Property of)
FAMILY OF FAITH
LIBRARY

W9-BEC-239

FA   H
Shaw   442

Family of Faith Library

an introduction to the elements of
MATHEMATICS

an introduction to the elements of

JOHN N. FUJII, *Oakland City College*

New York · London, John Wiley & Sons, Inc.

MATHEMATICS

Copyright © 1961 by John Wiley & Sons, Inc.

All rights reserved. This book or any part
thereof must not be reproduced in any form
without the written permission of the publisher.

Library of Congress Catalog Card Number: 61-15397

Printed in the United States of America

PREFACE

For many years, introductory courses in mathematics have been a rehash or review of secondary school mathematics. The usual undergraduate mathematical curricula have been those leading toward an engineering or physical science program. It has become apparent that there are many other areas in which an appropriately modified mathematical curriculum would be of value to the thinking of a maturing college student.

Mathematicians have been so busy with the development of their subject that they have failed to keep teachers and students informed about new ideas. Contemporary mathematics is now such an extensive subject that no one man in his lifetime could expect to master even a small portion of it.

In recent years, the teaching of mathematics in the United States has been undergoing a series of reforms. Many groups have been active in these reform movements. Four of these groups deserve mention here: the Committee on the Undergraduate Program (CUP), sponsored by the Mathematical Association of America; the Commission on Mathematics of the College Entrance Examination Board (CEEB); the School Mathematics Study Group (SMSG), working under a grant from the National Science Foundation; and the University of Illinois Committee on School Mathematics (UICSM).

This textbook puts into effect some of the results of these reform movements. In general, it is designed to give students with a nontechnical background some understanding of the ideas underlying mathematics, its history, and an elementary treatment of problem-solving and decision-making. The intention is not to emphasize mathematical "skills" or "computational" facility; rather, it is to develop some of the conceptual ideas underlying mathematics and science. The text does not assume that the reader has mastered certain "language" and "reasoning" skills.

However, a certain maturity is expected of the reader; he must also have the desire to start and the perseverance to finish.

This book is not a set of directions, nor is it a collection of assertions. Its intent is to help direct and encourage critical examinations of certain useful ideas. A preliminary browsing is recommended to give the reader a general feeling for the material. A second more serious reading is a must for each section and topic. A third reading is advisable upon completion of the second reading. Unlike newspapers or fiction, material of this kind usually takes the average person one-half hour to two or more hours per page to digest.

Unfortunately, many students think of textbooks and courses solely as lists of exercises and hurdles to overcome. The exercises are intended to help make the ideas developed in each chapter the reader's own. Occasionally, exercises introduce new ideas and require initiative and resourcefulness on the part of the reader. This is intentional.

Any study of forms of reasoning or of mental discipline must, to a great extent, be devoid of interpreted content. In introductory material this abstraction can easily lead to confusion and misdirection. Thus illustrations and examples of interpreted content have been included in the text. The intent in the text, however, is to develop the ability to distinguish between the vague and specific, between loose and careful thinking. It must be admitted that an understanding of abstract reasoning and form does not automatically result in clear and careful thinking on all subjects. There must be the desire and effort to use the understanding in other areas of learning.

Whatever a liberal education may imply, it should give some consideration to the conceptual tools used in human endeavor. With this in mind, the text begins with a study of language. From this discussion of the problems of communication, it proceeds to a consideration of the meaning of *truth* and *validity*. If the search for truth is worthy of effort, then mathematics, which has played such an important part in its discovery, should likewise be worth as much effort.

Concerning the arrangement of the material in the text, each of the chapters is separated into a number of sections and items. The sections and items are referenced at the left margin. The reference consists of two or more numbers separated by periods, for example, 2.1.2.

The numbers indicate the chapter, the section, and the item, respectively. For example, 5.4.1 would refer to Chapter 5, section 4, and the first item in that section. Complete sections are referred to by a pair of numbers. For example, 7.2 refers to section 2 of Chapter 7.

A selected list of books for further reading and reference is included in Appendix A. The books have been selected for both relevance to the material and for ease of reading. It is hoped that readers will use these references.

I wish to thank Oakland City College for granting me some released time from teaching duties to prepare the original syllabus which led to the writing of this textbook. Thanks are also due to the many persons who have given their valuable advice and criticism in the development and final preparation of the material. I owe a sincere debt of gratitude to my publishers, John Wiley and Sons, Inc., and their editors for their confidence, faith, and patience in the writing and editing of the final manuscript.

Finally, I wish to acknowledge the part my wife played in patiently encouraging me throughout the process of writing.

Oakland City College   JOHN N. FUJII
July, 1961

CONTENTS

1
LANGUAGE

1.1 NATURAL LANGUAGE

Man has yet to attain direct telepathic communication. It is a fact that ideas can be conveyed from one person to another only through some form of language. The recognition of this fact, and of the difficulties implied by it, is a first step in learning a subject precisely.

Everyday conversations include a mixture of vague and ambiguous statements. We are often metaphorical in our language usage. Literal translations of our words would often be inaccurate or even unintelligible. When a student states with feeling that he "hates examinations" he surely does not mean this literally. He is simply expressing an emotion. When a person is referred to as "a square," presumably this is not to be understood literally.

The exclamation "Look out!" is understood almost universally among English-speaking people. The particular words are almost free of the communication. Words of greeting and of parting are often similar expressions. On the other hand, when stating rules for a game or giving instructions, we desire to be as specific as possible. When we state, "This class will meet every Monday, Wednesday, and Friday in room 43," we are communicating information as specifically as possible.

The reader should be able to give many more illustrations of variety in the usage of language in ordinary conversations. It is not surprising that confusion arises in the study of precise and exact concepts through the use of everyday language.

In order to proceed with our study, then, we must consider carefully the difficulties which we may encounter in the use of ordinary language. Our language may fail to communicate in two ways: the meaning of a statement may be misunderstood, or there may be a lack of understanding altogether. Misunderstandings occur when an unintended communication

1

takes place. When no communication takes place, there is a lack of comprehension.

When familiar words are used in a communication, many meanings may be attached to them. The words may have meaning according to the ways in which they are used in relation to other words, or according to their relations to objects, or according to the purpose for which they are used. Consequently, a recipient of a communication may associate an unintended meaning to familiar words and presume erroneously that he knows what was intended.

For example, *scale* has many meanings. To scale the heights, to scale a fish, to establish a scale, that is a scale, etc.

Lack of understanding arises from a number of possible sources. Unfamiliarity with the words used, elaborate and complex phraseology, and, occasionally, the inherent complexity of an idea may lead to incomprehension. Many words have special technical as well as ordinary meanings. Such words as *difference, product, base, reciprocal, relation, similar, prime, and so on* have precise technical meanings when used in mathematics. The association of different meanings to these words can easily lead to misunderstanding, confusion, and erroneous conclusions. However, the difficulty of understanding such words as *geodesic* and *logarithm* is usually recognized. Meaning and understanding can then be controlled and carefully developed through experience and observation.

Although closely allied, *meaning* and *understanding* refer to two different aspects of communication. Meaning refers to the direct content of words and symbols, whereas understanding implies an awareness of the cause and effect relationship of a communication. For example, the meaning of the statement, "When yellow and blue are mixed together, the result is green," may be clear although understanding may be lacking. Meaning may very often be "read into" a statement, but understanding requires an integrating process.

Ordinary words are often ambiguous, may have many meanings, and may easily be misunderstood. Unfamiliar words and complex phraseology may lead to a complete lack of understanding. Yet ideas can be conveyed from one person to another only through some form of language. Thus, as we proceed, we must use language with caution. As in the conversation between Humpty Dumpty and Alice:

"When I use a word," Humpty Dumpty said, "it means just what I choose it to mean—neither more nor less."

"The question is," said Alice, "whether you can make words mean so many different things."

"The question is," said Humpty Dumpty, "which is to be master—that's all."

Lewis Carroll

I.I.I We do not know just how or where language first developed. At one time it might have been argued that language was given to man by his Creator. Since Darwin pointed out the biological kinship of man with the lower animals, students of language have speculated on the evolution of formal speech. However, it seems clear that the development of language was complex and intimately associated with the sociological organization of man.

Once a child is able to make reasonably distinctive sounds, he begins to communicate. Conscious, purposeful sound-making takes place long before any words are learned. The first words are generalized and refer to total situations. *Mama* does not refer to a person, but to a generalized feeling. The early words refer to situations as a whole, with classification and specific meanings coming later. As the child grows he experiments with words and invents new words. Through daily experiences and repeated associations, the child develops a growing vocabulary of words. He must have names for the things around him. He must be able to explain their use. By the time the child is six he may have a vocabulary of 5,000 different words. These early words, and many others learned later in life, form a "natural" vocabulary which is understood in terms of the past experiences and associations of the person.

When two people converse, they usually communicate by means of their "natural" language. Since the communication in ordinary conversations is relatively adequate, we are prone to forget that it is, at most, approximate. No two people have learned the same words under precisely the same conditions. Past associations and experiences differ, and to each person the words are recalled in the past contexts of his or her unique circumstances. In spite of the foregoing considerations, we will proceed with the use of a "natural" language as a basis of communication because it is the only common means of communication available to us.

Although we will go no further in the study of "natural" language at this time, all that we do later in this text will be influenced by the existence of a "natural" language and its general content.

Exercises 1.1
1. Write five sentences illustrating five distinct uses of language in everyday situations.
2. Look up the word "abstract" in a dictionary and list its possible acceptable meanings in ordinary language situations.
3. Write sentences using words in each of the following ways. Underline the word in each sentence.
   (*a*) A word having meaning according to the way in which it is used in a sentence.

(*b*) A word having meaning according to the way in which it is related to an object.

(*c*) A word having meaning according to the purpose for which it is used.

4. Write a list of one hundred words which you feel belong to your "natural" vocabulary. Be able to discuss their origin in your vocabulary.

5. Describe in your own words how a child might make the transition from spoken to written words and letters on a page.

1.2   SEMANTICS

Let us now take a closer look at the process of communication. Alfred Korzybski, who died in 1950, was the originator of what he called "General Semantics." He published two books. The thesis of his first book, *The Manhood of Humanity*, is that man is distinguished from the rest of the earth's creatures by his language and the ability to communicate what he learns from one generation to the next. The word *semantics* first appeared about sixty years ago and was originally defined as "studies having to do with meaning." Our interest in semantics is limited to the study of the relations between signs or symbols and what they mean or denote, and of behavior as it is influenced by signs or symbols.

1.2.1 Signs are kinds of communication experiences. When a baby sees a bottle, the baby may react as if he expects to be fed. To the baby, the bottle can be a sign for food. Many studies of animal learning have shown the effectiveness of signs. Pavlov, in his experiments with dogs, showed that ringing a bell could be made an effective sign for food.

In *The Meaning of Meaning*, published in 1921, C. K. Ogden and I. A. Richards presented the triangle relationship of sign-organism-context. That is, to every sign situation there is associated an organism and a context, the implication being that we must keep in mind the context of our discourse. For example, nimbus clouds in the sky are only potential signs; an organism must see the clouds and associate from past experiences the expectation of rain. A raised hand may mean stop or friend, depending on the context of the situation.

The sign-organism-context relationship might be described as follows:

1. There must be an object or arrangement which we have called a sign situation.

    (*a*) The organism must have experienced a similar situation in the past. There must be a certain frequency of occurrence of the sign situation.

    (*b*) The sign must be sufficient in its intensity or strength to attract the attention of the organism.

2. There must be an organism to interpret and give meaning to the sign situation.
   (*a*) The organism must have an interest, desire, or urge to give meaning to the sign.
   (*b*) The organism must recall, from past experiences and associations, occurrences of the sign situation and must relate a remembered experience to the sign.
3. There must be a context. That is, there must be an experience to which some meaning is attached. The past experiences and associations of the organism determine the context of the sign situation.

It is well to note that the organism is the connecting link between the sign and the contextual meaning of the sign. A sign is a part of the experience of an organism. It has the effect of bringing back an experience to the memory of the organism.

1.2.2 A symbol is the name of a sign used in the absence of a sign to communicate thought. For example, the word "Typhon" is a symbol which refers to a monster in Greek and Roman mythology. "Mammals" refer to a group of vertebrates. No one has experienced a Typhon, nor can we isolate the experiencial situation for mammals. However, we can associate the symbols in use and communicate ideas with them.

The late Benjamin Lee Whorf, who took up linguistics as a hobby, said that the forms of a man's thoughts are controlled by patterns learned early in life, that thinking is a language process. Many believe that talking is merely a tool which we use to communicate something deeper called "thinking." Thinking, it is assumed, depends on a reason and logic common to all mankind. Listening to discussions of "The American Way," "Big Business," and "Communism" will soon convince the listener of the importance of language as an integral part of thinking.

The existence of a symbol depends upon its inventor, for symbols are invented. The fulfillment of a symbol situation also requires a "sensing" organism which associates the symbol to a referent. The referent is the object referred to, while the symbol is the name of the referent. A symbol properly used abstracts an interpretation from experienced situations. Man, through his interpretive abilities, can create a hierarchy of symbols which successively abstracts greater and greater subtleties from the concrete world around him.

Consider the word *apple*, for example. As a physical event in the world it may be described as a certain collection of molecules which we recognize as an apple. As a sensory event it is a patch of reflected light of a certain color, size, and shape. To the touch it feels round, smooth-skinned, hard when green, soft when overripe. As a botanical event it is the seed-pod of the genus *Malus*, a member of the rose family. As an edible fruit it has such properties as a distinctive flavor, a caloric value, a market value, and so on. It belongs to folklore; it is the thing which fell to the ground and inspired Newton with the law of gravity; it is the object which comforted King Solomon when he was sick with love; it is the thing which gives little boys stomachaches when eaten green, and keeps the doctor away when eaten daily.

Let us illustrate the process of abstraction which is involved here with the following list, descending in the order of abstraction:

The physical event called an apple.

The sensory event with color, size, shape, odor.

The edible event with flavor and food value.

The historical event which gave Newton the idea of gravity, King Solomon comfort, and Johnny Appleseed his fame.

When misunderstanding or lack of understanding occurs, it can often be traced to the fact that we are abstracting different meanings associated with a word. That is, we often forget the relationship of the word to its referent or erroneously associate an incorrect referent with respect to the communication. We must determine the referent being referred to, and the referents *not* being referred to.

Almost every time we use a word, we are abstracting one or more of its possible meanings—and immediately we are taking the risk of being misunderstood, because the meaning *we* have chosen to associate with our particular use of the word may not be the one our hearer associates with it.

The usefulness of symbolic language is undeniable, but there is always the danger of expecting too much. It is an easy step from talking or writing symbolically, as a means of communicating and organizing our thinking, to simply talking or writing without regard to referents. Symbolic language should be a means to clearer and more specific thoughts. The symbols are like arrows pointing to thoughts and concepts, but to be effective the arrows must fly straight and strike the mark.

How can we remind ourselves of the dangers in talking and writing? By reminding ourselves that:

1. Symbols do not tell the whole story. There is always a "and so forth" trailing every sentence and statement.
2. Symbols identify things, but things are not static. Identities change, ideas are modified, there is diversity all around us.
3. Time passes and with passing time, symbols change their meanings.
4. Symbols categorize, classify, and divide. But concepts and ideas have a unity.
5. Symbols mean many different things to people.

Man profits by the experience of past generations. Man can be consciously reoriented, can learn and improve on past experiences. Man can abstract and proceed from the concreteness of personal experience successively to further and further abstractions. Man, the organism, is the connecting link between his invented symbol and its referent.

Exercises 1.2

1. Give an illustration of a sign situation and describe the sign-organism-context relationship for your illustration.
2. Give two examples of successive abstractions from a sign situation to an abstract concept.
3. Invent a language of not more than ten symbols which would enable simple communication.
4. Select a word, say "anthropomorphic." Refer to an encyclopedia, dictionaries, and any other sources necessary, and determine a chain of symbols for the development of a clear referent for the word. That is, reduce the word to terms in your "natural" vocabulary. If possible, visualize the referent. Learn the historical significance of the word as well as the referent. Delve into the word as deeply as possible.
5. Give an example of each of the five points noted as dangers in talking and writing. Add to the list, if possible.

1.3   DEFINITIONS

Words and symbols are not static; referents change; thoughts change; and the symbols themselves are often changed. As we proceed from rough general ideas to more precise thinking, there will be changes in our perception of referents as well as in the symbols and words which we use.

Early in this chapter, we discussed "natural" language. This "natural" language is of necessity limited for each person. Often it is not precise, nor is it concise. As our insights develop, there will be a need to expand and increase our symbol language. This process is accomplished through definitions. There are definitions which we use from day-to-day; these include all processes of clarification or explanation of a symbol. A more restricted and formal kind of definition is used in special and technical universes of discourse. The former we will call "informal" definitions and the latter "formal" definitions.

1.3.1 A definition is like a road: it has a starting point, a route, and an ending. It can go directly, circuitously, or it can become a maze. For example:

(*a*) A chair is a seat for one person; it usually has four legs and a back.
(*b*) By a chair we mean a piece of furniture which is usually used by a single person to sit upon; it is often made of wood or metal; it may

or may not be comfortable and can be large or small; it usually has four legs, a place to sit, and a back to lean upon.

(c) The word *chair* has many possible meanings: it may mean a seat, usually with four legs and a back, on which one person may sit; it may mean an office or position of dignity, such as a judgeship, professorship, or chairmanship; it may be used to indicate a person who presides over a meeting; it may mean a special seat of honor which is carried on poles; it may mean to place a person in a position of authority. Thus the word *chair* may mean many things to many people in many situations.

In informal definitions, any process which clarifies or explains a symbol or sign may be used to expand, increase, develop, or shorten our symbol language. Various kinds of definitions may be included: "Joe," spoken while pointing to the person to whom we are referring; "sayo-nara," meaning "good-bye"; and "eminent," meaning "rising above other things or places."

Remembering that the purpose of a definition is to clarify and explain, let us consider the structures of definitions. In all definitions, we should find three parts:

1. The symbol being defined. Here we will not quibble about whether it is the symbol or the referent that is being defined.
2. The process of definition; that is, the route that it takes in defining the symbol.
3. The common starting point. This is assumed known and understood.

For example; the word *binary* is an adjective meaning "made up of two parts." In chemistry we refer to a substance made up of two elements as a "binary compound."

In this example, the word *binary* is the symbol being defined. The process or route of the definition is (a) a classification of the word, (b) a translation of the word into presumably known and understood words, (c) an example of the word as used in the field of chemistry. The common starting point is the set of words used and the context of the definition. The elements of the common starting point are assumed known and understood by the reader.

When a symbol must be defined, we expand it, clarify it with further symbols, explain it, describe it in use, and so forth. If a definition does not define clearly, it may cause difficulties. If it is too long or too short, it will confuse. Learning the processes or routes for definitions requires experience. Nonetheless, it is useful to suggest possible forms for the processes of informal definitions.

Some definitions may take the form of directly sensed experiences: "This is a chair," spoken while pointing to a chair.

A definition may be a translation of one symbol into another known symbol: "A divot is a lump of turf."

It is often convenient to describe a symbol by exhibiting similar, opposite, or contrasting symbols: "A tiger is an animal like a big cat." "Black is the opposite of white." "Hot can be contrasted with cool."

We can often describe the form, shape, material, size, or state: "A football is an inflated elliptical leather ball about the size of a small watermelon."

We might classify, partition, or locate: "A whale is a fishlike mammal." "A Neanderthal was one of the types of men of the stone age."

A description of behavior, the cause of, the effect from, or the use of a referent may be used: "A mouse is a timid or spiritless person." "A poison is a substance that causes illness or death when eaten, drunk, or absorbed by the body."

The above do not, by any means, exhaust the possible ways of defining symbols. In the broadest sense of the term, any other kind of simple or complex connection that can be thought of might be included in the possible forms for the processes of definition.

The practical aspect of a study of definitions in the above sense is not so much to develop a formal system but to become aware of a process which we use daily. It should make us more resourceful and careful in explaining and clarifying communications. We should learn to be careful in the choice of a common starting point. If a common starting point is not established, a definition may be a waste of time and effort.

A useful purpose should be served in defining a new symbol. The definition should enable us to express a communication more concisely, or help us to organize a thought more clearly. If used in a special or restricted context, a symbol might well be clarified or explained further by a new definition.

When defining symbols, we should also beware of "circularity." For example: "A dollar is equal to 100 cents. A cent is equal to a 100th part of a dollar."

Although we seem to communicate adequately with vague and ambiguous language in ordinary conversations, in a more critical study, in which words and symbols must be understood independently of the sentence context, vagueness and ambiguity would soon lead to utter confusion. Examining instances in the use of a word or symbol and extracting a meaning as is done in ordinary conversations and in writing dictionaries would often be impossible.

1.3.2 In technical subject areas new words and symbols must often be created to serve as abbreviations for less convenient language. Thus, within given areas of discourse, we frame formal definitions which serve to facilitate precise and concise communication.

Formal definitions are more restrictive and structured in their form than informal definitions. Bertrand Russell has remarked that definitions in this sense are simply and solely statements of symbolic abbreviations; they are statements concerning symbols, not concerning what is symbolized. That is, a formal definition facilitates the study of a technical subject but does not add anything new to the subject. For example, in electronics a "pentode" is defined as an "electronic vacuum tube with five internal elements." This definition enables the individual in electronics to discuss pentodes without becoming tiresome and ineffective due to lengthy repetitions.

A formal definition may thus be regarded as simply a stipulation on how a symbol is to be used. The user should eliminate all preconceptions concerning the meaning of the symbol being defined. He should proceed on the basis of the definition alone. A formal definition, to be useful, should give a single unique meaning to the defined symbol, and this meaning should be invariably applicable. For example, in mathematics we define $2 = 1 + 1$. Also, we define $3 = 2 + 1$; $4 = 3 + 1$. This enables us to write "4" whenever "$3 + 1$" appears or, as can be seen by a little writing, whenever "$1 + 1 + 1 + 1$" appears.

In framing a formal definition we attempt to make it fruitful in the sense that the definition lends itself to applications. Definitions should also be "natural"; they should tend to agree with our intuitive feelings about the thing being defined. Formal definitions should classify and describe the properties and characteristics unique to the symbol.

For example:

1.3.2.1 Definition: By a **triangle** we mean a plane figure formed by connecting three points not in a straight line by straight line segments.

1.3.2.2 Definition: By the **vertices** of a triangle we mean the three points used in forming the triangle.

1.3.2.3 Definition: By the **sides** of a triangle we mean the three straight line segments connecting the vertices of the triangle.

In the development of a subject, formal definitions may appear in a serial order. That is, a first definition, a second definition, a third, and so on. Thus we may speak of preceding definitions as well as refer to the number of a definition in the order of its occurrence. Successive definitions, in these instances, may use preceding definitions to define new symbols.

This property of formal definitions will become apparent in later chapters of this text.

In conclusion, we note that formal definitions as well as informal definitions are created for convenience. Defined symbols are formed from root derivations or historical origins, or arise out of the suggestive nature of a situation. Definitions are in a sense arbitrary agreements on the usage and meaning to be associated with a given symbol for the purposes of communication.

Exercises 1.3

1. Write short, informal definitions for the following words: *precise, concise, condition.*
2. Look up the following words in a dictionary and discuss the routes of the definitions given for them: *rift, gimp, koa.*
3. Write a short discussion on the similarities and differences between formal and informal definitions as described in the text.
4. Starting with the word *quartz* in a dictionary, look up the defining terms, the terms defining the defining terms, and so on. Discuss your observations.
5. Write formal definitions for the following words in the fields indicated: *coordinate* (mathematics), *mixture* (chemistry), *pitch* (music, architecture, and engineering).

Exercises 1

1. Arrange the following words in order, from the most clear to most vague in meaning:
   (a) *heavy, pound, gravity, weight.*
   (b) *cover, cloak, conceal, disguise.*
2. Write four sentences using the following word in different senses: *condition.*
3. Give an example which illustrates the difference between the meaning and the understanding of a term.
4. Compile a list of twenty-five words which have a special meaning in mathematics as well as a common meaning in English.
5. Look up the word *geodesic* in a dictionary and discuss the possible origin of the word.
6. Write lists of at least five synonyms for each of the following words: *degree, skill, direction.*
7. Give two examples which illustrate the difference between a symbol and its referent.
8. Write short informal definitions for the following words: *quantity, form, structure.*
9. Write formal definitions for the following words in the fields indicated: *erg* (physics), *stock* (zoology), *composite* (botany), *flare* (photography).
10. Discuss the processes of definition and the relationship between the formal definitions numbered 1.3.2.1, 1.3.2.2, 1.3.2.3.

11. Arrange the one hundred words listed for problem 4 of exercise 1.1 into five word classes according to their syntactical usage in sentences.
12. Write short etymologies for the following words: *form, reason, clear.*
13. Write a short essay on "A guide to the use of an ordinary English dictionary."
14. What is the difference between an ordinary English dictionary and an English–German translating dictionary?
15. Read and write a short discussion of the article titled "Loglan" in the June 1960 issue of *Scientific American* magazine.

2
SYMBOLS

2.1 CLASSIFICATION

Familiarity with symbols is not sufficient for an understanding of the ways in which they are used. Symbols must be "put-together" and integrated into an intelligible structure. Consider how a small child begins to put ordinary words together. For example, "Daddy naughty baby hurt cry." Who hurt whom? Was there an accident?

Older English grammarians asserted that nouns were names of things and that verbs designated actions. Symbols were grouped and classified according to their grammatical usage. For example, the word *house* was called a noun; the word *frowzy*, an adjective. Today many words may be classified in more than one way, according to their usage. The study of grammatical classifications, usage, and structure of words properly belongs in an English text, and so we will not pursue it further here.

The emotional classification of words belongs to the fields of psychology and sociology. Words and symbols have emotional content in the sense that their referents relate to human experiences and feelings. The word *worm* will often elicit an emotional response different from that of the word *wood*. The word *good* has an emotional tone different from that of the word *bad*.

Words and symbols can also be grouped in terms of the areas in which they are used. We might consider grouping words according to the languages used in various geographical areas of the world. Or we might classify words according to their special fields of usage, such as musical, psychological, medical, mathematical, and so forth. Note that there are two points of view above. In terms of ordinary languages, words and symbols are commonly used to cause a rich, full sensing of the referents. This may lead to vagueness and ambiguity in communication. In fields of special usage, words and symbols are more commonly used in specific and restricted senses.

13

2.1.1 In the study of the structures of symbols, we will find it convenient to consider a classification of all symbols into five categories:

1. **Nominal elements.** This first group will consist of all words and symbols with the characteristics of nouns and pronouns in ordinary English grammar. For example, John, apple, you, 2, 3, x, y, and so on. The word *those* in "Hand me those." The word *music* in "Listen to the music." The symbols naming numbers in mathematics will often be considered to be in this category.

2. **Functional elements.** This second group will consist of all words and symbols which indicate relationships between nominal elements of the first category. These are the elements which report the doings or actions attributed to the nominal elements. For example, the term *father* in "Mr. Williams is the father of James." The word *harder* in "Oak is harder than pine." In mathematics, the symbols for the operations of addition, subtraction, multiplication, and division fall into this category.

3. **Logical elements.** All words and symbols indicating logical connections are to be placed in this group. In ordinary English the words *and*, *or*, *one*, *many*, *some*, *not*, *if* . . . *then*, and *is* are to be included in this category. For example, the words *all* and *and* in "All words and symbols . . . ." The words *If* and *then* in "If I try, then I will succeed."

4. **Grouping elements.** Words and symbols which do not contribute to the content of statements but which are necessary integral parts of statements are to be placed in this category. For example, punctuation marks, such as commas, periods, parentheses, and quotation marks, belong to this group. In mathematics, parentheses, brackets, and braces are important elements of statements which belong to this category.

5. **All other elements** not falling into one of the first four groupings are to be placed in this group. This category is convenient for those elements which give smoothness and contiguity to statements without being essential elements of communications. Common examples are the uses of *a*, *an*, and *the* in ordinary sentences.

Example of classification of symbols:

Snow is wet and white.

We can conveniently indicate the classification by copying the statement and writing N, F, L, G, or O just below the terms of the statement as follows:

Snow is wet and white.
  N   L   F   L   F

Note the importance of the logical elements. We might rephrase the statement as: Snow is wet and snow is white. Now we note that the statement has at least two distinct "levels" of classification: [Snow is wet] and [snow is white]. The phrases in brackets can be thought of as nominal elements connected by a logical symbol. The phrases in turn can be classified:

    Snow is wet.
     N   L   F

EXAMPLE. If John is Mary's uncle, then Mary's father or mother is John's sister or brother.

Using brackets, we can separate the sentence into three distinct parts: If [John is Mary's uncle], then [Mary's father or mother is John's sister or brother]. The two words *If . . . then* form a single logical connective joining the phrases in the brackets. The bracketed phrases at this stage can be thought of as nominal elements.

The phrase "John is Mary's uncle" can be separated in turn as follows: [John] is [Mary's uncle]. The terms in brackets can then be thought of as nominal elements connected by the logical term *is*. Finally "Mary's uncle" can be rephrased as "The uncle of Mary." The word *the* is purely grammatical and belongs to the "all other" category. *Uncle* is a nominal element and also, in "uncle of Mary," acts as a functional element along with the word *of*. *Mary* is clearly a nominal.

The phrase "Mary's father or mother is John's sister or brother" is separated into "[Mary's father or mother] is [John's sister or brother]." The phrases in brackets are then nominal elements and *is* is a logical element. Now "Mary's father or mother" can be rephrased into "Mary's father or Mary's mother" in which *Mary's father* and *Mary's mother* act as nominal elements connected by the logical element *or*. We can conclude our classification by noting that the terms *father* and *mother* have dual uses as both nominal and functional elements and that *Mary* is a nominal element.

Diagrammatically, we might indicate the process of classification as follows:

If John is Mary's uncle, then Mary's father or mother is John's sister or brother.

	N			N		N	
L————————		L	————————		————————		

    John is Mary's uncle   Mary's father or mother is John's sister or brother.

$$N \quad L\underline{\quad N \quad} \qquad \underline{\quad N \quad} \quad L\underline{\quad N \quad}$$

    Mary's uncle   Mary's father or mother   John's sister or brother.

$$N \quad L\underline{\overset{NF}{\quad}} \qquad \underline{\overset{N}{\quad}} \quad L\underline{\overset{NF}{\quad}} \qquad \underline{\overset{N}{\quad}} \quad L\underline{\overset{NF}{\quad}}$$

    Mary's father   John's sister

$$N \quad L\underline{\overset{NF}{\quad}} \qquad\qquad N \quad L\underline{\overset{NF}{\quad}}$$

The last phrase in the diagram, "John's sister or brother," has been classified in the same way. Because of the richness and complexities of the English language, the classification of words becomes very complicated.

In fields of special usage, the classification of symbols is less confusing. Differences of opinions and interpretations are minimized, and usage is more specific and restricted, enabling us to classify and categorize words much more easily.

Exercises 2.1

1. Classify the words and symbols in the following sentences according to the categories given in 2.1.1, using the method of the example.
  (*a*) "Words are the counters of wise men, and the money of fools."   Hobbes.
  (*b*) "The moving power of mathematical invention is not reasoning but imagination."   De Morgan.
2. Do as in exercise 1:
  (*a*) What is the area and perimeter of a square, if each side is 3 inches long?
  (*b*) The sum of two numbers is 113, and their difference is 23.   Find the numbers.
3. Do as in exercises 1 and 2:
  (*a*) It is always permissible to add the same number to both members of an equation.
  (*b*) If n is a positive whole number, then $1 + 2 + 3 + \cdots + n = n(n + 1)/2$.

2.2   MATHEMATICAL SYMBOLS

It is often said that the symbols of mathematics are abstract. Symbols are created by man; they are abstract, they are arbitrary. Symbols reflect interpretations and mental processes which are not directly experienced. Most of our ordinary language is also abstract.

We grow from early childhood in an environment of ordinary words. Familiarity with the symbols used in ordinary language grows rapidly with use and time. We are not so obviously surrounded by mathematical symbols. The results of man's use of mathematical symbols is all around us, but we as individuals seldom come directly into contact with the mathematical language itself.

2.2.1 Mathematics is a language especially well-suited for situations in which the notions of quantity, size, or relationships enter. Mathematical symbols can be used in many ways as a language. Some of the ways are:

1. Mathematical symbols can be used **to describe objects precisely** in terms of size, order, or number. For example, rather than saying that a person is tall and middle aged we might better describe him as 6 feet tall and 40 years of age. Rather than saying that the class is large, we might say that there are 35 students in the class.

2. Mathematical symbols can be used **to describe** the **relationship** between objects **or to indicate** some **change or action** to be taken on an

object. For example, rather than saying that one object is larger than another, we might say that the first object has 3 times the volume of the second. Rather than requiring that the brakes of an auto be "good," we can specify that the brakes stop the auto within 50 feet when traveling at a rate of 30 miles per hour.

3. Mathematical symbols can be used **as concise expressions** of other symbols. For example, instead of writing $5 \times 5 \times 5 \times 5 \times 5 \times 5 \times 5 \times 5 \times 5 \times 5$ we can write 5^{10}. Instead of $1 + 2 + 3 + 4 + 5 + 6 + 7 + 8 + 9$ we write 45. In an appropriate symbolic form, mathematical symbols will often reveal relationships which might otherwise not be evident to the eye.

4. Mathematical symbols can be used **to express** the **notion** of a general object of a specified group of objects. For example, we might use the letter m to stand for any mammal. Symbols used in this way may be used as selective or descriptive devices. For example, the x in $x + 2 = 5$ may be thought of as a selective device. That is, the symbol is used to indicate a selection from a set of numbers, the number 3. In the statement $a + b = b + a$, the symbols a and b describe a relationship between elements in a set. Specific examples from arithmetic are $2 + 3 = 3 + 2$ and $10 + 4 = 4 + 10$.

Mathematics is often considered a difficult and mysterious science, because of the numerous symbols which it employs. Of course, nothing is more incomprehensible than a symbolism which we do not understand. Also a symbolism, which we only partially understand and are unaccustomed to use, is difficult to follow . . . . But this is not because they are difficult in themselves. On the contrary they have invariably been introduced to make things easy. A. N. Whitehead, *Introduction to Mathematics*.

Exercises 2.2
1. Form a list of ten illustrations of practical uses of mathematical symbols in your daily life.
2. Give examples of the four general ways in which mathematical symbols can be used.
3. Give an example of a special symbol used in each of the following fields: Chemistry, English, History, Music.

2.3 HISTORY

We have mentioned that written records are relatively recent in man's cultural history. The first attempts at recording ideas probably belong to the history of art. Events were first depicted through the use of simple pictographs.

Egyptian hieroglyphs represent an early stage in the stylizing of ideas. From these stylized representations, called ideographs, we have the development of alphabets. Early Greek had its origin in some Semitic alphabet dating back to about 1500 B.C. There are also indications that some of these early symbols were directly connected to Egyptian hieroglyphs.

2.3.1 Although the most important written symbols are words, it is not easy to solve problems using words. Even the most primitive men had need for quantitative symbols. From counting objects, when bartering, to telling time and giving directions, quantitative symbols were of practical use in their daily existence.

TABLE 1
Early Number Symbols

Egyptian	I	III II	∩	∩∩∩ ∩∩	)
Babylonian	▌	▼▼▼ ▼▼	<	<<< <<	▐▬
Roman	I	V	X	L	C
Mayan	·	—	══		〇
Modern	1	5	10	50	100

Quantitative number symbols developed slowly from more general terms. At first the symbols devised for numbers were simple and few. The earliest number symbols probably originated in Egypt and Mesopotamia about five thousand years ago. Our present day symbols didn't come into use until the fifteenth century and the Renaissance.

The names for numbers occurred early in spoken language. The use of fingers in counting probably led to the term "digits," meaning fingers in Latin, for the numerals one through nine. It is interesting to note that there are striking similarities in the words used for number names in different languages. In some cases the words have not changed in thousands of years.

In the development of the number concept, higher number names were formed by "adding" the names. For example, an Australian tribe used the word *enea* for "*one*," *petcheval* for "two," *petcheval-enea* for "three," and *petcheval-petcheval* for "four." Larger numbers were formed by bunching or grouping in fives, tens, twenties, and other quantities.

The number names used in counting are called **cardinals**. The adjectives that show the order of the objects counted, such as first, second, third, are called **ordinals**. Examination of the words used for cardinals and ordinals in various languages indicates that early people did not connect the idea of "three objects" with the "third object."

TABLE 2

Cardinal Number Names

Modern English	French	German	Old English	Latin	Greek
one	un	ein	an	unus	oinos
two	deux	zwei	two	duo	duo
three	trois	drei	threo	tres	treis
seven	sept	sieben	seofon	septem	hepta
eight	huit	acht	ahta	octo	okto
nine	neuf	neun	nigon	novem	enneas

Our present-day symbols for numerals are often spoken of as Arabic. They were probably never used by the Arabs! The symbols apparently originated in India about twelve hundred years ago in a book on arithmetic. The book was translated into Arabic and soon afterward merchants carried the book to Europe where it was translated into Latin. The original forms of the number symbols were quite different from our present day numerals. In fact, our present day numerals are constantly undergoing change with new methods of printing and writing.

TABLE 3

Cardinal and Ordinal terms in Various Languages

Language	Cardinal	Ordinal
English	one	first
German	ein	der erste
Latin	unus	primus
Russian	od-in	pervi
Hebrew	akh-d	rishon

2.3.2 The symbols for numerals were just a beginning. The symbols for addition and subtraction evolved through many stages. Our modern symbols, + and −, first appear to have been used in Europe in the fifteenth century. Leibniz (1646–1716) experimented for years with different symbols for multiplication, equality, and the like. He tried six different symbols for multiplication: the dot and cross, which are in general use today, and a cup, comma, semicolon, and asterisk.

The equality symbol also has a long and interesting history. Our modern symbol for equality, =, was invented by Robert Recorde (c. 1510–1558) who used it first in his work *The Whetstone of Witte* (1557). His works were usually in the form of dialogues between master and student, which he justified by saying, "I judge that to be the easiest way of instruction when

TABLE 4
Hindu-Arabic Numerals

Century	1	2	3	4	5	6	7	8	9	0
First										
Twelfth										
Fourteenth										
Fifteenth										
Twentieth	1	2	3	4	5	6	7	8	9	0

the Scholar may ask every doubt orderly, and the Master may answer his questions plainly." Descartes (1596–1650) used the symbol ∞ for equality. The survival of Recorde's symbol for equality may be partly due to its simplicity, but it is more probably due to the wide use of his textbooks and to the fact that Newton and Leibniz both used this symbol rather than Descarte's.

TABLE 5
Symbols Used for Equality

c. 275	ι^6	Diophantus
1557	=	Recorde
1559	[	Buteo
1575	‖	Xylander
1634	⌐	Herigone
1637	∞	Descarte
c. 1680	⌐	Leibniz

It would seem reasonable to think that mathematicians would adopt a uniform and consistent symbolism, but this has not been the case. The development of the symbols which we use today has been diverse and haphazard. The evolution of our present symbolism gives just cause for the comment:

No one could have imagined that such tricks of abbreviation could lead to the creation of a language so powerful that it has actually itself become an instrument of research which can point the way to future progress.

J. W. L. Glaisher

2.3.3 The priests and architects of early Egypt needed symbols to describe their temples and the great pyramids. They also needed ground plans and methods for leveling and squaring stone blocks. For irrigation and taxation, they needed surveying methods and recording devices. These needs led to the development of the symbolism which we call practical geometry.

Egyptian architects learned that a drawing and a building could be of different sizes but of the same shape, that the relationships in one were the relations in the other. Drawing straight lines and constructing straight edges might have been relatively easy, but to square a corner was a much more difficult task. Ingenious methods were developed to determine the directions of the compass, to square a corner, and to determine the exact vertical or zenith.

In both Babylonia and Egypt engineers could place their temples to face a precise point of the compass as demanded by their gods. They were so far in advance of the rest of civilization at that time that scholars would journey far distances to study and learn their methods. It is probable that Egyptian "rope-stretchers" constructed right angles by using a rope knotted into segments whose ratios were 3:4:5. Their surveyors used a plumb line in conjunction with an "A" frame to obtain horizontal lines. The Ahmes Papyrus (c. 1650 B.C.) shows the use of formulas in calculating areas.

When Athens became a leading city of Greece, many important mathematicians immigrated to that center of learning. Many Greeks were often teachers and philosophers and delighted in public study and debate. Modern mathematics with its interest in the question of "why" and the struggle to arrange ideas in logical chains was born in this Golden Age of Greece. The Greeks were interested in understanding man's place in the universe according to a rational scheme rather than in the "practical" questions of the "how" and "what" of a situation.

Thales (c. 640–546 B.C.), who was named among the "Seven Wise Men" of Miletus in Asia Minor, is traditionally considered the father of Greek mathematics. He showed how the height of a pyramid could be measured by measuring its shadow and comparing it to the shadow of a post. Thales is better known, however, for the study of demonstrative geometry based on logical reasoning. A noted pupil of Thales was Pythagoras (c. 572–501 B.C.) who devoted much attention to the study of areas, volumes, proportions, and regular solids. It was Pythagoras who noticed the constant relationship between the sides of a right triangle. The rope-stretchers' right triangles had the sides 3:4:5 and 5:12:13. Pythagoras noted that the sum of the squares of the two shorter sides of these triangles equaled the square of the longer side. He asked, "Is this always true? If the sides of a triangle are in this relationship, is the triangle a right triangle?" Instead of being content with examining a few cases of such triangles, Pythagoras proceeded to show that this relationship was invariably true of right triangles.

The Greeks studied geometry for recreation. Yet their methods and results found many practical applications in navigation, astronomy, and the building arts. About 300 B.C. a Greek named Euclid wrote a series of texts. His work, titled the *Elements*, has proved to be one of the best-sellers of all time. It was translated and used as a textbook in European and American schools until some fifty years ago. Even today, many schools teach geometry in essentially a Euclidean manner.

Although the early Egyptians seem actually to have recognized a graphical method of describing towns and regions, the use of grid lines and symbols in map making was probably due to the Greeks. The first men to clearly make symbolic use of graphs were two Frenchmen named Fermat (c. 1608–1665) and Descarte, in 1636 and 1637. This development brought about the joining of numerical and algebraic methods with purely geometric methods. Thus we have the development of the symbolic tools which played such an important part in the subsequent Age of Discovery in science.

Exercises 2.3

1. Find three examples of the use of Roman numerals in our present everyday lives.
2. Find examples of words in our ordinary vocabulary whose origins can be traced to the Latin and Greek names for the cardinal numbers in Table 2.
3. What is the difference in meaning between the words *numeral* and *number*?
4. Write a short essay on the Ahmes Papyrus (c. 1650 B.C.).
5. Write a brief biography of one or more of the following men of mathematics: Pythagoras, Archimedes, Al-Khowarizmi, Fibonacci, Johann Widman, Robert Recorde, Galileo Galilei, Rene Descartes, Pierre de Fermat, Blaise Pascal, Isaac Newton, Gottfried Wilhelm von Leibniz, Jacques Bernoulli, Abraham de Moivre, Leonard Euler, Joseph Louis Lagrange, Pierre-Simon Laplace, Carl Friedrich Gauss.

Exercises 2

1. Write down the capital and small letters of the Greek alphabet. (Copy the alphabet on a convenient file card for reference.)
2. What symbols, other than the + and − symbols, were used to indicate addition and subtraction?
3. Describe and illustrate a method for determining the exact vertical or zenith position.
4. Describe how to use a common map of your local area, e.g., a map supplied by a gasoline station.

5. Many justifications have been given for Pythagoras' conclusions concerning the relationship between the sides of a right triangle. A President of the United States found time to "prove" the conclusion. Can you?

6. Write a brief biography of one or more of the men of mathematics listed in exercise 5 of Section 2.3.

7. Find further examples of the four general ways in which mathematical symbols can be used.

8. Form lists of at least ten words which might be classified in the following categories: emotionally charged words, medical terms, psychological terminology, musical phrases, French words.

9. Classify the words and symbols in the following sentence according to the classification given in 2.1.1: "Mathematics in its widest signification is the development of all types of formal, necessary, deductive reasoning."

A. N. Whitehead.

10. Do as in exercise 9 (above) with:
   If a, b, and c are real numbers and $a < b$ and $b < c$, then $a < c$. This is called the transitive property of the real numbers.

11. Understanding traffic signs and symbols is very important for good driving. Write a short dictionary of the standard signs and symbols used in driving an automobile.

12. We use the English alphabet to form words and sentences for communication. Write a short essay on the history and development of the English alphabet.

13. Established rules are available for spelling words. Where can these rules be found? Give a few examples of these rules.

14. What is meant by the "mood," "voice," and "person" of a word, phrase, or sentence? Give examples.

15. Write a short essay on the similarities and differences in the meaning of the "How," "What," and "Why" questions of a situation.

3
COMPOUND
STATEMENTS

3.1 STATEMENTS

Through the years a symbol structure has been developed which forms a powerful tool for the study of languages. Special symbols permit us to exhibit with greater clarity the structure of statements. As observed by A. N. Whitehead in his *An Introduction to Mathematics*, ". . . by the aid of symbolism, we can make transitions in reasoning almost mechanically by the eye, which otherwise would call into play the higher faculties of the brain."

We have noted how difficulties can arise from the confusion between names and the things named. We shall not only make statements but will also talk about them and the relations between them. In making statements, we *use* names to *mention* objects. That is, in making statements about other statements, we are using a name for the statement, rather than the statement itself. It is convenient to omit quotation marks wherever there is no danger of confusion as to the meaning intended.

We will restrict our attention to a very small portion of the possible kinds of statements that might be made. By a **simple statement** we will mean a declarative assertion with the property of being true or false, and such that it does not contain any other statement as a part. For example, "It is hot" and "It is a pepper" are simple statements. The statement "I believe that it is hot" will not be included in the statements under consideration because the truth or falsity of the statement is indeterminate. The statement "It is a hot pepper" is not simple since it contains the two statements "It is hot" and "It is a pepper." The statement "It is a hot pepper" will be called a **compound statement**.

3.1.0.1 Definition: By a **simple statement** we mean a declarative assertion which is true or false but not both simultaneously, and such that it does not contain more than one assertion.

3.1.0.2 Definition: By a **compound statement** we mean a statement consisting of two or more simple statements.

3.1.1 There are various ways in which a statement can be made without changing its meaning. For example, "It is raining," "Il pleut," "Es regnet," "Ame ga futelu" are plainly different but have similar content. The statements "It is raining" and "Rain is falling" say essentially the same thing. "It is a hot pepper" can be rewritten to read "It is a pepper and it is hot." Statements which have the same meaning but differ in the way they are symbolized will be considered equivalent. That is, we will call them different formulations of a single statement.

We will distinguish the content of a statement from the form of the statement. That is, in order to study the structure of compound statements, we will often let a capital letter stand for a statement. For example, we might use the letter A to stand for "Men are mortal." If we let H stand for "It is hot" and P stand for "It is a pepper," then we can write "P and H" for "It is a hot pepper." Now, if A and B stand for two simple statements, we can consider the *structural* properties of the statements "A and B," "If A, then B," "A or B," and so forth. An economy is attained in using single letters for statements. Such use also frees us from the content of specific statements, permitting us to concentrate on the form of compound statements. This convention of letting letters stand for statements will be termed symbolic representation of statements, and the representation will occasionally be called the **statement form** of the statement.

It may seem unreasonable to attempt to develop precision in language through the use of ordinary words, but such an attempt is not as unrewarding as it may seem. The rules of many precise games, such as chess, are written in ordinary language. Our purpose, of course, is not so arbitrary. However, the rules which we state will be similar in the sense that they govern the usage of our language. Our purpose is to organize and systematize the symbolism so that clear and precise communication is indeed possible.

Exercises 3.1

1. Form a list of ten simple statements.
2. Using the list of simple statements of exercise 1, form a list of ten compound statements.
3. Using convenient capital letters for simple statements, write symbolic representations of the list of compound statements of exercise 2.

4. Reformulate each of the compound statements of exercise 2.

5. How can the truth or falsity of a statement be determined? Give an example of a statement for which the truth or falsity might change. Give an example of a statement for which the truth or falsity cannot be determined.

3.2 "AND," "OR," "NOT"

Let us now turn to some of the ways in which simple statements may be compounded. Let A stand for "It is a book" and B stand for "It is difficult." The statement "It is a difficult book" can be reformulated as "It is a book *and* it is difficult." Note the word *and* inserted between the statements A and B. This is called a **conjunction** and the two statements joined by the conjunction are called **conjuncts**. The conjunction is symbolized by $\wedge$. The statement "It is a book and it is difficult" can be symbolically represented as "$A \wedge B$."

A simple statement is, by definition, true or false. The determination of the truth or falsity of a simple statement is a matter for empirical testing. For example, the question of whether A is true or false can be answered only by empirically determining whether the *it* in "It is a book" does in fact have a book as a referent, or not. However, it can be asserted that every simple statement, by our definition, is in fact true or false in any given specific situation.

Now let us consider the possible truth or falsity of the compound statement formed by connecting the simple statements A and B. A and B might both be true. A might be true, while B could be false. A might be false, while B could be true. Finally, both A and B might be false. The possible situations can be set up as in Table 6.

TABLE 6

A	B	$A \wedge B$
T	T	T
T	F	F
F	T	F
F	F	F

From our past experience in the use of the connective *and* we can agree to say that the compound statement form $A \wedge B$ should be considered true if both conjuncts are true, and false otherwise. That is, if "It is a book" is true and if "It is difficult" is true, then we will agree to say that the statement "It is a difficult book" is true. Otherwise we shall say that the statement is false.

The statements A and B refer to particular simple statements. If we consider *any* two simple statements P and Q, we note that they must have the characteristic of being true or false. The statement $P \wedge Q$ formed by taking the arbitrary simple statements P and Q and connecting them with $\wedge$, will thus have a well defined property of being true or false, depending only upon the truth or falsity of P and Q. That is, $P \wedge Q$ will be true if both P and Q are true; otherwise $P \wedge Q$ will be false.

3.2.1 The statement "It is a book *or* it is difficult" has the connective word *or* between the two simple statements. The word *or* might have two possible meanings: "either one or the other or both," or "at least one but not both." It is conventional to use the symbol $\vee$ in the former or inclusive sense of "either one or the other or both." The connective is called a **disjunction** and the simple statements which are connected are called **disjuncts**. The statement "It is a book or it is difficult" is then symbolized by "$A \vee B$."

From our interpretation of the usage to be made of the word *or*, we conclude that the statement form $A \vee B$ is false only when both A and B are false. Furthermore, if P and Q are *any* two simple statements, we conclude that the statement form $P \vee Q$ will be false only when both P and Q are false.

TABLE 7

P	Q	$P \vee Q$
T	T	T
T	F	T
F	T	T
F	F	F

3.2.2 It we wish to deny the statement "It is difficult," we would say, "It is *not* difficult." This is called a **denial** and is symbolized by $\sim$. The statement "It is not difficult" would be symbolically represented as "$\sim B$." In general, if P is any simple statement, then if P is true, $\sim P$ is false. Also if P is false, $\sim P$ is true.

TABLE 8

P	$\sim P$
T	F
F	T

3.2.3 Using the above symbolic representations, we can form still more complicated compound statements. For example, $A \wedge \sim B$ stands for "It is a book and it is not difficult." The statement form $A \wedge (B \vee \sim B)$ states "It is a book and it is difficult or not difficult." Note that the example $A \wedge (B \vee \sim B)$ introduces the symbols ( ) which are commonly used to indicate a grouping. They are called parentheses and serve to indicate the order in which the connectives are to be applied. Using parentheses, we can avoid ambiguity in the statement form $A \wedge B \vee \sim B$, which might also be interpreted as $(A \wedge B) \vee \sim B$.

The interpretation of the meaning "at least one but not both" in writing "A or B" can be symbolized as $(A \vee B) \wedge (\sim A \vee \sim B)$.

In summary, we see that if P and Q are simple statements, then we can form compound statements by using the connectives $\wedge$, $\vee$, $\sim$ represented as $P \wedge Q, P \vee Q, \sim P$. Furthermore, we can form compound statements using compound statements as parts. When we form compound statements using compound statements, we will often introduce grouping symbols to avoid ambiguity of the final compounds. We note also that the problem of determining the truth or falsity of complicated compound statements may be quite difficult without appropriate tools to work with.

Exercises 3.2

1. Give symbolic representations of the following statements, using the letters indicated at the end of each statement.

(a) It is warm and sunny. (W, S)

(b) The book is interesting but it is not easy. (I, E)

(c) I must work or I will go hungry. (W, H)

(d) Sam saw Bill but not Ann, or Ann but not Nancy. (B, A, N).

2. Determine the truth or falsity of the statements in exercise 1 above, given that in

(a) W is true, S is false.

(b) I is true, E is false.

(c) W is true, H is false.

(d) B is false, A is true, N is true.

3. If S stands for "I will study," T for "I will watch television," and U for "I will sleep," then write out the statements symbolized by:

(a) $S \wedge (\sim T \wedge \sim U)$.   (b) $(U \vee T) \wedge \sim S$

(c) $S \wedge \sim T$ (d) $\sim(\sim S \vee U)$

3.3   TRUTH TABLES

All the statements which we shall consider are true or false (in the exclusive sense). We can think of truth or falsehood as being a property of every statement. We shall call this the **truth value** of each statement. Compound statements consist of two or more simple statements. The simple statements in a compound statement will be called the **components** of the compound statement. With these agreements as to vocabulary, we can develop a very convenient method for analyzing the possible truth values of a compound statement.

3.3.1 In discussing the possible truth values to be associated with the connectives *and*, *or*, and *not* we formed Tables 6, 7, and 8. These tables are called **Truth Tables** and, when properly constructed, list the possible ways in which component statements can occur as true or false. Such tables also exhibit the resulting truth values of the compound statements under consideration when the component statements have given truth values.

For brevity we let T stand for the truth value "true" and F stand for the value "false." In our discussion of the connective *or*, we noted that the term might have two possible meanings. If P and Q are simple statements, we can examine the two meanings of *or* as symbolized by $P \lor Q$ and $(P \lor Q) \land (\sim P \lor \sim Q)$ by means of a truth table. Recall that $\lor$ meant "one or the other or both" while the other was to be read as "at least one but not both."

TABLE 9

P	Q	$P \lor Q$	$(P \lor Q) \land (\sim P \lor \sim Q)$
T	T	T	F
T	F	T	T
F	T	T	T
F	F	F	F

Examination of Table 9 shows that the truth values of the compound statement forms differ in the first row. When both P and Q are true the inclusive sense of *or* as symbolized by $P \lor Q$ is to be considered true. The exclusive sense of the term *or* is to be considered false as we would expect intuitively from our common past experiences. The distinction may seem slight; however, in a critical situation it could well be all-important.

Truth tables can be used to clarify the meaning to be associated with the use of certain symbols. For example, if P, Q, and R are statements, we can specify the way in which parentheses are used.

TABLE 10

P	Q	R	$(P \land Q) \lor R$	$P \land (Q \lor R)$
T	T	T	T	T
T	T	F	T	T
T	F	T	T	T
T	F	F	F	F
F	T	T	T	F
F	T	F	F	F
F	F	T	T	F
F	F	F	F	F

The fifth and seventh rows of the truth table differ for the two compound statements. Examination of the statement forms show that the parentheses are used to group statements to form single statements on which the external connectives apply.

The application of the denial symbol is clarified by considering various situations in which it is used. For example, Table 11 illustrates four possible compound statement forms in which the denial symbol occurs.

TABLE 11

P Q	$\sim(\sim P)$	$\sim P \land Q$	$\sim(P \land Q)$	$P \land \sim Q$
T T	T	F	F	F
T F	T	F	T	T
F T	F	T	T	F
F F	F	F	T	F

Examination of the table shows that the denial is, by this convention, to be applied to the first statement on the right.

3.3.2 The proper construction of a truth table is, from the foregoing, quite important for the analysis of the truth values to be associated with compound statements. Our first step in the construction of a truth table is to list and form the possible combinations of truth values for the component statements involved. Next, we write the compound statement, leaving sufficient space between symbols so that we can form columns of truth values below each symbol. Now, beginning with the truth values of the component statements, we begin to fill in the truth values, column by column.

The simplest, innermost columns are filled in first and the more complex forms later. For example, let us construct in detail a truth table for the compound statement $\sim(P \land \sim Q)$.

STEP ONE. We note that the compound statement has two component statements, P and Q, and so we construct two columns of truth values. There are four possible ways in which we can pair the truth values T and F.

P Q	
T T	
T F	
F T	
F F	

STEP TWO.   Now we write the compound statement form to the right of the components, leaving ample room.

P	Q	$\sim(P \wedge \sim Q)$
T	T	
T	F	
F	T	
F	F	

STEP THREE.   Now, fill in the columns for P and Q by copying the truth values from the appropriate left-hand column.

P	Q	$\sim(P \wedge \sim Q)$	
T	T	T	T
T	F	T	F
F	T	F	T
F	F	F	F

STEP FOUR.   With the truth values of Q known, we can fill the column under the denial of Q.

P	Q	$\sim(P \wedge \sim Q)$		
T	T	T	F	T
T	F	T	T	F
F	T	F	F	T
F	F	F	T	F

STEP FIVE.   Now we can fill the column below the conjunction.

P	Q	$\sim(P \wedge \sim Q)$			
T	T	T	F	F	T
T	F	T	T	T	F
F	T	F	F	F	T
F	F	F	F	T	F

STEP SIX.   Finally, we can fill the column for the denial of the statement in parentheses.

P	Q	$\sim$	$(P \wedge \sim Q)$			
T	T	T	T	F	F	T
T	F	F	T	T	T	F
F	T	T	F	F	F	T
F	F	T	F	F	T	F

STEP SEVEN. The truth table is now complete. The truth values for the compound statement are those in the column completed last. They are the truth values which the compound statement would have for the various possible values of the component statements P and Q. If we are interested only in the truth values of the compound statement, we can construct a new table showing just the truth values of the components and the compound statement.

TABLE 12

P	Q	$\sim(P \wedge \sim Q)$
T	T	T
T	F	F
F	T	T
F	F	T

The following tables, given with all the columns filled in, should help to illustrate the procedure. Below the columns in the tables are listed the sequence of steps used in filling the columns with truth values. (Writing the compound statement has been counted as part of step one.) The column completed last gives the truth values of the compound statement.

TABLE 13

P	Q	$(P \vee Q)$	$\wedge$	$\sim P$
T	T	T T T	F	F T
T	F	T T F	F	F T
F	T	F T T	T	T F
F	F	F F F	F	T F
1	1	2 3 2	4	3 2

TABLE 14

P	Q	$\sim[$	$\sim(\sim P \wedge Q)$	$\vee$	$\sim Q]$
T	T	F	T F T F T	T	F T
T	F	F	T F T F F	T	T F
F	T	T	F T F T T	F	F T
F	F	F	T T F F F	T	T F
1	1	7	5 3 2 4 2	6	3 2

TABLE 15

P	Q	R	(P ∧ ~Q)	∨	(Q ∧ ~R)
T	T	T	T F F T	F	T F F T
T	T	F	T F F T	T	T T T F
T	F	T	T T T F	T	F F F T
T	F	F	T T T F	T	F F T F
F	T	T	F F F T	F	T F F T
F	T	F	F F F T	T	T T T F
F	F	T	F F T F	F	F F F T
F	F	F	F F T F	F	F F T F
1	1	1	2 4 3 2	5	2 4 3 2

3.3.3 Since in the above truth tables we are considering all possible cases of truth values of the component statements, the components can be thought of as being arbitrary statements (within the restrictions which we have mentioned previously). That is, the truth table values may be thought of as giving all the possible values of the compound statement. The actual truth or falsity of the component statements is not known and the truth value of the compound statement is not known until the truth values of its component statements can be specified.

If the truth values of the component statements of a compound statement are known, then it is not necessary to construct a complete truth table for the compound statement. A single row of the truth table with the specified truth values of the components will quickly determine the truth or falsity of the compound statement. For example, if A and B are true statements and C is a false statement, then the compound statement $\sim[A \vee \sim(C \wedge B)]$ must be false.

TABLE 16

~[	$A \vee \sim (C \wedge B)$]
F	T T T F F T

In concluding this section, we note that the converse problem of finding appropriate compound statements which satisfy (i.e., have the same truth values as) a given set of truth values is an instructive exercise in familiarizing oneself with the truth table technique. For example, if in a truth table the truth values are F, F, T, F respectively, the statement $\sim P \wedge Q$ will satisfy the table.

Exercises 3.3

1. If A and B are true statements and C and D are false statements, find the truth values of the following statements.
  (a) $\sim(A \wedge C)$ (b) $A \vee (C \wedge \sim D)$ (c) $\sim[\sim A \vee (\sim C \vee D)]$
  (d) $\sim[\sim(\sim C)]$ (e) $(A \vee C) \wedge (B \wedge \sim D)$

2. Do as in exercise 1 with:
  (a) $A \wedge [B \wedge (C \vee \sim D)]$ (b) $A \vee [B \vee (C \wedge D)]$
  (c) $(\sim C \wedge A) \vee [\sim(C \wedge D) \wedge (C \vee \sim B)]$

3. If P, Q, and R are statements, construct truth tables for the following statements.
  (a) $\sim(P \wedge Q)$ (b) $\sim P \vee \sim Q$ (c) $\sim(P \vee Q)$ (d) $\sim P \wedge \sim Q$

4. Do as in exercise 3 with:
  (a) $P \vee (Q \wedge R)$ (b) $(P \vee Q) \wedge (P \vee R)$
  (c) $\sim[\sim(P \vee \sim Q) \vee (Q \wedge \sim R)]$

5. Find compound statements which have the following truth tables.

(a) T	(b) F	(c) F	(d) F	(e) T	(f) F	(g) F	(h) T	(i) F
F	T	F	F	T	T	T	T	F
F	F	T	F	F	T	F	T	F
F	F	F	T	F	F	T	T	F

3.4 IF ... , THEN ...

We are all familiar with statements like "If it is a book, then it is difficult." The words *if* and *then* are used in a variety of ways. For example, the statement "If men are mortal and Socrates is a man, then Socrates is mortal" is called an argument in which the "if" portion of the statement is presupposed and the "then" portion is concluded as a consequence of this supposition. In "If you play with fire, then you will be burned," the "if" portion conditions the "then" portion. The consequent "you will be burned" depends upon an empirically determined investigation. The sense of statements of the form "If it is a mouse, then it is a rodent" depends upon the linguistic meaning of the words *rodent* and *mouse*.

3.4.1 In many situations, we use the connective "if ... , then ... " in a conditional sense. That is, we assert that a statement is true providing a specified condition is met. In this sense, we can define a connective for

TABLE 17

P	Q	$P \to Q$
T	T	T
T	F	F
F	T	T
F	F	T

forming compound statements as follows: If P and Q are statements as defined in 3.1.0.1 and 3.1.0.2, then the statement "If P, then Q" is a compound statement symbolized by "$P \rightarrow Q$" satisfying the truth values in Table 17.

Note that Table 17 specifies the truth value to be associated with the compound statement given any of the possible truth values of the component statements. In comparing truth tables, the compound statement forms $P \rightarrow Q$, $\sim P \vee Q$, and $\sim(P \wedge \sim Q)$ are seen to have the same set of truth values for given values of their components.

TABLE 18

P Q	$P \rightarrow Q$	$\sim(P \wedge \sim Q)$	$\sim P \vee Q$
T T	T	T	T
T F	F	F	F
F T	T	T	T
F F	T	T	T

Compound statements of the form $P \rightarrow Q$ are called **material implications**. The statement, P, between the *if* and the *then* is called the **antecedent**; the statement, Q, following the *then* is called the **consequent**. A material implication is, according to Table 17, a convenience in expression.

Note that the statement $P \rightarrow Q$ is to be considered true whenever P is false, regardless of the truth value of Q. Two questions may arise in this connection: first, why couldn't the material implication be considered false when P is false or when both components are false?; second, why should the statement "If black is white, then cows are green" be considered true? The answer to the first query is that the choice of truth values is made arbitrarily for convenience rather than for any inherent reason. It will be found that our arbitrary choice is consistent with our intuitive notion as to the use to which we will put the compound statement. The answer to the second query is that we are concerned here only with the form of statements and not with their content. That is, we are to use the material implication in the formal sense in which it is defined by the truth table.

3.4.2 Now suppose we wish to state that two statements P and Q are equivalent to each other? We might write the statement $(P \rightarrow Q) \wedge (Q \rightarrow P)$. Since this form of statement occurs frequently, we define a new symbol, $\leftrightarrow$, to indicate the connection. The new symbol is called an **equivalence** and is read as "if and only if." The equivalence asserts that if P is true, then Q is true, and if P is false, then Q is false.

TABLE 19

P	Q	$P \leftrightarrow Q$
T	T	T
T	F	F
F	T	F
F	F	T

The equivalence introduces an interesting and important concept concerning the relationship of compound statements. Consider the statements $\sim(P \wedge \sim Q)$ and $\sim P \vee Q$ in Table 18, if we let R stand for $\sim(P \wedge \sim Q)$ and S stand for $\sim P \vee Q$, then form $R \leftrightarrow S$, we have Table 20.

TABLE 20

P	Q	$\sim(P \wedge \sim Q)$	$\sim P \vee Q$	$R \leftrightarrow S$
T	T	T	T	T
T	F	F	F	T
F	T	T	T	T
F	F	T	T	T

When two statements such as R and S are related in this way, we say that they are **materially** or **logically equivalent.** That is, if the components of two statements are the same, and they are logically equivalent, then the statement forms of the two statements must have the same set of truth values. In subsequent considerations, we will consider logically equivalent statements as asserting or naming the same referent or condition.

A natural question to ask now is whether there are statements which would result in all false values of the equivalence. The answer is yes. Statements related in this way are called **contradictory** statements. For example, the statements $P \wedge Q$ and $\sim P \vee \sim Q$ are contradictories.

TABLE 21

P	Q	$(P \wedge Q)$	$\leftrightarrow$	$(\sim P \vee \sim Q)$
T	T	T	F	F
T	F	F	F	T
F	T	F	F	T
F	F	F	F	T

In conclusion, we note that the implication and equivalence refer to the form of a particular compound statement. "Logically equivalent" and "contradictory" refer to a relationship of truth value sets between two statements. A test of logical equivalence or contradiction is to form the equivalence statement to ascertain whether the resulting compound statement is true or false in every case.

Exercises 3.4

1. If A and B are true statements and C and D are false statements, find the truth values of the following statements.
    (a) $\sim(A \vee C) \to \sim(C \wedge B)$ (b) $(\sim C \wedge A) \to [(B \vee D) \vee C]$
    (c) $\sim[\sim(\sim A \wedge D) \to (\sim B \vee C)]$
2. Do as in exercise 1 with:
    (a) $(\sim A \vee B) \leftrightarrow [(C \wedge B) \to (D \vee A)]$
    (b) $\sim C \wedge [\sim(B \vee D) \leftrightarrow (\sim A \to C)]$
    (c) $\{\sim B \vee [\sim(C \vee A) \to D]\} \leftrightarrow [\sim(B \wedge D) \vee C]$
3. If P, Q, and R are statements, construct truth tables for the following statements.
    (a) $R \to (\sim P \vee Q)$ (b) $\sim[\sim P \to (Q \wedge R)]$
    (c) $\sim(\sim P \wedge \sim Q) \leftrightarrow R$ (d) $(P \to Q) \vee (\sim P \leftrightarrow R)$
4. Using truth tables, determine whether the following pairs of statements are logically equivalent.
    (a) $\sim(\sim P \wedge Q)$ and $\sim Q \vee P$
    (b) $P \wedge \sim(Q \vee R)$ and $(\sim Q \vee P) \wedge (P \vee \sim R)$
    (c) $(\sim P \vee Q) \to R$ and $P \to (\sim Q \vee R)$
5. If P, Q, and R are statements, construct truth tables for the following statements.
    (a) $[(P \to Q) \wedge P]$ (b) $[(P \to Q) \wedge \sim P] \to \sim Q$
    (c) $[(P \to Q) \wedge (Q \to R)] \to (P \to R)$

3.5 SUMMARY

In the foregoing sections we have taken the first direct step in the analysis of statements and problems.

Our first step was to focus and restrict our attention to a small portion of the possible kinds of statements that might be made. We defined statements called *simple* and *compound*. We then proceeded to consider five **logical connectives**. These connectives, called *conjunction, disjunction, denial, material implication*, and *equivalence*, were symbolically represented and defined. The essential character of the logical connectives is summarized in Table 22.

In our definitions of simple and compound statements we noted that we would only consider those statements which were true or false. This was called the **truth value** of the statement. In considering the truth value of statements, we considered an important and useful tool for the analysis of statements, *truth tables*. Using truth tables, it was possible to indicate the way in which the parentheses and bracket symbols, that is, the *grouping* symbols, were to be used. The denial symbol was also clarified.

TABLE 22

Truth Tables for Logical Connectives

P Q	$P \wedge Q$	$P \vee Q$	$\sim P$	$P \rightarrow Q$	$P \leftrightarrow Q$
T T	T	T	F	T	T
T F	F	T	F	F	F
F T	F	T	T	T	F
F F	F	F	T	T	T

We concluded by noting that pairs of statements can be compared and related. That is, statements might be **logically equivalent, contradictory,** or related in other ways. In the next chapter, we will continue our analysis of statements and consider at some length the ways in which collections of statements may be related.

3.5.0.1 Definition: By the **truth value** of a statement we mean T if and only if the statement is true, and F if and only if the statement is false.

3.5.0.2 Definition: Two statements are said to be **logically equivalent** if and only if they have the same truth tables.

3.5.0.3 Definition: Two statements are said to be **contradictory** if and only if they are never both true or both false.

Exercises 3.5

1. Indicate with an *S* or a *C* whether the following sentences are simple or compound. If neither, denote this by *N*.
   (*a*) He is a good boy.
   (*b*) He is big.
   (*c*) A tall boy should play basketball.
   (*d*) Let's go bowling or to the movies.
   (*e*) He isn't too bright.
   (*f*) I believe that I'll stay home.
   (*g*) If $a = b$, then $a + c = b + c$.
   (*h*) Whenever $a = b$, we have $b = a$.
   (*i*) He is taking mathematics or English, but not history.
   (*j*) If $a < b$ and $b < c$, then $a < c$.
2. Reformulate the sentences in exercise 1 into a form which is convenient to symbolize.
3. Using capital letters for simple statements, write symbolic representations for all of the sentences in exercise 1 which are simple or compound.
4. Construct truth tables for the symbolic representations of exercise 3.

Exercises 3

1. Symbolize the following statements, using the letters indicated.
   (a) Shirley is blond and not shy. (B, S)
   (b) If taxes were lower, we would receive fewer services. (T, R).
   (c) It is hot or it is cold and wet. (H, C, W)
   (d) If the car is new and expensive, it is large and shiny. (N, E, L, Y)
   (e) I can spend my money, or if I save it, then it will earn interest for me in the bank. (D, I)

2. Determine the truth or falsity of the statements in exercise 1, if S, R, H, L are false and the remaining simple statements are true.

3. If A stands for "man is mortal," B stands for "Joe is a man," and C stands for "Joe is a mortal," then write out the statements symbolized by
   (a) $(A \wedge B) \to C$ (b) $\sim B \to \sim C$ (c) $B \vee \sim B$ (d) $B \leftrightarrow C$

4. Construct truth tables for the statement forms of exercise 3.

5. If A and B are true statements and C and D are false statements, find the truth values of the following compound statements.
   (a) $(A \vee C) \to B$ (b) $(A \wedge C) \to \sim B$ (c) $(A \wedge D) \vee (C \to B)$
   (d) $[(C \wedge D) \vee (A \wedge B)] \to \sim[\sim(\sim A)]$

6. Construct truth tables for the following statement forms.
   (a) $R \to (P \vee Q)$ (b) $(P \wedge Q) \leftrightarrow (\sim P \to \sim Q)$
   (c) $\sim[P \wedge (\sim Q \vee R)] \wedge (\sim R \vee P)$ (d) $[(P \to Q) \wedge \sim Q] \to \sim P$

7. Find statement forms which are logically equivalent to the following statements.
   (a) $P \to Q$ (b) $\sim(P \wedge Q)$ (c) $\sim P \wedge \sim Q$ (d) $P \to (Q \to R)$

8. Find statement forms which are contradictory to the following statements. (Do not use the denial of the statement.)
   (a) $P \wedge \sim Q$ (b) $P \vee Q$ (c) $P \to \sim Q$ (d) $P \leftrightarrow Q$

9. Symbolize the following statements, using the letters indicated.
   (a) If Sam goes to school, he will be successful; and if he does not go, he will be a failure. (G, S)
   (b) Our nation can be made safe from aggression, if and only if our taxes are raised. (S, T)
   (c) If either Johnson or Kelly win, then it will be a victory for labor and the common man. (J, K, L, C)
   (d) It is not the case that reading the *Times* will prejudice you in the coming election. (T, P)

10. If A and B are true statements and C and D are false statements, find the truth values of the following compound statements.
    (a) $\sim(\sim A \vee C) \wedge B$ (b) $\sim(\sim[\sim A \wedge (B \wedge \sim C)])$
    (c) $\sim(A \to C) \vee (C \to D)$ (d) $(C \leftrightarrow D) \vee (A \to \sim B)$

11. Construct truth tables for the following statement forms.
    (a) $P \wedge (Q \vee \sim Q)$ (b) $Q \vee (P \to Q)$
    (c) $\sim P \vee (Q \to R)$ (d) $(\sim P \vee Q) \leftrightarrow (Q \wedge \sim P)$

12. Using truth tables, determine whether the following pairs of statements are logically equivalent.

    (a) $P \rightarrow (Q \wedge R)$ and $\sim R \rightarrow \sim P$ (b) Q and $(\sim Q \rightarrow \sim P) \leftrightarrow Q$

    (c) $P \vee Q$ and $P \vee (\sim P \wedge Q)$ (d) P and $P \wedge (P \vee \sim Q)$

13. For each of the following, find as simple a logically equivalent form as you can.

    (a) $P \vee \{\sim P \rightarrow [Q \vee (\sim Q \rightarrow R)]\}$

    (b) $[(P \wedge Q) \vee (Q \wedge R)] \vee [(P \wedge R) \vee R]$

    (c) $\sim\{\sim[\sim P \vee (Q \wedge \sim P)]\}$ (d) $[\sim(P \rightarrow Q) \vee P] \wedge [(P \wedge \sim Q) \vee Q]$

14. In examining the truth tables of various statement forms, note that the sets of truth values for the statements may be classified into three types: those which have the value true for all truth values of their components, those which have the value false for all truth values of their components, and those which have both true and false values for truth values of their components. Statements are called **tautologies, false statements,** and **conditional statements,** respectively, when characterized in the above way. Using T, F, C, and truth tables, determine and indicate the group in which each of the following statements should be placed.

    (a) $P \rightarrow \sim P$ (b) $\sim(P \wedge \sim P)$ (c) $(\sim P \wedge Q) \rightarrow P$

    (d) $(P \vee \sim Q) \wedge (\sim P \vee Q)$ (e) $\sim[\sim(P \wedge Q) \vee \sim(\sim P \wedge Q)]$

15. Write a short discussion on the logical use of the words *but*, *yet*, and *however* in the English language.

4
ARGUMENTS
AND PROOFS

4.1 ARGUMENTS

The intellectual processes which we call logical characterize man's struggle to solve problems. The processes of deriving inferences range from the consequences anticipated by a child who has knocked over a vase, to the analytic and subtle behavior of a physicist, who pieces out the story of his instrument readings.

It would be a hopeless task to discuss the logical processes using ordinary language alone. A symbolic language has been developed to avoid the ambiguity of ordinary language as well as to obtain a compactness which would otherwise be impossible.

The early Greeks recognized the usefulness of logical discourse; the famous Greek philosopher Plato and his student Aristotle were firm believers in the deductive processes using logical elements. In the Renaissance period Leibniz is regarded as the first to consider seriously the desirability of a symbolic logic. More recently an Englishman, George Boole (1815–1864), published a small pamphlet entitled *The Mathematical Analysis of Logic*. In 1854 Boole had published *An Investigation into the Laws of Thought*. A German logician, Gottlob Frege (1848–1925), and an Italian mathematician, Guiseppi Peano (1858–1932), developed the modern approach to symbolic logic which culminated in the monumental work, *The Principia Mathematica* (1910–1913), of A. N. Whitehead (1861–1947) and Bertrand Russell (1872– —).

In the use of language and symbols, we can make a distinction between the relationship between symbols and the association of symbols to referents. Traditionally the two areas are called formal logic and semantics. Logic is the study of the methods and principles used in distinguishing "correct" from "incorrect" arguments. That is, logic concerns itself with the connections that hold between symbols and a symbol structure. We began our study of logic with the consideration of compound statements and their form.

4.1.1 Statements are said to be true or false. Arguments are said to be **valid** or **invalid**. By valid and invalid arguments, we do not mean true or pragmatic (practical) arguments. By valid arguments, we mean that the inferences follow rules and specifications agreed upon. To illustrate:

We begin with **premises**:

The book is difficult or it is easy.

The book is not difficult.

We **conclude**:

Therefore, the book is easy.

In an argument, the concluding statement is said to follow logically from the premises if the argument is valid. Otherwise, it is not known from the argument itself whether the concluding statement is true or false. An invalid argument may lead to truth as well as a valid argument. To illustrate:

EXAMPLE 1. If lions eat meat, then sheep are carnivorous.

                Sheep are carnivorous.

                Therefore, lions eat meat.

In this argument, the premises are false, the conclusion true, and the argument is invalid.

EXAMPLE 2. Lions are vegetarians or sheep are carnivorous.

                Lions are not vegetarians.

                Therefore, sheep are carnivorous.

In this argument, the first premise is false, the conclusion is false, and the argument is valid.

EXAMPLE 3. If the moon is made of green cheese, then there are mice on the moon.

                The moon is not made of green cheese.

                Therefore, there are no mice on the moon.

In this argument, both premises and conclusion are true, but the argument is invalid.

EXAMPLE 4. If the moon is made of green cheese, then there are mice on the moon.

                There are no mice on the moon.

                Therefore, the moon is not made of green cheese.

In this argument, both premises and conclusion are true, and the argument is valid.

The above examples also illustrate the fact that the terms "premises" and "conclusion" are relative terms and refer to the role of statements in a particular argument. That is, a statement may have the role of a premise in one argument and the role of conclusion in another argument.

4.1.1.1 Definition: By an **argument** we mean a sequence of statements which have the following properties:
1. There are given statements which are called the **premises**.
2. The last statement, which is called the **conclusion** is said to **follow** from the statements in the sequence preceding it.

In examining arguments, it will be convenient to refer to the symbolic representations of the statements of the arguments. The symbolic representation of an argument will be called the **argument form** of the argument.

For example, for the four numbered examples above, we have:

$$
\begin{array}{cccc}
(1)\ P \to Q & (2)\ P \lor Q & (3)\ P \to Q & (4)\ P \to Q \\
\underline{Q} & \underline{\sim P} & \underline{\sim P} & \underline{\sim Q} \\
\therefore P & \therefore Q & \therefore \sim Q & \therefore \sim P
\end{array}
$$

where the letters stand for the statements in the respective arguments and the symbol $\therefore$ is read "therefore."

4.1.1.2 Definition: By the **argument form** of an argument we mean the sequence of symbolic representations of the statements of the argument.

An argument form is said to be valid if, whenever the premises are true, the conclusion is true. Otherwise, the argument form is said to be invalid or to be a fallacy. For convenience, we will say that an argument is valid if its argument form is valid.

4.1.1.3 Definition: By the **validity** of an argument we mean that whenever the premises are true, the conclusion is true. Otherwise, we will say that the argument is invalid or is a **fallacy**.

A truth table can be constructed to test the validity of an argument. Note that the validity of an argument does *not* imply truth or falsity with respect to the statements of the argument. A valid argument only asserts the "correctness" of the structure of the argument.

To illustrate, consider the argument:
The book is difficult or it is easy.
The book is not difficult.
Therefore, the book is easy.

This can be symbolically represented as:

$$A \lor B$$
$$\sim A$$
$$\therefore B$$

with the truth values as given in Table 23.

TABLE 23

A B	$A \lor B$	$\sim A$	$\therefore B$
T T	T	F	T
T F	T	F	F
F T	T	T	T
F F	F	T	F

The statements of the argument may or may not be true. The first row of the truth table indicates a possible situation in which the premise statement, "The book is not difficult," is false while the conclusion, "The book is easy, is true. The second row gives the possibility of a false conclusion. In a test of validity, however, we are interested only in those rows in which all of the premises are true. This occurs only in the third row. Since the conclusion B is also true in the third row, we conclude that the argument is valid. The validity of an argument depends solely on the structure of the argument form of the argument.

Argument forms can also be written in the form of compound statements. Note that, when the premises are true, the conclusion must be true in order for the argument to be called valid. If any premise is false, the truth or falsity of the conclusion is immaterial to the validity of the argument. For the above illustration, we can form the material implication: $[(A \lor B) \land (\sim A] \to B$. The truth table for this compound statement shows an interesting property, as in Table 24.

TABLE 24

A B	$[(A \lor B) \land (\sim A)] \to B$
T T	T
T F	T
F T	T
F F	T

Compound statements with all truth values true are called **tautologies** and represent valid argument forms. The implication formed by the conjunction of all the premises as the antecedent and the conclusion as the consequent from a valid argument form will always result in a tautology. Testing compound statements to see whether they are tautologies is thus equivalent to testing an argument for validity.

   4.1.1.4 Definition: By a **tautology** we mean a statement which has the truth value true for all possible truth values of its components.

   Three classical valid arguments which are used frequently are:

$$(a)\ P \to Q \qquad (b)\ P \to Q \qquad (c)\ P \to Q$$
$$ P \qquad\qquad\quad \sim Q \qquad\qquad\quad Q \to R$$
$$ \therefore\ Q \qquad\qquad \therefore \sim P \qquad\qquad \therefore\ P \to R$$

These are called **modus ponens, modus tollens,** and **hypothetical syllogism,** respectively. The reader should verify the validity of these argument forms by means of a truth table.

   Two invalid argument forms , called the Fallacy of Affirming the Consequent and the Fallacy of Denying the Antecedent, can be expressed as

$$(a)\ P \to Q \qquad (b)\ P \to Q$$
$$ Q \qquad\qquad\quad \sim P$$
$$ \therefore\ P \qquad\qquad \therefore \sim Q$$

TABLE 25

P Q	$P \to Q$	$\sim P$	$\sim Q$
T T	T	F	F
T F	F	F	T
F T	T	T	F
F F	T	T	T

   Examination of the third row of the truth values in Table 25 should make invalidity of these arguments clear.

   We should not be too hasty in judging the validity or invalidity of an argument. For example, the unlikely argument $\sim A,\ \therefore\ \sim(A \wedge \sim B)$ is valid according to Table 26 for $\sim A \to \sim(A \wedge \sim B)$.

TABLE 26

A B	$\sim A \to \sim(A \wedge \sim B)$
T T	T
T F	T
F T	T
F F	T

In concluding this section, we consider a short method for testing the *invalidity* of an argument. If the truth table of an argument contains a row in which the premises are all true and the conclusion false, the argument is invalid. Instead of constructing the entire truth table, if the argument is invalid, we can choose the truth values of the component statements in such a way that the premises are made true and the conclusion false. Thus one row of truth values is sufficient to show the invalidity of the argument. For example, the invalid argument $(P \wedge \sim Q) \vee (Q \wedge \sim R)$, $\sim(P \wedge Q)$, $\therefore \sim(Q \vee \sim R)$ can be shown to be invalid by choosing P true, Q false, and R false.

TABLE 27

$P \quad Q \quad R$	$(P \wedge \sim Q) \vee (Q \wedge \sim R)$	$\sim(P \wedge Q)$	$\therefore \sim(Q \wedge \sim R)$
T F F	T	T	F

The above test of invalidity is much shorter than making up an entire truth table.

Exercises 4.1

1. Symbolize the following argument and test for validity:
Shirley is either blond or brunette.
If Shirley is blond, then she is friendly.
Shirley is not friendly.
Therefore, Shirley is brunette.

2. Do as in 1:
If it rains, then I will stay indoors.
The television is broken and it is raining.
Therefore, I will stay indoors.

3. Test the validity of the following:

(a) $\sim(\sim P \wedge \sim Q)$ (b) $\sim P \rightarrow \sim Q$
      $\sim(\sim P)$ $\sim(P \wedge \sim R)$
     $\overline{\therefore \ Q}$ $\sim R$
                  $\overline{\therefore \ \sim Q}$

4.2 PROOFS

The meaning of the word *proof* depends on the audience for whom the proof is intended. "Proofs" quite adequate to a historian may not be comprehensible to a physicist. A "proof" understood by an advanced student in a special field might be completely confusing to the beginning student in that field. However, the aim of a proof is to convince an audience of the truth of some conclusion based on some preliminary agreements and assumptions. As with definitions, there are two levels of proofs: informal and formal.

All proofs can be considered as belonging to one of two categories: proofs of factual truth or content, and proofs based on structure and form. We will concern ourselves with the latter type of proof, and restrict its meaning to the establishment of the concluding statement of an argument in which the premises are assumed true. We will say that a statement is **proved** when the statement is the conclusion of a valid argument in which the premises are assumed true. We will use the word "proof" and the phrase "prove a statement," meaning "assume the given premises to be true and exhibit a sequence of valid arguments such that the last concluding statement is the statement which was to be proved." It should be evident that the preceding truth-table methods might be used to exhibit the validity of arguments used in a proof.

4.2.1 A more convenient method of establishing the concluding statement of an argument is to separate the argument into a sequence of shorter arguments whose validity is already established. If the premises are "given" or assumed true, we can form a connected chain of valid arguments such that the conclusion of the last valid argument is the statement to be proved. For example, the following argument, which requires sixteen rows in a truth table, can be separated into a short sequence of valid arguments to establish its validity.

> Sam saw Bill but not Ann or Ann but not Nancy.
> If he saw Bill, then he saw Mary.
> He did not see Mary.
> Therefore, Sam did not see Nancy.

A symbolic representation results in:

$(A \wedge \sim B) \vee (B \wedge \sim C)$	premise.
$A \rightarrow D$	premise.
$\sim D$	premise.
$\therefore \sim C$	conclusion.

If the premises are assumed true, then a proof can be written as follows:

1. $(A \rightarrow D), \sim D, \therefore \sim A$
2. $\sim A, \therefore \sim(A \wedge \sim B)$
3. $(A \wedge \sim B) \vee (B \wedge \sim C), \sim(A \wedge \sim B), \therefore (B \wedge \sim C)$
4. $(B \wedge \sim C), \therefore \sim C.$

Note that each of the four arguments is a valid argument. The premises of the individual arguments are either premises of the argument or conclusions of a previous argument of the proof. The conclusion of the final short argument is the required conclusion of the original argument. It is reasonable to suppose that the conjunction of the four short arguments would also form a valid argument with the final conclusion as its conclusion.

It will be convenient to have a reference list of valid argument forms and logically equivalent statements to use in testing the "correctness" of proofs as well as in forming and constructing proofs. The use of any of the argument forms or equivalences in the reference list is then justified without further verification. Finally, if we are to use this procedure, we should refer each short argument of a proof to this list.

TABLE 28

Valid Argument Forms

1. Modus ponens:	$P \rightarrow Q$, P, $\therefore Q$.	
2. Modus tollens:	$P \rightarrow Q$, $\sim Q$, $\therefore \sim P$.	
3. Hypothetical syllogism:	$P \rightarrow Q$, $Q \rightarrow R$, $\therefore P \rightarrow R$.	
4. Disjunctive syllogism:	$P \lor Q$, $\sim P$, $\therefore Q$.	
5. Constructive dilemma:	$(P \rightarrow Q) \land (R \rightarrow S)$, $P \lor R$, $\therefore Q \lor S$.	
6. Destructive dilemma:	$(P \rightarrow Q) \land (R \rightarrow S)$, $\sim Q \lor \sim S$, $\therefore \sim P \lor \sim R$.	
7. Simplification:	$P \land Q$, $\therefore P$.	
8. Conjunction:	P, Q, $\therefore P \land Q$.	
9. Addition:	P, $\therefore P \lor Q$.	

TABLE 29

Logically Equivalent Statements

(a) P and $\sim(\sim P)$	(h) $[(P \land Q) \rightarrow R]$ and $[P \rightarrow (Q \rightarrow R)]$
(b) P and $(P \lor P)$	(i) $[P \land (Q \lor R)]$ and $[(P \land Q) \lor (P \land R)]$
(c) P and $(P \land P)$	(j) $[P \lor (Q \land R)]$ and $[(P \lor Q) \land (P \lor R)]$
(d) $(P \lor Q)$ and $(Q \lor P)$	(k) $\sim(P \land Q)$ and $(\sim P \lor \sim Q)$
(e) $(P \land Q)$ and $(Q \land P)$	(l) $\sim(P \lor Q)$ and $(\sim P \land \sim Q)$
(f) $(P \rightarrow Q)$ and $(\sim Q \rightarrow \sim P)$	(m) $[P \lor (Q \lor R)]$ and $[(P \lor Q) \lor R]$
(g) $(P \rightarrow Q)$ and $\sim(P \land \sim Q)$	(n) $[P \land (Q \land R)]$ and $[(P \land Q) \land R]$

With the above lists agreed upon, we are in a position to stylize the arguments used in a proof.

EXAMPLE 1. If the weather is fair, then we will go on a picnic. I will study, or I will watch television and not go on a picnic. I will not study. Therefore, the weather is not fair.

Proof:

1. $F \rightarrow P$ premise.
2. $S \lor (T \land \sim P)$ premise.
3. $\sim S$ premise.

4. $T \wedge \sim P$ 2, 3, disj. syll.
5. $\sim P$ 4, simpl.
6. $\therefore \sim F$ 1, 5, mod. tol.

Symbolic representations of the premises, which are assumed true for the purposes of the proof, are listed first. Steps 4, 5, and 6 are conclusions of valid arguments referred to in the column to the right. The last statement symbolized by $\sim F$ is the statement which is asserted to have been proved.

The stylizing of the form and structure in the above way results in a compact and relatively easy to "check" proof. That is, each argument and equivalence used can be easily verified. Since we are usually interested in "correct proofs" we will use the term "proof" to mean "correct proof." This is not to imply that all proofs are "correct."

4.2.1.1 Definition: By a **formal proof** of a given statement we mean a sequence of statements such that:
1. The statement is a premise which is given as true, or
2. The statement is the conclusion of a valid argument from a given list of valid arguments such that its premises are from preceding statements in the sequence, or
3. The statement is a logically equivalent statement to a preceding statement in the sequence, and such that
4. The last statement in the sequence is the statement to be proved.

Briefly, a **formal proof** of a given statement consists of a valid argument in which the premises are all true and such that the conclusion is the statement to be proved. In contrast to an argument which is said to be valid or invalid, in a proof we use valid arguments to assert the truth of a statement as being deduced from true premises.

Although a formal proof may be given, we should not conclude that it is necessarily correct. That is, we should check to see that it satisfies all the requirements for a formal proof. This can be accomplished by comparing each step in the sequence forming the proof with the list of elementary valid arguments and logical equivalences.

EXAMPLE 2. *Given:* $(A \wedge \sim B) \vee (B \wedge \sim C)$, $A \rightarrow D$, $\sim D$.
Prove: $\sim C$.
  Proof:
  1. $(A \wedge \sim B) \vee (B \wedge \sim C)$ premise.
  2. $A \rightarrow D$ premise.

3. $\sim D$ premise.
4. $\sim A$ 2, 3, mod. tol.
5. $\sim A \lor B$ 4, add.
6. $\sim(A \land \sim B)$ 5, equiv. (k).
7. $(B \land \sim C)$ 1, 6, disj. syll.
8. $\therefore \sim C$ 7, simpl.

To check a proof is mechanical and requires little ingenuity, but the discovery and writing of proofs is seldom easy. Before discussing how to find appropriate valid arguments for a proof of a given statement, let us examine some examples.

4.2.2 The following illustrates a type of proof called a **Direct Proof**. In a direct proof, each statement is deduced from the premises and succeding statements. The examples previously given are of this type.

EXAMPLE 3. *Given:* If it is big and soft, then it is warm. If it is warm and alive, then it is my dog. If it is an animal, then it is soft and alive. It is false that it is not an animal or small.

Prove: It is my dog. (Let the symbolic representations of the given premises be as shown in steps 1 through 4.)

Proof:
1. $(B \land S) \to W$ premise.
2. $(W \land A) \to D$ premise.
3. $N \to (S \land A)$ premise.
4. $\sim(\sim N \lor \sim B)$ premise.
5. $W \to (A \to D)$ 2, equiv. (h).
6. $(B \land S) \to (A \to D)$ 1, 5, hypoth. syll.
7. $[(B \land S) \land A] \to D$ 6, equiv. (h).
8. $[B \land (S \land A)] \to D$ 7, equiv. (n).
9. $[(S \land A) \land B] \to D$ 8, equiv. (e).
10. $(S \land A) \to (B \to D)$ 9, equiv. (h).
11. $N \to (B \to D)$ 3, 10, hyp. syll.
12. $(N \land B) \to D$ 11, equiv. (h).
13. $\sim D \to \sim(N \land B)$ 12, equiv. (f).
14. $\sim D \to (\sim N \lor \sim B)$ 13, equiv. (k).
15. $\therefore D$ 4, 14, mod. toll.

4.2.3 Another type of proof is called a **Conditional Proof**. A conditional proof asserts the conclusion in the form of an implication.

We have noted that argument forms may be written as implications with the conjunction of the premises as the antecedent and the conclusion as the consequent. If we let P stand for the conjunction of the premises of an argument and $Q \to R$ stand for the conclusion of the argument, then in the form of an implication the argument can be represented by $P \to (Q \to R)$. Now this compound statement is logically equivalent to the statement $(P \wedge Q) \to R$. If we show that the argument represented by the latter statement is valid, it will be equivalent to showing the argument represented by $P \to (Q \to R)$ is valid. Thus, in a conditional proof, we assume the antecedent of the implication, which is the conclusion, as an added premise and deduce the consequent of the conclusion.

EXAMPLE 4. *Given:* Bill is a disgrace and a nuisance or he is a student. If Bill is a student, then he is not in jail.
   Prove: If Bill is not a disgrace, he is not in jail.
   Proof:

1. $(D \wedge N) \vee S$	premise.
2. $S \to {\sim}J$	premise.
3. ${\sim}D$	conditional premise.
4. $S \vee (D \wedge N)$	1, equiv. (d).
5. $(S \vee D) \wedge (S \vee N)$	4, equiv. (j).
6. $S \vee D$	5, simpl.
7. S	3, 6, disj. syll.
8. ${\sim}J$	2, 7, mod. pon.
9. $\therefore {\sim}D \to {\sim}J$	3, 8, conditional concl.

4.2.4 In some situations we find it convenient to form a proof by assuming the denial of the conclusion and showing that this assumption leads to a contradiction. This type of proof is called the method of proof by **reductio ad absurdum**, or, more simply, a type of **indirect proof**.

The method stems from an application of logical equivalences to the implication form of an argument. That is, if P stands for the conjunction of the premises of a valid argument and C for the desired conclusion, then the associated implication $P \to C$, which represents the argument, must be a tautology. Now, since ${\sim}C \to {\sim}P$ is equivalent to $P \to C$, showing that the argument represented by ${\sim}C \to {\sim}P$ is valid is equivalent to showing that $P \to C$ is a tautology, that is, represents a valid argument. The form ${\sim}C \to {\sim}P$ is called the **contrapositive** of $P \to C$. In practice, the following logically equivalent forms to $P \to C$ are used:

(1) ${\sim}C \to {\sim}P$	(contrapositive)
(2) $(P \wedge {\sim}C) \to {\sim}P$	(conditional form)
(3) $(P \wedge {\sim}C) \to C$	(an application of Aristotle's *Law of Excluded Middle*)
(4) $(P \wedge {\sim}C) \to (R \wedge {\sim}R)$	(reductio ad absurdum)

In carrying out an indirect proof, note that we can always begin with the denial of the conclusion as an added premise. If the arguments of the proof lead us to assert the denial of any premise, the conclusion, or contradictory statements, then we will be able to assert the required conclusion.

EXAMPLE 5. An indirect proof of Example 1, 4.2.1.

Proof:

1. $F \rightarrow P$	premise.	
2. $S \lor (T \land \sim P)$	premise.	
3. $\sim S$	premise.	
4. F	premise for indirect proof.	
5. $T \land \sim P$	2, 3, disj. syll.	
6. P	1, 4, mod. pon.	
7. $P \lor \sim T$	6, add.	
8. $\sim(\sim P \land T)$	7, equiv. (k).	
9. $\sim(T \land \sim P)$	8, equiv. (e).	
10. $(T \land \sim P) \lor \sim F$	5, add.	
11. $\therefore \sim F$	9, 10, disj. syll.	

Note that in the above proof the contradiction occurs in steps 5 and 9 to form a reductio ad absurdum proof which is carried to the required conclusion in steps 10 and 11.

EXAMPLE 6: *Given:* If Bill drinks or is in one of his ugly moods, he will ruin the party. Bill will drink or ruin the party.

Prove: Bill will ruin the party.

Proof:

1. $(D \lor M) \rightarrow R$	premise.
2. $D \lor R$	premise.
3. $\sim R$	premise for indirect proof.
4. D	2, 3, disj. syll.
5. $D \lor M$	4, add.
6. $\therefore R$	1, 5, mod. pon.

Note that this is in the form $(P \land \sim C) \rightarrow C$. That is, we have shown that $\sim C \rightarrow (P \rightarrow C)$.

Exercises 4.2

Each of the following represents a formal proof. Give the numbers of the previous steps used and the valid argument or logical equivalence applied in each step of the proof.

1. (a) *Proof:*

1. $A \lor (B \land C)$	premise.
2. $\sim C$	premise.
3. $(A \lor B) \land (A \lor C)$	

(b) *Proof:*

1. $\sim(L \land E)$	premise.
2. $\sim E \rightarrow S$	premise.
3. L	premise.

4. $A \lor C$
5. $\therefore A$

2. (*a*) *Proof:*

1. $A \to B$ premise.
2. $B \to C$ premise.
3. $A \land D$ premise.
4. $A \to C$
5. A
6. C
7. D
8. $\therefore C \land D$

3. *Proof:*

1. $(A \land B) \to N$ premise.
2. $(A \land C) \lor (A \land D)$ premise.
3. $B \land \sim C$ conditional premise.
4. $A \land (C \lor D)$
5. $A \to (B \to N)$
6. A
7. $B \to N$

4. *Proof:*

1. $\sim A \to (\sim B \lor \sim C)$ premise.
2. $B \land (A \lor C)$ premise.
3. $\sim A$ premise for indirect proof.
4. $\sim B \lor \sim C$

5. *Proof:*

1. $(A \land \sim B) \lor (B \land \sim C)$ premise.
2. $A \to D$ premise.
3. $\sim D$ premise.
4. C premise for indirect proof.
5. $C \lor \sim B$
6. $\sim B \lor C$

4. $L \to \sim E$
5. $\sim E$
6. $\therefore S$

(*b*) *Proof:*

1. $\sim P \to \sim Q$ premise.
2. $\sim (P \land \sim R)$ premise.
3. $\sim R$ premise.
4. $P \to R$
5. $Q \to P$
6. $Q \to R$
7. $\therefore \sim Q$

8. B
9. N
10. $C \lor D$
11. $\sim C$
12. D
13. $N \land D$
14. $\therefore (B \land \sim C) \to (N \land D)$

5. $\sim (B \land C)$
6. $(B \land A) \lor (B \land C)$
7. $B \land A$
8. $\therefore A$

7. $\sim (B \land \sim C)$
8. $A \land \sim B$
9. A
10. $\sim A$
11. $A \lor \sim C$
12. $\therefore \sim C$

4.3 DISCOVERING PROOFS

To discover appropriate valid arguments and/or equivalences for a proof is not always easy. It is necessary to *THINK*, to "figure out" where and how to begin. Simple proofs are often discovered by recognition, recollection, or by an immediate insight into the proof. For difficult proofs we may resort to lengthy study, planning, or discussion.

As G. Polya might remark, it is hard to have good ideas if we have little knowledge of the subject, and it is impossible if we have no knowledge. Good ideas are based on past ideas, experience, and recollections. Experience, intuition, and *PRACTICE* play large roles in the discovery of proofs.

Memory alone is not enough; we need imagination and the creative spirit of experiment to be successful. We must ask questions, follow suggestions, and observe how others have succeeded.

4.3.1 Given a statement to prove, our first task is to determine the given premises and the symbolic representation of the resulting argument. We list the premises and the conclusion separately.

For example:

Given: If Steve studies, he will graduate from school. If he graduates, he will work for his father or travel. Steve studies but will not work for his father.

Prove: Steve will travel.

Let S stand for Steve studies.

G for Steve will graduate from school.

W for Steve will work for his father.

T for Steve will travel.

Then $S \rightarrow G$ premise.

    $G \rightarrow (W \vee T)$ premise.

    $\underline{S \wedge \sim W}$ premise.

    $\therefore T$ conclusion.

Now examine the argument form to "see" if it suggests an immediate proof. Which type of proof should we try? Could the argument be invalid? Can we apply an elementary argument form to one or more of the premises? Do we recognize any logically equivalent statement forms? Does the argument appear similar to one we have used previously? At this point, it is wise to have a list of valid argument forms and logical equivalences handy.

Note that the first two premises can be combined by applying the argument form called a hypothetical syllogism. The third premise can be written as two separate statements S and $\sim W$ by simplification. Note that the conclusion T could be obtained by a disjunctive syllogism from the statement $(W \vee T)$. Do we "see" the proof?

Tentatively, we first list the premises:

1. $S \rightarrow G$ premise.
2. $G \rightarrow (W \vee T)$ premise.
3. $S \wedge \sim W$ premise.

Now apply the hypothetical syllogism to the first two premises to obtain:

4. $S \rightarrow (W \vee T)$ 1, 2, hyp. syll.

Let us simplify the third premise to obtain S. If we do this, we can apply the modus ponens argument to obtain $(W \vee T)$.

5. S 3, simplification.
6. $(W \vee T)$ 4, 5, mod. pon.

Another simplification of the third premise enables us to obtain $\sim W$. But this will allow us to apply the disjunctive syllogism.

7. $\sim W$ 3, simpl.
8. $\therefore T$ 6, 7, disj. syll.

The result in step 8 is our conclusion! Do not dismiss the proof just yet; re-examine it. Note how modus ponens and the disjunctive syllogism were applied. A simplification was useful twice. Look at the premises, see how the proof was suggested.

4.3.2 Another argument: If Bill went to school, he forgot his appointment with Sam and does not know about Clancy. If James acts and Bill is not aware of Clancy, a lawyer will not be necessary. Therefore, if James acts and Bill went to school, a lawyer will not be necessary.

Focus on the argument; symbolize it. List the premises and the conclusion.

$$S \rightarrow (A \wedge K) \qquad \text{premise.}$$
$$\underline{(J \wedge K) \rightarrow L} \qquad \text{premise.}$$
$$\therefore (J \wedge S) \rightarrow L \qquad \text{conclusion.}$$

Look at the structure of the argument. Are there any distinctive characteristics? Note the conclusion; it is in the form of an implication. Let us consider a conditional proof. Restate the modified argument.

$$S \rightarrow (A \wedge K) \qquad \text{premise.}$$
$$(J \wedge K) \rightarrow L \qquad \text{premise.}$$
$$\underline{(J \wedge S)} \qquad\qquad \text{conditional premise.}$$
$$\therefore L \qquad\qquad\quad \text{conditional conclusion.}$$

Examine the statements. Can we simplify? Is it possible to apply an equivalence? The statement $(J \wedge K) \rightarrow L$ can be written as $J \rightarrow (K \rightarrow L)$ by an equivalence. But J can be obtained by a simplification! Then a modus ponens argument will result in $A \wedge K$. Now we can obtain K by simplification. This is the antecedent of the implication $K \rightarrow L$. Modus ponens! And thus a proof is suggested.

Proof:

1. $S \rightarrow (A \wedge K)$ premise.
2. $(J \wedge K) \rightarrow L$ premise.
3. $J \wedge S$ conditional premise.
4. $J \rightarrow (K \rightarrow L)$ 2, equiv. (h).
5. J 3, simpl.
6. $K \rightarrow L$ 4, 5, mod. pon.

Steps 4, 5, and 6 indicate our first line of approach. Now, we begin our second line of attack.

    7. S 3, simpl.

    8. $A \wedge K$ 1, 7, mod. pon.

    9. K 8, simpl.

Our two lines of approach have resulted in the statements K and $K \rightarrow L$. Combining these, we obtain

    10. L 6, 9, mod. pon.

Finally, we can assert the conditional conclusion in the form of the given implication.

    11. $\therefore (J \wedge S) \rightarrow L$ 3, 10, cond. concl.

Note that in this proof we have joined a conditional premise to the given premises. When proofs are difficult, it may help to ask oneself whether adding a particular premise would be useful in deducing the conclusion. If so, we might try to deduce the useful added premise from the given premises. On occasion, this might lead to a contradiction and either an indirect proof or to showing that the argument is invalid.

An examination of the proof shows that there were two distinct sequences of statements. Proofs can sometimes be discovered by writing the possible sequences of direct steps which can be obtained from the premises, then a comparison of the steps of the sequences will often suggest a method of joining the short sequences to obtain a single sequence of steps leading to the desired conclusion. A short sequence of steps may again suggest another parallel sequence of steps. Finally, parallel sequences may lead to contradictory statements indicating an invalid argument.

4.3.3 A final example: If Mr. Stone went to the city, he went for business and pleasure. If he went to the city, he did not go for business. Therefore, Mr. Stone did not go to the city.

Symbolically

$$C \rightarrow (B \wedge P) \quad \text{premise.}$$
$$\underline{C \rightarrow \sim B \qquad\quad \text{premise.}}$$
$$\therefore \sim C \qquad\qquad \text{conclusion.}$$

Let us work for an indirect proof. This is natural since, if we have the denial of the conclusion, C, we would be able to apply modus ponens to each of the premises. If we obtain a contradiction, then we will be able to assert the desired conclusion.

Proof:

    1. $C \rightarrow (B \wedge P)$ premise.

    2. $C \rightarrow \sim B$ premise.

    3. C premise for indirect proof.

The assertion of the premise for an indirect proof is a "suppose this were true" hypotheses. If it is true, then our conclusion is false. If it is false, then our conclusion must be true. That is, the argument must be invalid or valid according to whether we can make the assertion of the denial of the conclusion or not.

Now let us proceed by applying the suggested modus ponens argument.

4. $B \wedge P$ 1, 3, mod. pon.

5. $\sim B$ 2, 3, mod. pon.

6. B 4, simpl.

From our supposition of the denial of the conclusion we have obtained the contradiction $\sim B$ and B. This does *not* mean that the argument is invalid; it tells us that our added supposition C leads us to a contradiction. Thus we can deduce our conclusion $\sim C$ as the only alternative to our supposition. This completes the main portion of the proof. To complete the proof, we adjoin the desired conclusion to one of the contradictory statements and then, using a disjunctive syllogism, effect the desired conclusion

7. $B \vee \sim C$ 6, add.

8. $\therefore \sim C$ 5, 7, disj. syll.

The discovery and writing of a proof should not be the end of our concern for the proof. The ease with which the next proof is discovered depends on the useful experience we gain from the discovery of the previous proof. If we succumb to the temptation to put our work away and look for something else to do, we miss an important and instructive phase of discovery. We should look back, re-examine our proofs, consolidate our position, establish our learning.

4.3.4 In this chapter we have considered the nature of arguments and proofs. In practice, arguments and proofs are most often expressed informally, and much of the time concern the content of statements as well as the form and structure of the assertions. Informal arguments and proofs are often more practical and convincing, but are never as adequate as a formal proof. Acceptance of informal arguments and proofs should be based upon the belief that they can be formalized; that is, that there exists a formal proof for the assertion being made.

Most mathematical proofs are informal. Indeed, if formal proofs were written, as they sometimes are, the length of the proofs would all but defeat the purpose of the proof to convince the reader of the truth of an assertion. Most proofs are thus abbreviations, sets of clues to suggest the existence of a formal proof. The degree of abbreviation depends upon the intended audience. Many proofs in modern technical journals and advanced texts are so brief as to be meaningless except to the specialist in the field.

In the following chapters, we will write many proofs. Most of the proofs will be informal. The reader should convince himself of the existence of formal proofs wherever possible.

Exercises 4.3

Represent the following arguments symbolically and write formal proofs for them, assuming the premises as given and the conclusion to be proved.

1. If he is a bachelor, he is lonely. If he is lonely, he should get married. He is a young bachelor. Therefore, he should get married.
2. It takes time or is difficult or it is tedious or difficult. If it takes time, then it is not difficult or costly. It is easy. Therefore, it is costly.
3. If he is smart or fast, he will succeed. If he fails, he is fast. Therefore, he will succeed.
4. If Steve is in school, he is not a nuisance. If he is a nuisance, he will hurt himself. Steve is in school or he will not hurt himself. Therefore, he is not a nuisance.
5. If he is an executive and a stockholder, he will be interested. He will be interested if and only if he is a friend or cooperates. He is a stockholder but not a friend. Therefore, if he is an executive, he will cooperate.

Exercises 4

1. Test the following arguments for validity or invalidity:

   (a) $\sim(P \vee Q)$ premise.   (b) $(\sim Q \vee P) \wedge (P \to Q)$ premise.

   $\underline{R \to P}$ premise. $\overline{\therefore\ P \leftrightarrow Q}$ conclusion.

   $\therefore\ R$ conclusion.

2. Each of the following is a formal proof. Give the numbers of the previous steps used and the valid arguments or logical equivalences applied in each step of the proof.

   (a) *Proof:*   (b) *Proof:*

   1. $(K \vee J) \to \sim N$ premise.   1. $M \to (\sim P \wedge \sim Q)$ premise.
   2. $H \wedge \sim K$ premise.   2. $N \to P$ premise.
   3. $\sim H \vee N$ premise.   3. $\sim(\sim N)$ premise.
   4. H 4. N
   5. N 5. P
   6. $\sim(K \vee J)$ 6. $P \vee Q$
   7. $\sim K \wedge \sim J$ 7. $M \to \sim(P \vee Q)$
   8. $\therefore\ \sim J$ 8. $\therefore\ \sim M$

3. Do as in exercise 2 with:

   (a) *Proof:*   (b) *Proof:*

   1. $(\sim A \wedge B) \vee C$ premise.   1. $(P \to Q) \vee (M \to R)$ premise.
   2. $(A \vee \sim B) \wedge D$ premise.   2. $\sim(\sim P \vee K) \wedge \sim Q$ premise.
   3. $(C \wedge D) \to B$ premise.   3. $\sim R$ premise.
   4. $A \vee \sim B$ 4. $\sim Q$
   5. $\sim(\sim A \wedge B)$ 5. $\sim(\sim P \vee K)$
   6. C 6. $P \wedge \sim K$
   7. $C \to (D \to B)$ 7. P
   8. $D \to B$ 8. $P \wedge \sim Q$
   9. D 9. $\sim(P \to Q)$
   10. B 10. $M \to R$
   11. $\therefore\ A$ 11. $\therefore\ \sim M$

4. Do as in 2 and 3 with:
  Proof:

  1. $\sim A \vee (K \wedge L)$ premise.
  2. $(M \wedge L) \to (N \vee A)$ premise.
  3. $\sim(N \vee K) \wedge L$ premise.
  4. $(\sim A \vee K) \wedge (\sim A \vee L)$
  5. $\sim A \vee K$
  6. $(\sim N \wedge \sim K) \wedge L$
  7. $\sim N \wedge \sim K$
  8. $\sim K$
  9. $\sim A$

  10. $\sim(N \vee A) \to \sim(M \wedge L)$
  11. $(\sim N \wedge \sim A) \to \sim(M \wedge L)$
  12. $\sim N \to [\sim A \to \sim(M \wedge L)]$
  13. $\sim N$
  14. $\sim A \to \sim(M \wedge L)$
  15. $\sim(M \wedge L)$
  16. $\sim M \vee \sim L$
  17. L
  18. $\therefore \ \sim M$

Symbolize the following arguments and then give formal proofs for them, assuming the premises as given and the conclusions to be proved.

5. Horse A will win if it rains. Horse B will win if it does not rain. Horse B will lose. Therefore, horse A will win.

6. I will buy a television set or a hi-fi set. I cannot work and watch television. I must work. Therefore, I will buy a hi-fi set.

7. He won or lost and he was not pleasant. If he won, then he went on a trip. If he went on a trip, then he would be pleasant. Therefore, he lost.

8. If Mr. Williams sells his furniture, then he is moving or buying new furniture. If he is moving, then he has a new job. If he goes to the bank, then he is not buying new furniture. Mr. Williams does not have a new job and he went to the bank. Therefore, Mr. Williams is not selling his furniture.

9. The object is hot or it is hard and bright. If it is hard, then it is metal and heavy. It is not metal. Therefore, the object is hot.

10. If I had the time and money, I would take a long trip. I have the time or ambition and I have the money. Therefore, if I am not ambitious, then I would take a long trip.

11. If it is worth the effort, then it is valuable or hard to obtain. It is not the case that it is hard to obtain or not worth the effort. Therefore, it is valuable.

12. It is not the case that the class is large and the course is easy. If the course is difficult, then it will require a great deal of study. The class is large. Therefore, the course will require a great deal of study.

13. If I go bowling, I will not study. I will study or take a nap. I will not take a nap. Therefore, I will not go bowling.

14. The object is valuable, or he would not want to buy it. Either the outward appearance is not an indication of its value, or the object is not valuable. He wants to buy the object. Therefore, outward appearance is not an indication of its value.

15. If Bill failed in Science, he would be on probation. If he were on probation, he would leave school and go to work. Bill has not left school. Therefore, Bill did not fail in Science.

5
THE AXIOMATIC METHOD

5.1 THE METHOD

In previous chapters, we have discussed how we can examine the structure of language and the symbolic processes as such, devoid of much of their content. In this chapter, we will proceed to examine how this structure can be "married" to observations and facts which we wish to assume. This process is called the **axiomatic** or **postulational** method. The method unifies and systematizes many important results which, when considered separately as to content, seem quite unrelated.

5.1.1 Historically, the Greeks first developed the notion of a logical discourse based on a set of initial statements assumed at the outset. Aristotle (384–322 B.C.) noted that "every demonstrative science must start from indemonstrative principles; otherwise, the steps of demonstration would be endless."

Euclid's work, *The Elements*, is no doubt the earliest attempt at developing an *axiomatic structure* based on definitions and a few common notions. His work has become so famous that the method and content have been almost completely identified. Entirely aside from content, the plan and method of logical organization turned out to be a contribution of the first magnitude. The method used by Euclid was employed by Archimedes (287–212 B.C.) in his books on the foundations of theoretical mechanics.

The European Renaissance marked the revival of Greek learning. A Latin translation of Euclid's *Elements* from the Greek was produced in 1572. This translation served as the reference for many subsequent translations used in European and American schools. In 1686 Newton published his famous *Principia*, which was organized as a deductive system.

Lagrange in 1788 published a systematic treatment of analytical mechanics, which moved from initial statements to other deduced statements.

Although the moden development of deductive systems cannot be attributed to any single person, Gottfried William Leibniz (1646–1716) must be recognized as a prime mover in its use. His philosophy embraced history, theology, linguistics, geology, mathematics, diplomacy, and the art of inventing. The search for a universal method by which he could obtain knowledge and understand the unity of the universe was the driving motivation in his life.

It was not only in the fields of pure science and mathematics that the deductive method was used. The seventeenth century philosopher, Spinoza (1632–1677), organized his *Ethics* into a deductive system. A Frenchman, J. Rueff, advocated the use of the axiomatic method in the study of the social sciences in his book, *Des Sciences physiques aux sciences morales* (1922). C. J. Keyser (1862–1947) shows how the deductive axiomatic method may be applied in the study of legal science in the *Yale Law Journal* (February 1929).

5.1.2 Even though the method popularized by Euclid has been recognized as a fundamental part of the scientific method in every area of human endeavor, our understanding of the axiomatic method has resulted to a great extent from studies in the field of geometry. Since the content of geometry was associated intimately with the realm of the physical universe, there arose the conviction that the axiomatic method possessed a character of logical necessity; that is, that there was something "universal" or "absolute" or beyond opposition when the axiomatic method was applied.

The modern *relative* concept of the axiomatic method can be traced to the bold achievements of Lobachevsky (1793–1856) and Bolyai (1775–1856) in their creation of non-Euclidean geometry. Hermann Grassmann (1809–1877), who wrote on such varied subjects as electric currents, colors, acoustics, linguistics, botany, and folklore, expresses the modern point of view. His *Ausdehnungslehre*, published in 1844, developed in abstract axiomatic form the doctrine of space. Its significance lay in the fact that it freed the development from all special intuitions. Its principles of procedure were the rules of logic; its basic beginnings, assumptions freed from the real world of necessity.

Although the origins of the theory and structure of a subject undeniably lie in the things called "practical," the form in which it evolves may be conceived as being independent of this "practical" world of necessity. That is, the modern point of view distinguishes between the form of a theory and its application.

As commonly used today, the axiomatic method sets forth certain statements about the concepts to be studied. Using a few undefined terms as well as the classical methods of logic, it then deduces further statements as logical consequences of the basic statements.

Of course, the systematic structuring and study of a subject need not proceed from logically deductive method alone. For a variety of reasons we may arrive at conclusions by induction, analogy, and even sheer guess-work. The axiomatic structuring of a subject even under these circumstances can prove to be invaluable.

Perhaps one or two informal suggestions will be illuminating. Consider the structure of a formal debate. In any debate, it is conventional to list, for clarity, a certain number of assumptions about which all the participants agree. The technical words used must be well defined. The participants then make assertions which they attempt to "prove" by the use of systematic arguments.

The *Declaration of Independence* and the *Constitution of the United States* form the basic structure of the "law of the land" in the United States. The Supreme Court and all lower courts in the United States presumably base their decisions on these documents.

5.1.3 In our discussion of language, it was recognized that there were words and symbols which could not be defined in terms of other words without circularity or an indefinite process which must be continued without end. If the meaning and understanding of a word arises from the contexts in which it is used, we say that the word is **implicitly defined.** Implicitly defined words are words which arise out of our experience in the use of the word rather than from any formal definitions. Using implicitly defined words, further words can be defined. When a new term is defined formally in terms of words which are already accepted in our vocabulary, we say that the word has been **defined explicitly.**

Since we cannot define all terms explicitly, it is necessary to accept some terms as undefined. When we have determined a list of undefined terms, we *assume* them as primitive conceptual terms and nothing more. These terms may then be used to define all other technical terms formally and explicitly. Since the primitive terms name concepts, we must list the properties which these terms are to have. The list of properties which describe our assumptions concerning the primitive terms are called **axioms.** If our primitive terms and axioms are accepted and assumed true, then we can deduce consequences logically through the use of valid arguments and proofs. These consequences are then called **theorems.**

The basic notion is that of selecting beginning links in a chain of reasoning. Once the beginning links have been selected, a chain of consequences can be formed through the use of the methods of logic. The resulting structure of the chain is called an axiomatic structure and the method is called the axiomatic or postulational method.

The choice of a profitable set of primitive terms and axioms is difficult. The origin and growth of an axiomatic structure cannot be framed in simple terms. Most branches of knowledge begin with simple observations and descriptions. There is a phase in which observations are merely recorded and collected. Data may be isolated and uncoordinated; there may be a lack of organization of the known facts. Eventually some intelligent, diligent, and perceptive investigator may begin to discern a pattern emerging in his subject. When this pattern has taken shape, the investigator is ready to select his undefined terms and axioms.

The above is not to imply that an axiomatic structure must necessarily concern observations from the real world. Primitive terms and axioms may be derived from other abstract sources. Indeed, the importance and value of the axiomatic method was fully realized only through the consideration of possible structures of non-Euclidean geometries. In modern mathematics, the axiomatic method has been used to great advantage to study the structures of symbols devoid of "real" content.

Axiomatic structures are often abstractions of our concepts concerning the real world. They are models of the relationships which have been observed experimentally. The conclusions are conjectures about new relations. In order to put substance into these conjectures, we must interpret them and examine them to see if they correspond to reality. The practical value of this activity is that, without the structure, we would seldom have been able to guess the relationships which the structure has suggested to us.

Exercises 5.1

1. Obtain a common school geometry text and abstract from it a list of the primitive terms, the axioms, and a few illustrative examples of definitions and theorems.
2. Discuss the acceptability of the Declaration of Independence to a slave, a dictator, a beatnik, and an ordinary citizen of the United States.
3. Do ping pong, tennis, badminton, and volleyball have a similarity of structure and form? If so, discuss their similarities.

5.2 DISCUSSION

Now we are ready to describe the pattern of an axiomatic structure. As a preliminary comment, we assume a familiarity with the English language and some awareness concerning logic and the methods of valid deductive proofs.

An axiomatic structure consists of five types of statements:

1. Primitive terms.
2. Formally defined technical terms.

3. A list of assumed primary statements, called axioms.

4. Deduced statements, called theorems.

5. A list of statements asserting that the theorems "follow" as a consequence of the primitive terms, definitions, and axioms.

Examination of the fifth type of statement named above reveals that an axiomatic structure results in a list of conditional conclusions, that is, conclusions of the form "If P, then Q." Logically, any interpretation of the structure which makes the P true must have Q true as a consequence. Herein lies the "practical" value of an axiomatic structure.

5.2.1 A trivial but illuminating illustration is obtained in examining a familiar game as described axiomatically.

Recall the game of tick-tack-toe, in which two players take turns marking either a cross or a circle in a block of nine squares, the object being to complete a straight or diagonal line of one's mark before the other player does. Observation or the experience of playing a few games should prepare us for the selection of a few undefined terms and axioms with which to construct a logical structure of the game. For informal reference, we use Figure 1.

FIGURE 1.

There are two statements which we assume:

P_1: There exists a space consisting of cells.

P_2: There exist markers consisting of crosses and circles.

The above two statements use three primitive terms: *cells, crosses, circles*. The term *space* can be defined as the name of the collection of cells. The term *marker* is used to refer to crosses and circles. With the above "primitive notions" we proceed to a statement of axioms and definitions. Axioms are listed by the letter A with a subscript to denote the order. Definitions are listed using the letter D with a subscript.

A_1: There are nine cells in the space.

D_1: We name the cells: 1, 2, 3, 4, 5, 6, 7, 8, 9.

D_2: By a *corner cell* we mean one of the following cells: 1, 3, 7, or 9.

D_3: By the *center cell* we mean cell 5.

D_4: By a *side cell* we mean one of the following cells: 2, 4, 6, or 8.

D_5: A *move* consists of placing a marker in an empty cell.

A_2: Moves must alternate between the cross and circle markers.

D_6: By *game* we mean nine moves of markers into the cells of the space.

D_7: By *opening* we mean the first move of a marker into a cell.

A_3: No game may begin with a marker in a cell.

A_4: No cell may contain two or more markers.

D_8: By *cross* (or *circle*) *wins* we mean that one of the following triples of cells contain all crosses (or circles): $(1, 2, 3), (4, 5, 6), (7, 8, 9)$ $(1, 4, 7), (2, 5, 8), (3, 6, 9), (1, 5, 9), (3, 5, 7)$.

D_9: By *draw* we mean that neither cross nor circle win.

Note that the axioms assert the properties to be assumed of our primitive notions. The definitions, on the other hand, describe the special terminology which we wish to use for convenience. As a result of the above axioms and definitions, it is possible to deduce logically many consequences. A few consequences, called theorems, are listed by the letter T with a subscript to indicate the order in which they might be proved.

T_1: There are nine opening moves to a game.

T_2: If cross opens, then cross has five moves in the game.

T_3: If cross opens, there are 126 distinct games possible.

T_4: If cross opens, of the 126 distinct games possible, cross wins 120.

The following theorems concern "strategy."

T_{10}: If cross uses a corner opening, circle must move into the center cell to prevent cross from winning.

T_{11}: If cross uses a center opening, then circle must move into a corner cell to prevent cross from winning.

T_{12}: If cross uses a side opening, then circle must move into an adjacent corner cell, the opposite side cell, or the center cell to prevent cross from winning.

Perhaps the most interesting theorem and one which might be unexpected can be stated as follows:

T_{13}: If cross opens, circle can end every game in a draw.

In proving the above theorems, a certain amount of mathematics is necessary. In general, mathematics has proved itself to be a valuable tool in the proofs of theorems in many significant axiomatic structures. In later chapters we will consider the development of mathematics as a logical consequence of certain assumed primitive notions.

In concluding this illustration, we note that we could list conditional statements which summarize the results.

5.2.2 In the study of axiomatic structures, the question of whether it is possible to obtain contradictory theorems occurs. For example, in our structuring of tick-tack-toe, could we deduce theorems which contradict each other? If so, the usefulness of the structure would be destroyed since we could not be logically certain of the interpretation to be given a theorem. Both a theorem and its contradiction couldn't be "true." This question is described as the question of **consistency.**

    5.2.2.l Definition: An axiomatic structure is said to be **consistent** if contradictory statements are not implied by the axioms of the structure.

Another question which occurs in the study of axiomatic structures is whether the axioms say "too much." That is, is it possible to eliminate certain axioms without "losing" any of the consequences? For example, if in our example of tick-tack-toe we had an axiom which stated that "there are at least five cells in the space," would this axiom add anything to the structure? This question is described as the question of **independence.** In order to define this notion, it is necessary to consider whether there is an interpretation of the axiomatic structure under consideration; that is, whether meaning can be assigned to the primitive notions and axioms in such a way as to make them "true."

    5.2.2.2 Definition: An axiomatic structure is said to be **satisfiable** if there exists an interpretation of the system which makes the axioms true.

    5.2.2.3 Definition: An axiom of an axiomatic structure is said to be **independent** in the structure, if both the axiomatic structure and the structure formed by deleting the axiom and adding its denial are satisfiable.

A third question which occurs is whether an axiomatic structure enables us to answer all statements concerning the primitive notions. That is, is it possible to determine the truth or falsity of every meaningful statement which might be formed concerning the primitive notions? This question is described as the question of the **completeness** of an axiomatic structure. A complete axiomatic structure is one to which no independent axioms can be added.

    5.2.2.4 Definition: An axiomatic structure is said to be **complete** if there are no independent axioms which can be added to the given structure.

The study of the above properties of consistency, satisfiability, independence, and completeness are important to the logician and mathematician. The study is not trivial nor easy. For our purposes it suffices to comment on the importance of consistency as a requirement for any useful and profitable axiomatic structure. Furthermore, we note that independence and completeness of axioms in many cases is not required nor even desirable.

As with most techniques, there are advantages and disadvantages with the use of an axiomatic structure. The precision and economy that can be achieved through the use of an axiomatic treatment of a subject is an advantage. We have also mentioned the fruitfulness of the axiomatic structure in pointing to new results which might not have been suspected. The specification of implicitly defined and explicitly defined technical terms also leads to better organization and understanding. However, the advantages of the axiomatic method also lead to disadvantage in the formal nature of the method and the restrictions which are placed on the structure in the development of a subject. The very requirements which bring precision lead to the pedestrian development and formality which is so psychologically inhibiting to learning.

In the chapters which follow, we will proceed rather informally. However, underlying our discussion will be the assumption that, in the event the subject must be presented precisely and rigorously, the subject can be axiomatized. That is, the materials can be set forth in a consistent axiomatic structure. We will discuss primitive notions which may occur, and definitions and axioms in the sense of assumptions will be pointed out.

Exercises 5.2

1. Select a definite game, say, ping pong or tennis. Can you describe the primitive terms for the game? Define a few of the technical terms used in the game. Describe some of the "axioms" for the game. Are there any "naturally" suggested theorems which might be proved?
2. Consider your personal philosophy of "social actions." Can you make a list of your primitive assumptions? Are they consistent? Is your philosophy of "social action" complete?
3. Discuss the structure of the English language with respect to consistency, completeness, and independence.

Exercises 5

1. Write a short essay on your conception of the "absolute" as contrasted to the "relative" notions concerning axiomatic structures.
2. What is meant by "the logically deductive method?"
3. Read through Chapter 6 and determine the primitive terms used in the chapter.
4. Read through Chapter 6 and determine the formally defined terms in the chapter.
5. In your reading of Chapter 6, did you note a list of "axioms"? If so, give a definite reference so that a person who is unfamiliar with the text could find it rapidly.

6. What is the tool suggested in Chapter 6 which enables the reader to check the consistency of the "axioms"?

7. Discuss the distinction to be made between the concrete interpretation of a situation and the axiomatization of a conception. That is, what is the difference between "theory" and "practice"?

8. Discuss the relationship of "truth" and "validity" to axiomatic structures. That is, do axiomatic structures purport to describe "truths" concerning the "real" physical world?

9. To what extent does intuition play a part in the structure of an axiomatic system?

10. Discuss the essential differences between what is meant by an axiom, a definition, and a theorem.

6
INTRODUCTION
TO SETS

6.1 SETS

One of the most important and fundamental concepts to be found in modern mathematics and logic is that of **sets**. It is a concept which has clarified, enriched, and unified many branches of mathematics. The theory of sets is one of the strong links connecting mathematics and logic. Historically, the theory of sets came into being only toward the end of the last century. Once George Boole and Georg Cantor (1845–1918) introduced the concept, it was accepted and recognized as fundamental to mathematical thinking.

Three primitive undefined notions are involved in the development of sets. They are the notions of **sets**, **elements**, and **membership**. That is, we will speak of elements as being members of sets.

In abstracting the notion of **elements** it will be necessary to include all kinds of entities. We will use the word *element* to mean the most general notion associated with words such as *object, entity, thing*. For example, we may consider as elements the following variety of "conceptual entities": a pencil, a person, a grade, a word, a number, a sentence, a dream, a location, a musical note, an argument, a genetic relationship, a color, and so forth.

In thinking of elements, it will be found impossible to deal with them in the absence of an appropriate context. In general, any collection of elements will be called a **set**. In any given discussion, we will limit our discourse to certain elements. The elements will always be in sets. The sets of elements will occur at three "levels": the set of all possible elements in our discourse, which we will call the **universal set**; the sets of elements which are given in our discourse; and the sets of elements derived in the process of our discussion.

The elements comprising a set are said to **belong** to the set, or to be **members** of the set. An element belonging to a set is said to be **contained** in the set, and a set is said to contain the elements which belong to it. For example, consider the set consisting of the fingers of your right hand. The elements are the five fingers of your right hand called the thumb, forefinger, middle finger, ring finger, and the little finger. The right thumb is a member of the set called the fingers on your right hand. The right thumb belongs to and is contained in the set. The set called the fingers on your right hand contains the five fingers mentioned above.

The notions of sets and elements belonging to sets are deeply rooted in our experience. We often make distinctions between objects by separating them into those things which "belong" and those which do not "belong." More formally, we determine a set by a rule or property. Those elements which satisfy the rule belong to the set; those which do not, do not belong to it. For example, a basketball coach might well be interested in male students over six feet tall. He is defining a set with the rule: male and over six feet tall. The universal set is the set of all students eligible for basketball in his school. Given any element (a student) in the universal set, the coach must decide whether the element satisfies his rule or not. If the student satisfies the rule "male and over six feet tall," then he belongs to the set. Otherwise, the student does not.

6.1.1 Imagine how difficult life would be if objects, people, places, emotions, and so on had no names. Since we wish to talk about sets and elements, we will introduce symbols or labels for these conceptual objects. Capital letters will usually be used as names of sets and small letters for elements. Elements and sets will be shown to be related by the symbol $\in$. In describing sets, braces, $\{\ \ \}$, will be used to denote sets and the symbols within the braces will either list the elements of the set or will describe the properties of the elements in the set. For example, the set consisting of a chair, pencil, and a piece of paper might be symbolized by letting S stand for the name of the set. The small letters c, p, and a might be used to denote the three elements, respectively. The set is then symbolized by $S = \{c, p, a\}$, which is read "the set S is the set consisting of the elements c, p, and a." Furthermore, we could write $c \in S$ which is read "c is a member of S" or "c belongs to S." If d stands for a desk, we could write $d \notin S$ which is read "d is not a member of S."

The slash symbol, /, which occurs above, is used in a variety of ways. When used "over" other symbols, we will read it as a denial. That is, the logical notion of *not* belonging to a set, or *not* being a particular element, or *not* being a particular set, will be indicated by the slash as in $a \notin A$, $b \neq 2$, and $S \neq \{1, 2, 3, 4\}$ which are read "a is not an element of A," "b is not equal to 2," and "S is not the set consisting of the elements 1, 2, 3, and 4," respectively.

In our discussions a variety of sets may be encountered. When a set consists of only a few elements, a simple and unambiguous rule to use is: list all the elements in the set. When sets consist of a large number of elements, however, it may be awkward or impossible to list all the elements in braces. In this case, we describe the conditions under which elements are in the set by writing a rule within the braces. For example, $B = \{x$ is a book.$\}$ would be read "B is the set of all elements x which are books." We might write $C = \{x \in B \mid x$ is about mathematics.$\}$ to indicate the set named C consisting of all books belonging to the set B such that the book is about mathematics. Note the use of the slash symbol, which here is read "such that."

We must not conclude from the above that the elements of a set are always related in a simple way. The only obvious property common to all elements in a set may be that they belong to the same set. The following examples illustrate various sets.

$A = \{$Bill, Sam, Joe$\}$ is read "A is the set consisting of Bill, Sam, and Joe."

$B = \{a, c, e, m, k\}$ is read "B is the set consisting of the elements a, c, e, m, and k."

$C = \{$Bill, c, 5$\}$ is read "C is the set consisting of the elements Bill, c, and 5."

$D = \{x$ is a book in the library$\}$ is read "D is the set of all books in the library."

$E = \{x \in D \mid x$ is about history$\}$ is read "E is the set of all elements in the set D such that the elements are about history."

$F = \{x \in D \mid x$ is over 500 pages$\}$ is read "F is the set of all elements in the set D such that the elements have over 500 pages."

$G = \{x \in D \mid x$ is about history and over 500 pages$\}$ is read "G is the set of all elements in D such that the elements are about history and over 500 pages." *Note:* we might also write this as $G = \{x \in D \mid x \in E$ and $x \in F\}$.

Simple as these examples may seem, the reader should carefully study them to make sure that he feels absolutely at home with the symbolism used.

6.1.2 In describing sets, we note that the statements $a \in A$ and $b \in B$ say something about elements and sets. We will often wish to make remarks concerning the relationship between elements and between sets. The word *equals*, symbolized by $=$, is used in the same sense as the word "alias." By "a is equal to b," "$a = b$," we mean that they denote the same element or conceptual entity. When we write $A = B$, we mean that A and B are two names for the same set.

> **6.1.2.1 Definition:** We say that two sets A and B are **equal**, $A = B$, if and only if every element of A is an element of B and every element of B is an element of A.

For example, if $A = \{2, 4, 6, 8\}$ and $B = \{x$ is an even positive integer less than ten.$\}$, then $A = B$. Note that in the example, there is a tacit assumption of a set of all possible elements which can be considered. For the example this might be the set of all real numbers. This "all inclusive" set is called the **universal set**. On the other hand, consider the set $C = \{x$ is the square root of a negative number.$\}$. If the universal set is the set of real numbers, then there are *no* elements in C. Later in the text we will be able to show that there are *no* elements in the set $S = \{x$ is any odd whole number which is the sum of two odd whole numbers.$\}$. It will be convenient to admit sets with no elements.

> **6.1.2.2 Definition:** By the **universal set**, denoted by U, we mean the set consisting of all possible elements in a given discussion.

> **6.1.2.3 Definition:** By the **empty** or **null** set, denoted by $\emptyset$, we mean any set with no elements belonging to it.

Continuing our example, we might consider the set D formed by selecting the elements 2 and 4 from the set A: $D = \{2, 4\}$. We then say that the set D is a **subset** of the set A. A subset can be specified by telling exactly what properties the elements of the subset and only those elements should have; for example, $D = \{x \in A \mid x$ is less than 5.$\}$.

> **6.1.2.4 Definition:** A set A is said to be a **subset** of a set B, if and only if every element of A is an element of B. We write $A \subset B$ and read it "A is a subset of B."

Whenever we consider any set, we are considering the elements of the set and the sets which can be formed by selecting various elements from the given set. For example, consider the set $S = \{a, b, c\}$ where the elements are distinct. We recognize the following sets which can be formed: $\emptyset$, $A = \{a\}$, $B = \{b\}$, $C = \{c\}$, $D = \{a, b\}$, $E = \{a, c\}$, $F = \{b, c\}$, and $S = \{a, b, c\}$. Each of these sets are formed by selecting elements from the given set S. Any set obtained from a given set in this way is called a subset of the given set. Note that if $x \in M$ and $M \subset N$, then $x \in N$. But if $x \in N$ and $M \subset N$, then we cannot claim $x \in M$. Since every element of an empty set can be thought of as belonging to any set, the empty set is a subset of every set. That is, for any set G, we have $\emptyset \subset G$. Every set is a subset of itself; that is, since every element of any set G is an element of the set G, we have $G \subset G$.

The denial of the statement $B \subset A$ is indicated by a slash; $B \not\subset A$ is read "B is not a subset of A." That is, for some $c \in B$, we have $c \notin A$. If B is a subset of A and not equal to A, we say that B is a **proper** subset of A. That is, there is at least one element, say $a \in A$, such that $a \notin B$. If $C \subset D$ and $D \subset C$, then $C = D$. The notation $F \neq \emptyset$ means that the set F is not empty; that is, the set F must have at least one element. In a discussion there may be two sets M and N such that they have no elements in common That is, if $a \in M$ then $a \notin N$ and if $b \in N$ then $b \notin M$. When two nonempty sets have no elements in common, we say that they are **disjoint**. It is clear that disjoint sets cannot be subsets of one another.

6.1.2.5 Definition: Two nonempty sets are said to be **disjoint** if and only if they have no elements in common.

Exercises 6.1

1. Describe the following sets.
   (a) The set of objects in your wallet or purse.
   (b) The set of musical notes in an octave.
   (c) The set of primary colors of the spectrum.
   (d) The set of moons (satellites) of the planet Saturn.
2. List the elements of the following sets.
   (a) The set of all words which can be formed by using the letters R, T, and A exactly once.
   (b) The set of all subsets of the set $T = \{1, 2, 3, 4\}$.
3. Give examples of sets consisting of:
   (a) automobiles   (b) furniture   (c) stationary
4. Give an example of a subset of each of the sets given in exercise 3.
5. If $S = \{1, 2, 3, 4\}$, then give examples of:
   (a) proper subsets of S.
   (b) disjoint subsets of S.
6. Describe the property or condition which determines membership in each of the following sets.
   (a) {cussed, swig, tote, souse, gumption, ...}
   (b) $\{1, 4, 9, 16, 25\}$
   (c) {earth, air, fire, water}
   (d) {Euglena, Amoeba, Plasmodium, Paramecium}
7. If $A = \{1, 2, 3, 4, 5, 6, 7\}$, $B = \{2, 4, 6\}$, $C = \{3, 5, 7, 9\}$, then: (a) Is $A \subset B$? (b) Is $B \subset A$? (c) Is $C \subset A$? (d) Is $B \subset C$? (e) Are any two of the sets disjoint? (f) Is there a proper subset of another set?
8. If $a \in A$, $b \in B$, $A \subset C$, $B \subset C$, then: (a) Is $a \in C$? (b) Could $b \in A$? (c) Could there be an element $c \in C$ such that $c \notin A$ and $c \notin B$? (d) Could there be an element $c \in C$ such that $c \in A$ and $c \notin B$?
9. Construct examples of sets A, B, and C which will illustrate the properties questioned in exercise 8.
10. If $A \subset B$ and $B \subset C$, what can you conclude about the relationship between A and C? Illustrate with an example.

6.2   VENN DIAGRAMS

A convenient aid in the study of sets and subsets is a diagram called a **Venn diagram**. Venn diagrams graphically represent sets as closed figures. An outer boundary line is often drawn to indicate the universal set consisting of all "points" inside the boundary. Inner circles or convenient shapes are used to indicate subsets of the universal set. The elements are imagined as the "points" interior to the appropriate boundary. The sets are given names by using capital letters near the boundaries of the sets. As a simple example, where all of the elements are listed, consider the universal set $U = \{a, b, c, d, e, f, g, h, k, m, n, p, q, r, s, t, u, v, w, z\}$ and the subset $A = \{b, c, g, h\}$. Note, $A \subset U$.

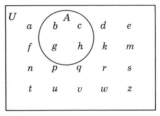

FIGURE 2.

The value and usefulness of a Venn diagram occurs, however, when the number of elements under consideration is too numerous to list or is unknown. The elements are then thought of as the "points" within the boundaries without specific mention. For example, in Figure 3, we have

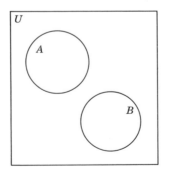

FIGURE 3.

drawn a universal set with two subsets called A and B. The elements of the universal set include all the region interior to the rectangle. The elements of set *A* are all of the "points" included within the circle marked *A*. The set of elements of *B* are all within the circle marked *B*. Note that $A \subset U$, $B \subset U$, and that the sets *A* and *B* are disjoint. It should also be clear that $A \not\subset B$ and $B \not\subset A$.

Various relationships between sets can easily be represented as illustrated in the following Venn diagrams. On occasion it will be convenient to shade the figure or set, to list elements within the figures, to letter the figures, and to write descriptions within the figures.

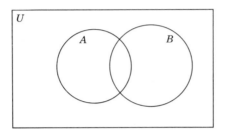

FIGURE 4.

In Figure 4: *A* and *B* are subsets of the universal set *U*. The sets *A* and *B* have elements in common as indicated by their overlapping areas. There are four distinct disjoint sets.

In Figure 5: The set *B* is a subset of the set *A*. Every element of *B* belongs to *A*. There are some elements of *A* which are not in *B*. We can write $B \subset A \subset U$.

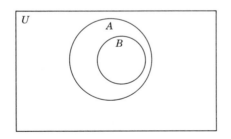

FIGURE 5.

In Figure 6: The universal set has three subsets *A*, *B*, and *C* indicated within it. The sets are *not* subsets of one another. That is, there are elements in *A* which are not in *B* or *C*, with a similar situation for *B* and for *C*. There are elements common to all three sets *A*, *B*, and *C*.

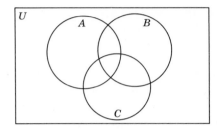

FIGURE 6.

In Figure 7: The set C has elements in set A, in set B, and in neither. The sets A and B are disjoint. Six distinct disjoint sets are shown in the Venn diagram.

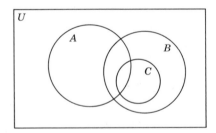

FIGURE 7.

In Figure 8: The set $C \subset B$ but $C \not\subset A$. We note that there is an element $c \in C$ such that $c \in B$ but $c \notin A$. There are elements common to both A and B but not in C. There are elements $x \in A$, $x \in B$, and $x \in C$. That is, there are elements common to all three sets A, B, and C. There are elements in the universal set which are not in any of the sets A, B, or C.

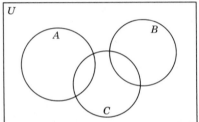

FIGURE 8.

When the universal set is clearly understood in a discussion, it may be omitted from the diagram. It is important to remember that Venn diagrams are informal representations of sets. They are useful aids, not logical means for the proof of any property, relationship, or assertion. Venn diagrams can assist us in gaining an understanding of the properties and relationships between sets.

Venn diagrams suggest a variety of questions to ask concerning sets and subsets. For example, in Figure 3, we might ask whether there are elements common to both the sets A and B. That is, what can we say about the set $C = \{x$ is an element common to both A and $B\}$? Or, $C = \{x \in A$ and $x \in B\}$? It is clear that there are no elements in the set C. That is, $C = \emptyset$. If we consider the same situation for Figure 4, we have for $C = \{x \in A$ and $x \in B\}$ the set of elements in the portion in which the sets A and B overlap. That is, $C \neq \emptyset$. For Figure 5, we have for $C = \{x \in A$ and $x \in B\}$ $= B$.

The conjunction *and* suggests that we might ask further questions concerning the logical connections between the elements of sets. For example, if x is an element, is it sensible to ask about the set of all elements *not* in a given set? In Figure 3, can we indicate the set $\bar{A} = \{x$ is not an element in $A\} = \{x \notin A\}$? Can we form a set $D = \{x$ is an element in A or $B\}$? Note how useful the logical connectives are in asking and suggesting these questions.

A further question which suggests itself is: How many sets can be formed, using two subsets of a universal set? When we compare the Figures 3, 4, and 5, we might ask: In what respects will our answers differ to the above questions? In the next section we will begin a consideration of these and further questions.

Exercises 6.2

1. Sketch a Venn diagram for the set of 52 playing cards in a bridge deck, with the set of aces as a subset and the set of hearts as another subset.
2. Using the Venn diagram constructed in exercise 1, list the elements in the sets
   (a) $C = \{x$ is an ace and x is a heart$\}$.
   (b) $D = \{x$ is not an ace and x is not a heart$\}$.
   (c) $E = \{x$ is an ace and x is not a heart$\}$.
   (d) $F = \{x$ is not an ace or x is not a heart$\}$.
3. Sketch a Venn diagram of all the people you know, showing the subsets which are described as relatives, males between twenty-one and thirty years old, females who are blonde and between eighteen and twenty-two years old. Name the elements in the set of relatives which do not belong to the other two sets mentioned. List three other subsets of the set of all the people you know by describing the conditions on the elements of the sets.
4. Let A, B, and C be subsets of a universal set U. Construct Venn diagrams which satisfy the following conditions:
   (a) Sets A and C are disjoint. Sets B and C are disjoint. Sets A and B have elements in common. There are elements x such that $x \notin A$, $x \notin B$, and $x \notin C$.

(*b*) If $x \in C$, then $x \in A$ and $x \in B$. There are elements $x \in A$ and $x \in B$ but $x \notin C$. There are elements $x \in B$ not in A or C. Also $x \in A$ not in B or C. Finally, there are elements in the universal set which are not in A, B, or C.

6.3 SET RELATIONS

Now we are ready to consider further relations between sets. We have already considered the relation of inclusion which refers to a subset of a given set: $A \subset B$. Note that a subset relation compares sets. The primitive notion of membership, $\in$, compares elements to sets. They are different kinds of relationships.

In 6.1.2.1 we defined formally our usage of the word *equal* with respect to set notions. In ordinary usage, the word *equal* is used in two senses: "equal in certain respects" and "equal in every respect." We often use the word *equivalent* to indicate the sense of "equal in certain respects" as contrasted to the use of *equal* to mean "equal in every respect." In a given discourse, when the usage is clear and unambiguous, the term *equal* is used for both.

6.3.1 If we consider any universal set and a subset A of the set, we note that the totality of elements under consideration is divided into two disjoint sets. The set called A and the set of elements $x \notin A$. The set formed by the collection of all elements $x \notin A$ is given the name "the **complement** of A" written $\bar{A}$. The complement of a set is the set of all elements *not* included in the set. For example, let U be the set $\{1, 2, 3, 4, 5, 6, 7, 8, 9\}$, and let A be the subset $\{2, 4, 6\}$. Then the complement of A is $\bar{A}$ containing the elements 1, 3, 5, 7, 8, and 9, that is, $\bar{A} = \{1, 3, 5, 7, 8, 9\}$. If $U = \{x \text{ is a college student}\}$ and $A = \{x \text{ is a student at Oakland City College}\}$, then $\bar{A} = \{x \text{ is a college student } \textit{not} \text{ at Oakland City College}\}$.

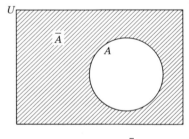

FIGURE 9. $\bar{A}$.

A Venn diagram is helpful in "seeing" this notion of the complement of a set. The shaded region of Figure 9 indicates the complement of the set A (unshaded). Note that the sets are disjoint. Disjoint sets, however, do not have to contain all the elements in a universal set. But if $x \in A$, then $x \notin \bar{A}$

and if $x \in \bar{A}$, *then* $x \notin A$. If $x \in U$, then $x \in A$ *or* $x \in \bar{A}$. That is, a set and its complement exhaust the elements in a universal set.

6.3.1.1 Definition: By the **complement** of a set A relative to a universal set U we mean the set of all elements of U which are not elements of A. When the universal set is clearly understood, we write $\bar{A}$ for the complement of A.

6.3.2 Whenever we wish to consider the totality of elements in either of two sets, we form a new set, say, C, which we call the **union** of the two sets. If U is understood and A and B are two sets in U, then we can form the set $C = \{x \in A \text{ or } x \in B\}$. That is, the set C, called the union of A and B, consists of all elements in the sets A or B. For example, if $A = \{2, 4, 6\}$ and $B = \{1, 3, 5\}$, then the union of A and B denoted by $A \cup B = C = \{1, 2, 3, 4, 5, 6\}$. If $A = \{1, 3, 4\}$ and $B = \{3, 4, 5\}$, then $A \cup B = C = \{1, 3, 4, 5\}$. If $A = \{2, 4, 6\}$ and $B = \{2, 4, 6, 8\}$, then $A \cup B = C = \{2, 4, 6, 8\}$. The Venn diagrams in Figure 10 (*a*), (*b*), (*c*) illustrate the union of the sets A and B as shaded.

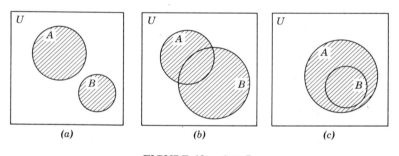

FIGURE 10. $A \cup B$.

Note that a single set may consist of disconnected portions in a Venn diagram. The logically inclusive sense of the word *or* is meant in $A \cup B = \{x \in A \text{ or } x \in B\}$. The union of any set and its complement is clearly the universal set: for any A, $A \cup \bar{A} = U$.

6.3.2.1 Definition: By the **union** of two sets A and B, written $A \cup B$, we mean the set of all elements which belong to A or to B.

As a further example, consider the universal set of all college students in the United States with the sets A of all students in "O.K." college and B of all students with a grade average of "B" or better. The set $C = A \cup B$ will be the set of all students either in "OK" college or making a grade average of 'B' or better. The shaded region of Figure 11 indicates the set C.

A few observations concerning the Venn diagram may help to illustrate set notations. On the Venn diagram, Figure 11, the universal set is represented by the entire region inside the outer rectangle. The sets A and B are indicated by the slant-shaded regions interior to the smaller rectangles.

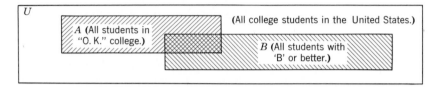

FIGURE 11.

The following sets are a few of the possible sets which might be considered with respect to the situation:

$A = \{x$ is a student in "O.K." college$\}$.
$B = \{x$ is a student with a grade average of "B" or better$\}$.
$\bar{A} = \{x$ is *not* a student of "O.K." college$\}$.
$\bar{B} = \{x$ is a student with a grade average *less than* 'B'$\}$.
$A \cup \bar{A} = B \cup \bar{B} = U = \{x$ is a college student in the U. S.$\}$.
$A \cup B = \{x$ is a student of "O.K." college *or* a student with a grade average of 'B' or better$\} = \{x \in A \ or \ x \in B\}$.
$\overline{A \cup B} = \{x$ is not a student of "O.K." college *and* does not have a grade average of "B" or better$\} = \{x \notin A \ and \ x \notin B\}$.

6.3.3 In the above example, we note that the sets A and B have some elements in common. The set formed by the elements belonging to both of two sets is called the **intersection** of the sets and is denoted by $A \cap B$, where A and B are the two sets being combined. That is, if A and B are sets, the intersection is a set $C = \{x \in A \ and \ x \in B\}$. In the above example, the intersection of A and B is the region indicated by the double-hatched area.

If $U = \{1, 2, 3, 4, 5, 6, 7, 8\}$ and $A = \{2, 4, 6\}$ and $B = \{1, 3, 5\}$, then the intersection of A and B, $A \cap B = \emptyset$. If $A = \{1, 3, 4\}$ and $B = \{3, 4, 5\}$, then $A \cap B = \{3, 4\}$. If $A = \{2, 4, 6\}$ and $B = \{2, 4, 6, 8\}$, then $A \cap B = \{2, 4, 6\}$. The shaded regions of Figure 12(a), (b), (c) illustrate the intersections of sets A and B.

Note that the intersection of disjoint sets A and B is empty (Figure 12 (a). If a set B is a subset of a set A, $B \subset A$, then their intersection, $A \cap B = B$ (Figure 12(c)). It would be wise for the reader to compare the four relations of **subsets, complements, unions,** and **intersections** at this point.

6.3.3.1 Definition: By the **intersection** of two sets A and B, written $A \cap B$, we mean the set of all elements which belong to both A and B.

The reader might note that in our example with the college students (Figure 11), $\overline{A \cup B} = \bar{A} \cap \bar{B}$. Since the intersection of disjoint sets is empty, we have for any two disjoint sets C and D, $C \cap D = \emptyset$. Also, for any set A, $A \cap \bar{A} = \emptyset$.

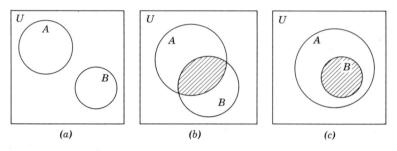

(a)   (b)   (c)

FIGURE 12. $A \cap B$

6.3.4 Before proceeding further, a few examples may help to clarify the operations on sets.

EXAMPLE 1. Let $U = \{x \text{ is a day in April 1959}\}$, $M = \{x \text{ is a Monday}\}$, $F = \{x \text{ is a Friday}\}$, $V = \{x \text{ is a day whose numerical date is a multiple of six}\}$.

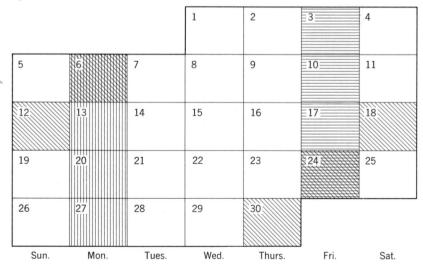

FIGURE 13.

The subsets of U can be listed by numerical dates as follows (shaded on Venn diagram as shown below).

$M = \{6, 13, 20, 27\}$

$F = \{3, 10, 17, 24\}$

$V = \{6, 12, 18, 24, 30\}$

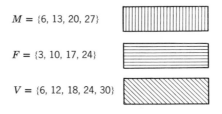

Some of the many sets which can be formed by the operations of union, intersection, and complementation are illustrated in the following list:

$M \cup F = \{3, 6, 10, 13, 17, 20, 24, 27\}$
$M \cup V = \{6, 12, 13, 18, 20, 24, 27, 30\}$
$M \cap V = \{6\}$ and $M \cap F = \emptyset$
$(M \cup F) \cap V = \{6, 24\}$, $(M \cap V) \cup F = \{3, 6, 10, 17, 24\}$
$\bar{V} = \{1, 2, 3, 4, 5, 7, 8, 9, 10, 11, 13, 14, 15, 16, 17, 19, 20, 21, 22, 23, 25,$
$26, 27, 28, 29\}$
$\overline{M \cup F} = \{1, 2, 4, 5, 7, 8, 9, 11, 12, 14, 15, 16, 18, 19, 21, 22, 23, 25, 26,$
$28, 29, 30\}$
$(M \cap V) \cup (F \cap V) = \{6, 24\}$ and $M \cap \bar{V} = \{13, 20, 27\}$

EXAMPLE 2. If U is the set of all people, A the set of all males, B the set of all people over six feet tall, C the set of all people with dark hair, then:
$\bar{A} = $ The set of all females.
$\bar{B} = $ The set of all people less than or equal to six feet tall.
$\bar{C} = $ The set of all people without dark hair.
$A \cup B = \{x$ is a male or over six feet tall$\}$.
$A \cap B = \{x$ is a male over six feet tall$\}$.
$\bar{A} \cap C = \{x$ is a female with dark hair$\}$.
$(A \cap B) \cap C = \{x$ is a dark haired male over six feet tall$\}$.

EXAMPLE 3: Venn diagrams can be used to examine a variety of problems. If we denote the number of elements in a set by $S(n)$ where S is the name of the set and n is the number of elements in the set, then we can find the number of elements in various subsets of a universal set in many cases.

A certain school had a total of 57 students in three classes: a mathematics class with 23 students, a history class with 29, and an English class with 19. Four students were taking both mathematics and history, five both English and history but not mathematics. Two students were enrolled in all three classes. We wish to know the number of students who were taking (*a*) mathematics and history but not English, (*b*) mathematics and English, (*c*) mathematics or English but not history, (*d*) at least two of the classes.

We must first determine the universal set and its subsets. The universal set $U = (M \cup H) \cup E$, where M is the set of mathematics students, H the set of history students, and E the set of English students. The set required for part (*a*) will then be $(M \cap H)$ less the number of these enrolled in English; (*b*) will be $(M \cap E)$; (*c*) will be $(M \cup E)$ less the number of these enrolled in history; and for (*d*) we will have $(M \cap H) \cup (M \cap E) \cup (H \cap E)$. The Venn diagram (Figure 14) indicates the various subsets.

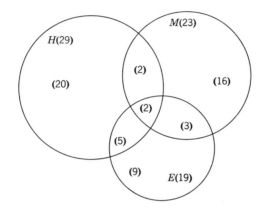

FIGURE 14.

(*a*) $(M \cap H)$ less E has 2 elements.
(*b*) $(M \cap E)$ has 5 elements.
(*c*) $(M \cup E)$ less H has 28 elements.
(*d*) $(M \cap H) \cup (M \cap E) \cup (H \cap E)$ has 12 elements.

Exercises 6.3

1. If $U = \{x$ is a letter in the English alphabet$\}$, $V = \{x$ is a vowel$\}$, $C = \{x$ is a consonant$\}$, and $N = \{x$ is a letter in your full name$\}$,
   (*a*) Describe the four sets by listing the elements of each set.
   (*b*) List the elements in the following sets: (i) $N \cup V$, (ii) $N \cap C$, (iii) $V \cup C$, (iv) $N \cap \bar{V}$, (v) $C \cap \bar{N}$, (vi) $\bar{C}$.
2. Given $M = \{1, 2, 3, 4, 5, 6, 7\}$, $N = \{3, 5, 6, 9\}$, and $P = \{1, 4, 7\}$:
   (*a*) Sketch a Venn diagram representing the sets M, N, and P.
   (*b*) Find and shade the set: (i) $M \cap (N \cap P)$ horizontally, (ii) $P \cup (\overline{M \cap N})$ vertically, (iii) $(M \cap N) \cup (\overline{P \cup N})$ with slant lines.
3. Describe symbolically in terms of the sets A, B, C, and D the sets shaded as shown in the Venn diagram on page 84.

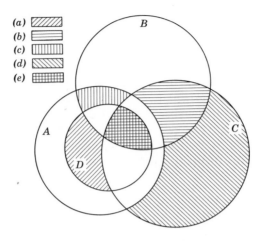

4. If A, B, C, and D are the sets shown in the Venn diagram of exercise 3, using the membership symbol, $\in$, indicate to which sets the element a belongs if:

(a) $a \in [(B \cap D) \cap \bar{C}]$ (b) $a \in ([(A \cap C) \cap B] \cap \bar{D})$

(c) $a \in [(A \cap C) \cap (\bar{B} \cup D)]$.

5. If A and B are two sets, we can form a set $D = \{x \in A \text{ and } x \notin B\}$.

(a) Using the membership notation, $\in$, show that $D = A \cap \bar{B}$.

(b) The set D is called the **difference** between the sets A and B, written $D = A - B$. Show that the set $B - A$ is usually different from the set $A - B$.

(c) If C is any set, show that $\bar{C} = U - C$, where U is the universal set.

(d) Show that the expression $(A - B) \cup (B - A)$ is analogous to writing the exclusive sense of *or*, that is, the set of all elements in A or B but not both: $\{x \in (A \cup B) \text{ and } x \notin (A \cap B)\}$.

6.4 BOOLEAN ALGEBRA

The set-forming operations of union, intersection, and complementation follow certain laws. The laws can be shown to be those which we would agree with intuitively when we construct Venn diagrams to illustrate them. The set operations can be translated into formal logical statements and arguments and then proved. The study and development of a formal symbolic structure describing sets and subsets is attributed to the British mathematician George Boole (1815–1864).

6.4.1 The postulational or axiomatic structure of sets is called Boolean algebra. There are several approaches to the study. The following sketch is based on a structure given by E. V. Huntington (*Transactions* of the American Mathematical Society, 5) in 1904.

We begin by asserting that there exists a set U of elements $A, B, C, \cdots$, with two rules of formation $\cup$ and $\cap$, called union and intersection, satisfying the following axioms (assumed properties).

P_1: For any A and B, we have: $A \cup B = B \cup A$ and $A \cap B = B \cap A$.

P_2: There exist elements $\emptyset$ and U such that for any A we have: $A \cup \emptyset = A$, $A \cap U = A$, and $\emptyset \neq U$.

P_3: For any A, B, and C, we have: $A \cup (B \cap C) = (A \cup B) \cap (A \cup C)$ and $A \cap (B \cup C) = (A \cap B) \cup (A \cap C)$,

P_4: There exists for any A an element $\bar{A}$ such that: $A \cup \bar{A} = U$ and $A \cap \bar{A} = \emptyset$.

The reader should satisfy himself of the interpretations which can be associated to the assertion and the axioms with respect to our previous discussions of sets, that is, that the structure is satisfiable and consistent. Notice also that the properties of union and intersection are interchangeable, as well as the elements $\emptyset$ and U. That is, the interchanging of the symbols for union and intersection and for $\emptyset$ and U in the axioms P_1 through P_4 would result in the same set of axioms again! When this situation arises, we call it a **duality**. The principle of duality for this structure can be enunciated as follows.

THE PRINCIPLE OF DUALITY FOR BOOLEAN ALGEBRA. Any theorem of Boolean algebra remains valid if the rules of formation, called union and intersection, and the elements $\emptyset$ and U, called the null and universe, are interchanged throughout the statement of the theorem.

The principle of duality enunciated above permits us to state all theorems in pairs and guarantees that the proof of one of the pair of statements will be sufficient for the establishment of both the statements. Following are a few theorems of Boolean algebra to illustrate the nature of the structure.

THEOREM 1. (Called the idempotent laws) $A \cup A = A$ and $A \cap A = A$.

Proof.
1. $A = A \cup \emptyset$ P_2.
2. $A = A \cup (A \cap \bar{A})$ 1, P_4.
3. $A = (A \cup A) \cap (A \cup \bar{A})$ 2, P_3.
4. $A = (A \cup A) \cap U$ 3, P_4.
5. $A = A \cup A$ 4, P_2.

THEOREM 2. $A \cup U = U$ and $A \cap \emptyset = \emptyset$.

THEOREM 3. (Called the absorption laws) $A \cap (A \cup B) = A$ and $A \cup (A \cap B) = A$.

THEOREM 4. (Called the associative laws) $A \cup (B \cup C) = (A \cup B) \cup C$ and $A \cap (B \cap C) = (A \cap B) \cap C$.

THEOREM 5.   For any A, $\bar{A}$ is unique. (There is exactly one $\bar{A}$ for any set A.)

THEOREM 6.   (Called De Morgan's laws) $(\overline{A \cup B}) = \bar{A} \cap \bar{B}$ and $(\overline{A \cap B}) = \bar{A} \cup \bar{B}$.

DEFINITION 1.   If A and B are elements of U (sets), then we say that $A \subset B$, read "A is a subset of B," if and only if $A \cup B = B$.

THEOREM 7. $A \subset A$.

Proof.   1. $A \cup A = A$ theorem 1.
                  2. $A \subset A$ 1, definition 1.

THEOREM 8.   If $A \subset B$ and $B \subset A$, then $A = B$.

THEOREM 9.   If $A \subset B$ and $B \subset C$, then $A \subset C$.

THEOREM 10. $\emptyset \subset A \subset U$ for any A.

The structure of Boolean algebra has found many applications, not only in the fields of pure mathematics and logic, but also in the design of electrical equipment and control devices.

6.4.2 In conclusion, the following tables list some of the laws governing set operations. *Note:* we assume the definition $A - B = A \cap \bar{B}$.

TABLE 30
Laws of Boolean Algebra I

In the following: U indicates the universal set, $\emptyset$ the null set, and A an arbitrary set in U.

(a) $\bar{U} = \emptyset$	(b) $U \cup A = U$	(c) $\emptyset \cup A = A$
$\bar{\emptyset} = U$	$U \cap A = A$	$\emptyset \cap A = \emptyset$
(d) $A \cup \bar{A} = U$	(e) $U - A = \bar{A}$	(f) $A - \emptyset = A$
$A \cap \bar{A} = \emptyset$	$A - U = \emptyset$	$\emptyset - A = \emptyset$
	(g) $A - A = \emptyset$	

TABLE 31
Laws of Boolean Algebra II

In the following: A, B, C are arbitrary subsets of some universal set U.

(a) $A \cup A = A$	(b) $A \cup B = B \cup A$	(c) $A \cup (B \cup C) = (A \cup B) \cup C$
$A \cap A = A$	$A \cap B = B \cap A$	$A \cap (B \cap C) = (A \cap B) \cap C$
(d) $A - B = A \cap \bar{B}$	(e) $(\overline{A \cup B}) = \bar{A} \cap \bar{B}$	(f) $A \cup (B \cap C) = (A \cup B) \cap (A \cup C)$
$B - A = B \cap \bar{A}$	$(\overline{A \cap B}) = \bar{A} \cup \bar{B}$	$A \cap (B \cup C) = (A \cap B) \cup (A \cap C)$
	(g) $\bar{\bar{A}} = A$	

Note the very close resemblance of the statements of the above laws for sets to the logically equivalent statements given in Table 29.

Exercises 6.4

1. Write formal proofs of theorems 2 and 3 similar to the proof given for theorem 1.
2. Write formal proofs of theorems 8 and 9 similar to the proof given for theorem 7. *Note:* we assume a **substitution** rule which states that if $a = b$ and $b = c$, then $a = c$.
3. Write informal proofs for the following theorems of Boolean algebra.
   (a) If $A \cup B = A \cup C$ and $A \cap B = A \cap C$, then $B = C$.
   (b) $A \subset (A \cup B)$ and $(A \cap B) \subset A$.
   (c) $A \subset B$ if and only if $A \cap \bar{B} = \emptyset$.

Exercises 6

1. Let $U = \{1, 2, 3, 4, 5, 6, 7, 8, 9\}$. List the elements in the subsets of U described as follows:
   (a) $E = \{x \in U \mid x \text{ is even (i.e., divisible by 2)}\}$.
   (b) $F = \{x \in U \mid x \text{ is odd (i.e., not divisible by 2)}\}$.
   (c) $P = \{x \in U \mid x \text{ is not divisible by any element other than 1 or itself}\}$.
2. If $U, E, F,$ and P are the sets given in exercise 1, list the elements belonging to:
   (a) $\bar{E}$ and $\bar{P}$ (b) $E \cup P$ and $F \cup P$
   (c) $E \cap P$ and $F \cap P$ (d) $F - P$ and $E - P$
   (e) $(F \cup P) \cap E$ (f) $\bar{E} \cup P$ and $\bar{E} \cap P$
3. If $U, E, F,$ and P are the sets given in exercise 1, determine which of the following are true.
   (a) $\bar{E} \cap \bar{F} = \emptyset$ (b) $\bar{E} \neq F$ (c) $P \subset F$
   (d) $E \cup F = U$ (e) $\overline{P \cup E} = \bar{P} \cap \bar{E}$ (f) $(P - E) \subset F$
   (g) $P \cap E = P - F$ (h) $P \cap F = \bar{E}$ (i) $\overline{P \cup F} \subset E$
4. Using membership notation, give arguments to show that, for arbitrary subsets $A, B,$ and C of a universal set U, we have
   (a) $A \cap (B \cup C) = (A \cap B) \cup (A \cap C)$
   (b) $(A \cup C) - B = (\bar{B} \cap A) \cup (C \cap \bar{B})$
5. Copy the Venn diagram of Figure 6 and label each of the eight disjoint subsets of U with an appropriate expression using $A, B,$ and C which describes the subset exactly. For example, the central region common to all three sets $A, B,$ and C might be labeled $A \cap (B \cap C)$.
6. Copy the Venn diagram of Figure 8 and do as in exercise 5.
7. Let $A, B,$ and C be subsets of a universal set U. Construct Venn diagrams which satisfy the following conditions.
   (a) Sets A and B are disjoint. There are elements x such that $x \in C$ and $x \in A$, $x \in C$ and $x \in B$, $x \in C$ and $x \notin A$ and $x \notin B$. Also there are elements $x \in A$ and $x \notin C$, and $x \in B$ and $x \notin C$, and elements in the universal set which are not in $A, B,$ or C.
   (b) Sets A and B have some elements in common. Sets A and C have elements in common. Sets B and C have elements in common. There are no elements x such that $x \in A$, $x \in B$, and $x \in C$. Finally, there are no elements x such that $x \notin A$, $x \notin B$, and $x \notin C$.

8. Using Venn diagrams, explain why the following equalities are true.
(a) $(A - B) - C = A - (B \cup C)$
(b) $A \cup (B - C) = (A \cup B) - (C - A)$
(c) $A \cap (B - C) = (A \cap B) - (A \cap C)$

9. Verify by manipulation according to the laws governing set operations (Tables 30 and 31) that the following equalities are true.
(a) $A - (C \cup B) = (A - B) \cap (A - C)$
(b) $(A \cap \bar{B}) \cup (A \cap \bar{C}) = (A - B) - C$
(c) $[(A \cap \emptyset) \cup (B \cap U)] - C = (\bar{C} \cup \emptyset) \cap B$

10. A careful study of the set operations should reveal a close analogue to the logical connectives studied in Chapter 3. For example, the denial of a statement, $\sim P$, can be compared to the complement of a set, $\bar{P}$. Find a simple set relation which is the analogue of each of the following compound statements.
(a) $P \vee Q$ (b) $P \wedge Q$ (c) $P \rightarrow Q$

11. Given that $U = \{a, b, c, d, p, q, r, s, x, y, z\}$, $A = \{a, b, c, d\}$, and $B = \{p, q, r, s\}$.
(a) Construct a Venn diagram representing the sets U, A, and B.
(b) Describe the following sets by listing their elements.
    (i) $\bar{A}$ (ii) $B \cup \bar{A}$ (iii) $A \cap \bar{B}$ (iv) $U - (A \cup B)$

12. Give examples, contrasting sets that are clearly and well defined with ambiguously defined sets.

13. Make up an example to illustrate the relationship between a universal set, given sets, and derived sets.

14. In 6.1.2.1 we have defined the meaning of *equal sets*. In many situations we are interested in sets which are related in a weaker way. When each element of a set can be made to correspond with an element in a second set and each element of the second set can be related to an element of the first set, we say that the sets are related by an **equivalence** relation.

6.1.2.6 Definition: We say that two sets A and B are **equivalent** to each other if and only if their elements can be related so that to every element of A there corresponds one and only one element of B, and conversely.

Discuss the similarities and differences in the use of equals and equivalence as defined above.

15. Give several examples of equal sets, of equivalent sets. Are equal sets always equivalent? Are equivalent sets always equal?

7

LOGIC AND SETS

7.1 TRUTH SETS

It should be evident to the reader that there is a connection between the structure of sets and the structure of compound statements and arguments. In forming sets, we have often specified conditions which the elements of the sets must satisfy.

Now let us consider a universal set consisting of all the possible simple statements which we might consider for a component statement in a given situation. That is, let U stand for the set of all possible simple statements, P, in a particular discourse. For convenience, we use a lower case letter, p, to stand for any one of these simple statements. We write $U(p)$ for the universal set of possible statements p.

We can divide $U(p)$ into two sets: the subset consisting of all those statements that are true, and the complement of this set which is the set of all statements that are false. We denote these sets by $T(p)$ and $F(p)$, respectively. Note that $U(p) = T(p) \cup F(p)$.

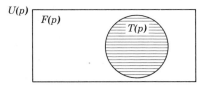

FIGURE 15.

Since we have considered only simple statements, all possible statements, p, must be contained in $T(p)$ or $F(p)$. Now, if we let the set $T(p)$ be denoted by P, the set of statements called the denial of p, $\sim p$, must be contained in the set $F(p) = \bar{P}$. Thus there is a parallel between the relationship of truth values of statements p and $\sim p$ and between the sets P and $\bar{P}$. That is, the complement of a set is analogous to the denial of a statement.

89

7.1.1 Since many statements are compound, let us consider a universal set consisting of pairs of component statements p and q. We can denote this universal set by $U(p,q)$.

For simplicity, first consider the portion which consists of the statements p. We have noted that this could be written $U(p) = T(p) \cup F(p)$. Next, in a similar manner, we consider the universal set $U(q) = T(q) \cup F(q)$. Now, imagine "superimposing" one universal set on the other to obtain a universal set in which each element consists of a p statement and a q statement. That is, an element of $U(p,q)$ consists of a p and a q statement, (p,q).

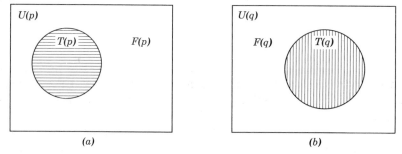

(a)   (b)

FIGURE 16.

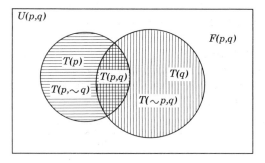

FIGURE 17.

Figure 17 is a Venn diagram of the situation. There are four possible disjoint subsets of $U(p,q)$. We have the two subsets $T(p,q)$ and $F(p,q)$. $T(p,q)$ consists of elements (p,q) such that both p and q represent true statements. $F(p,q)$ consists of elements (p,q) such that both p and q represent false statements. The horizontally shaded set in Figure 17 indicates the set in which p is true and q false. We can denote this set by $T(p,\sim q)$. Similarly, we have $T(\sim p,q)$ which is the set consisting of elements (p,q) such that p is false and q is true. The four sets result in $U(p,q) = T(p,q) \cup T(\sim p,q) \cup T(p, \sim q) \cup F(p,q)$. These four sets represent the sets in which the component statements can take on the possible combinations of truth values of p and q.

7.1.2 Now recall that the compound statement $p \lor q$ has the truth value true when p is true, q is true, or both are true. With respect to the above sets, this can be interpreted to mean that if we have an element of $T(p)$, $T(q)$, or $T(p,q)$, then the statement $p \lor q$ formed using the element (p,q) will be true. That is, we can represent the set $T(p \lor q)$ by the union of the sets $T(p)$ and $T(q)$: $T(p \lor q) = T(p) \cup T(q)$.

In a similar manner, we observe that the conjunction $p \land q$ is true only when both components are true. That is, we must have an element from the set $U(p,q)$ such that both p and q are true. This can occur only when we have an element from the set $T(p,q)$, that is, the set formed by the inter-section of $T(p)$ and $T(q)$: $T(p,q) = T(p) \cap T(q)$. We can denote this set $T(p \land q) = T(p) \cap T(q)$.

Finally, recall that the implication $p \to q$, was true for all truth values of the components except when p was true and q false. Any element from the set $T(p, \sim q)$ will then make the statement $p \to q$ false. This set can be represented by $T(p) - T(q)$. Now if we consider the complement of this set, $\overline{T(p) - T(q)}$, any element from this set will make the statement $p \to q$ true. That is, we can write $T(p \to q) = \overline{T(p) - T(q)}$.

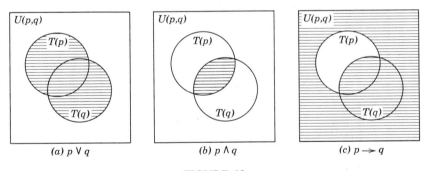

(a) $p \lor q$ (b) $p \land q$ (c) $p \to q$

FIGURE 18.

7.1.3 The above connections between compound statements and sets make it possible to "translate" statements into set relations. If p and q are statements such that $P = T(p)$ and $Q = T(q)$ are the sets of all state-ments p and q which are true, then

    (a) p is true if and only if $p \in P$ and $\sim p \in \bar{P}$.
    (b) $p \lor q$ is true if and only if $(p,q) \in (P \cup Q)$.
    (c) $p \land q$ is true if and only if $(p,q) \in (P \cap Q)$.
    (d) $p \to q$ is true if and only if $(p,q) \in \overline{(P - Q)}$.

The related sets of true compound statements are given the name "truth sets" for their corresponding compound statement forms. A **truth set** is thus the set of all statements which will make a given statement form true.

> 7.1.3.1 Definition: By the **truth set** of a statement form with components $p, q, r, \ldots$ we mean the subset of the universal set of statements $U(p,q,r,\ldots)$ such that if the element $(p,q,r,\ldots)$ is in the set, it will make the statement form true; and if the element is not in the set, it will make the statement form false.

The above remarks should indicate why there was such a resemblance between the set laws and logically equivalent statements.

Exercises 7.1

1. Give an argument to show that $U(p) = T(p) \cup F(p)$.

2. Discuss the meaning of the following notation:

(a) $F(p,q) = T(\sim p, \sim q)$ (b) $F(p,q) \neq \bar{T}(p,q)$

3. Sketch Venn diagrams and shade the truth sets which correspond to the following compound statements:

(a) $\sim p \vee q$ (b) $p \wedge \sim q$ (c) $p \leftrightarrow q$ (d) $\sim q \rightarrow p$

4. Construct a Venn diagram for compound statements with three components $p, q,$ and r. Label the truth value for each component in each of the eight possible disjoint subsets of $U(p,q,r)$.

5. Copy the Venn diagram of exercise 4 and shade the truth sets for each of the following compound statements.

(a) $p \wedge (q \vee r)$ (b) $(p \wedge q) \rightarrow r$ (c) $(\sim q \vee p) \rightarrow \sim r$

7.2 ARGUMENTS AND SETS

In the previous section, we noted that compound statements can be "translated" into set relations. For example, the compound statement form $(\sim P \vee Q) \wedge R$ can be translated into the set relation $(\bar{P} \cup Q) \cap R$, where the capital letters in the first symbolic expression stand for simple statements and in the second expression the same letters stand for the associated truth sets. That is, whenever the compound statement $(\sim P \vee Q) \wedge R$ is true, we must have an element of the set $(\bar{P} \cup Q) \cap R$.

Now recall that an argument consisted of a sequence of statements with a particular structure called its argument form. The argument was said to be valid if, whenever the premises were true, the conclusion would be true. It was also noted that arguments could be written in the form of implications with the conjunction of the premises as the antecedent and the conclusion as the consequent. Furthermore, if the implication was a tautology, the argument was valid. Otherwise, the argument was invalid.

For example, let us consider the valid argument called a disjunctive syllogism: $P \vee Q$, $\sim P$, $\therefore Q$. We can form the implication $[(P \vee Q) \wedge \sim P] \rightarrow Q$. Now, if we translate the implication into set relations, we note that the resulting set must be the entire universal set in order that the implication be a tautology. That is, a tautology is always true for any possible statements which might be written in for the components. In other words, the truth set of a tautology must be the universal set.

To illustrate the example, let us construct a Venn diagram of the associated sets for the statements $P \vee Q$, $\sim P$, and Q.

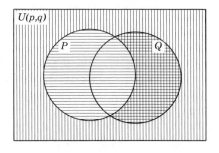

FIGURE 19.

In Figure 19, the truth set for $P \vee Q$ is the set $P \cup Q$, shaded horizontally. The truth set for $\sim P$ is vertically shaded. The truth set for $(P \vee Q) \wedge \sim P$ is cross-hatched. This is the set $Q - P$ which is the truth set of the premises of the argument. The truth set of the implication (i.e., the argument in the form of an implication) is then $\overline{(Q - P) - Q}$. Since $(Q - P) - Q = \emptyset$, we have $\overline{(Q - P) - Q} = U$, the universal set.

An alternate procedure is to note whether, whenever the premises are true, the conclusion is true. That is, we can see whether the truth set of the premises is contained in the truth set of the conclusion. For the disjunctive syllogism, we have the truth set $Q - P$ of the premises. Since $Q - P$ is clearly a subset of the truth set Q of the conclusion, we can say that the argument is valid.

More generally, if P_1, P_2, P_3, . . . are the premises of an argument and C is the conclusion, we can test the validity of the argument by forming the truth set of the conjunction of the premises and noting whether this truth set is a subset of the truth set of the conclusion C. If so, then the argument is valid; otherwise, invalid.

The following example illustrates the use of truth sets in testing the validity of an argument.

$B \vee M$ premise.
$B \rightarrow W$ premise.
$\sim W$ premise.
∴ M conclusion.

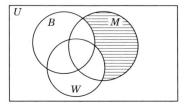

FIGURE 20.

The truth sets of the premises are for $B \vee M$, $B \cup M$; for $B \rightarrow W$ $\overline{B - W}$; for $\sim W$, $\overline{W}$. The truth set of the conjunction of the premises is then the intersection of the three truth sets: $(B \cup M) \cap [(\overline{B - W}) \cap \overline{W}]$. This is the set horizontally shaded in Figure 20. The truth set of the conclusion is the set M. Since the truth set of the premises is a subset of the truth set of the conclusion, the argument is valid.

As a second example, consider the invalid argument:

$P \wedge \sim Q$ premise.
$\sim Q \vee R$ premise.
∴ R conclusion.

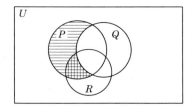

FIGURE 21.

The truth set of the conjunction of the premises is $(P \cap \overline{Q}) \cap (\overline{Q} \cup R) = P - Q$. The truth set of the conclusion is R. Since $P - Q$ need not be a subset of R, the argument is not valid. That is, if $x \in (P - Q)$, $x \in R$ or $x \in \overline{R}$. It is possible for the conclusion R to be false when the premises are both true.

Exercises 7.2

1. Using Venn diagrams, construct truth sets for the following compound statement forms.

(a) $P \vee (Q \wedge \sim R)$ (b) $(P \vee Q) \to R$ (c) $(P \wedge \sim Q) \vee (Q \wedge \sim R)$

2. Use truth sets and Venn diagrams to show:

(a) The validity of the argument called modus tollens.

(b) The invalidity of the argument called the Fallacy of Denying the Antecedent.

3. Test the validity of the following arguments using truth sets and Venn diagrams.

  (a) $\sim (P \vee Q)$ (b) $P \to Q$

       $Q \to P$ $\sim R \vee P$

       $\sim P$ R

       $\therefore Q$ $\therefore Q$

7.3 QUANTIFIERS

In discussing the structure of statements, we have considered only a very restricted group of statements which we called *simple*. We considered simple statements as "organic wholes" without internal structure. In ordinary usage, component statements of compound statements may themselves be interpreted in different ways. In this section, we will consider briefly a more detailed interpretation of component statements.

Statements such as "John is a fool," "All men are fools," "Some men are fools," and "He is a fool" can be considered to have an internal structure which separates into four parts:

(a) *A subject part.* The words *John, men,* and *He* in the above statements can be thought of as naming a "subject" being referred to.

(b) *A predicate part.* The word *fool* can be thought of as a condition on the subject, that is, that the subject has the particular property of being a "fool." We can interpret the condition, the predicate part, as defining a set which contains the subject part. (A word of caution: note that the subject and predicate property of the terms is dependent on the relative position of the terms with respect to the words *are* and *is.* For example, "Some fools are men" reverses the subject-predicate roles of the words *fools* and *men* as compared to "Some men are fools." That is, in "Some fools are men," the word *fools* is now the subject and *men* the predicate.)

(c) *A quantitative part.* All statements can be interpreted as implying a "grammatical number." That is, they are singular or plural in the English grammar sense. The word *John* refers to a single entity, whereas *men* refers to a collection. The words *all, some, one, few, many* refer to this quantitative aspect of statements.

(*d*) *A qualitative part.* Statements either affirm or deny the subject-predicate relationship. For example, "John is a fool" affirms the relationship while "John is not a fool" denies the relationship.

When statements such as "Frances is beautiful" and "Bill is a man" are interpreted as referring to a subject with the property of the predicate inhering to it, we can formulate a symbolic structure to describe their form and structural relationships. Statements interpreted in this way can also be described in terms of set relations.

Now let us consider any statement of the form "It has the property *P*." We can think of all these statements as defining a class of statements. If x stands for the subject and P the predicate, we can symbolize statements of this type by Px and understand it to mean "x has the property P." Statements formulated in this way are called **singular propositions**.

7.3.0.1 Definition: By a **singular proposition** we mean a statement which can be written in the form "x is P," where x is a subject and P is a predicate term. We write Px and read it as "x has the property P."

The statement "Frances is beautiful" can be symbolized as Bf and "Bill is a man" as Mb. Note that we use small letters to indicate the subject and capital letters to denote the predicate of the statement. When specific subjects such as *Frances* and *Bill* occur in singular propositions, the statements are either true or false. However, we may wish to make statements in which the subjects or predicates are not specified. In these situations, the statements can neither be true nor false. For example, the statement "He is a fool" can neither be true nor false until a specific substitution is made for the subject *He*. When we write "x is P" or Px, we can think of the symbols as "place holders" awaiting substitution of proper names. Statement forms containing unspecified terms are called **conditional statements**.

7.3.0.2 Definition: By a **conditional statement** we mean a statement with one or more unspecified terms.

7.3.1 Now we are ready to consider the quantitative part of statements. The singular proposition "Men are fools" can be modified to read "All men are fools." We might write "All *Fm*." The quantitative term *All* is symbolized by (x) where x is the subject of the statement. Note that the subject term *men* refers to a set of elements called "men." The quantitative term *All* refers to the members of the set. The statement "All men are fools" is then symbolized as $(m)Fm$.

The symbol (x) is called a **universal quantifier**, and statements which refer to "all" or "everything" or "any" are said to be **universally quantified.**

Typical formulations for this type of statement are: "For all x, x is P," "For every x, x is P," and "For each x, x is P."

> **7.3.1.1 Definition:** By a **universal quantifier** we mean the phrase "For all x" prefixed to a statement. We write (x), where x refers to the subject element of the statement which follows.

The statement "All men are fools," $(m)Fm$, is true if every element of the set called men, m, has the property F. If there is an element of the set m which does not have the property of being a "fool," F, then the statement is false. Alternatively, if we interpret *fool* to mean the set of all elements with the property of "being a fool," then $(m)Fm$ will be true if and only if the set of "men" is a subset of the set of "fools."

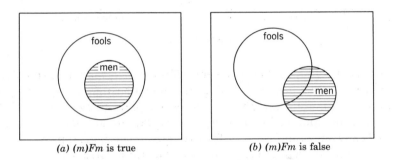

(a) $(m)Fm$ is true   *(b) $(m)Fm$ is false*

FIGURE 22.

7.3.2 The statement "Some men are fools," or "There is at least one man who is a fool," can be interpreted to mean that there is a nonempty subject set which is a subset of a predicate set or which has the predicated property. That is, a statement of the form "There is an x such that Px." asserts that an element of the subject set has the property P. Statements which refer to "some", "at least one", "there is" are said to be **existentially quantified**.

Statements which can be formulated to read "There is an x such that x is P" are symbolized by $(\exists x)Px$. The symbol $(\exists x)$ is called an existential quantifier which is read "There is an x such that . . . " For example, the statement "There is a man who is a fool" is symbolically represented by $(\exists m)Fm$.

> **7.3.2.1 Definition:** By an **existential quantifier** we mean the phrase "There is an x" prefixed to a statement. We write $(\exists x)$, where x refers to the subject element of the statement which follows.

An existentially quantified statement is true if there is, in fact, an element of the subject set belonging to the predicate set or with the predicated property. If there are no elements in the subject set with the predicated property, then the statement is false.

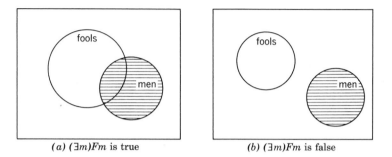

(a) (∃m)Fm is true   (b) (∃m)Fm is false

FIGURE 23.

7.3.3 We have noted that statements affirm or deny the subject-predicate relationship. The denial of either the quantification or the subject-predicate relationship can be denoted by our previous symbol ∼. With the denial, the universal quantifier, and the existential quantifier we can symbolically represent four basic forms of quantified singular propositions. These quantified singular propositions can be formulated as:

1. For all x, x is *P*.   1′. There is no x such that x is not *P*.
2. There is an x such that x is *P*.   2′. It is false that for all x, x is not *P*.
3. For all x, x is not *P*.   3′. There is no x such that x is *P*.
4. There is an x such that x is not *P*. 4′. It is false that for all x, x is *P*.

Table 32 gives the set of four pairs of symbolic representations of the

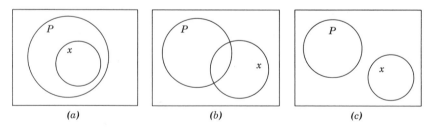

(a)   (b)   (c)

FIGURE 24.

(a) $(x)Px$ and $(\exists x)Px$ are true. $(x) \sim Px$ and $(\exists x) \sim Px$ are false.
(b) $(\exists x)Px$ and $(\exists x) \sim Px$ are true. $(x)Px$ and $(x) \sim Px$ are false.
(c) $(x) \sim Px$ and $(\exists x) \sim Px$ are true. $(x)Px$ and $(\exists x)Px$ are false.

above formulations for quantified singular propositions. Figure 24 illustrates interpretations of the statements in terms of sets.

TABLE 32

1. $(x)Px$	1′. $\sim(\exists x) \sim Px$
2. $(\exists x)Px$	2′. $\sim(x) \sim Px$
3. $(x) \sim Px$	3′. $\sim(\exists x)Px$
4. $(\exists x) \sim Px$	4′. $\sim(x)Px$

7.3.4 A further structuring of statements is possible when we note that
the subject and predicate terms can be interpreted as naming sets. That is,
we can separate the subject element named from the condition on the
subject. If S and P stand for the subject and predicate sets of quantified
statements and x stands for an arbitrary element, then we can consider
the four following situations depicted by the Venn diagrams of Figure 25.

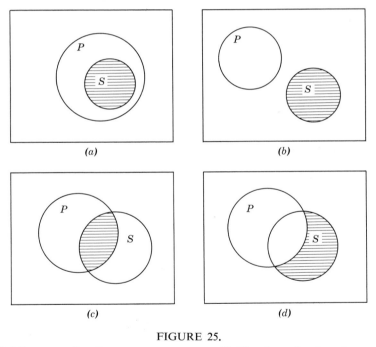

(a)   (b)

(c)   (d)

FIGURE 25.

(a) All s are p: $S \subset P$.   (b) No s is p: $S \cap P = \emptyset$.
(c) Some s are p: $S \cap P \neq \emptyset$.   (d) Some s are not p: $S - P \neq \emptyset$.

The statement "All men are fools" can be reformulated as "For all
elements x; if x is a man, then x is a fool." Note that an interesting

phenomenon has occurred; the singular propositions "x is a man" and "x is a fool" are clearly conditional statements in themselves. That is, they contain the unspecified term x and are thus neither true nor false. On the other hand, the quantified proposition "For all x; if x is a man, then x is a fool" is clearly true or false. The quantified proposition is true if the set of all men is in fact a subset of all fools.

The statement "Some women are fools" can be reformulated as "There is an x such that x is a woman and x is a fool." The statement "Some women are not fools" can be interpreted as "There is an x such that x is a woman and x is not a fool." The statement "No man is a fool" can be written "For all x; if x is a man, then x is not a fool."

The above four types of statements are given names and standard formulations as follows:

1. The universal affirmative: For all x; if x is P, then x is Q. Symbolized: $(x)[Px \rightarrow Qx]$.
2. The universal denial: For all x; if x is P, then x is not Q. Symbolized: $(x)[Px \rightarrow {\sim}Qx]$.
3. The particular affirmative: There is an x, such that x is P and x is Q. Symbolized: $(\exists x)[Px \wedge Qx]$.
4. The particular denial: There is an x, such that x is P and x is not Q. Symbolized: $(\exists x)[Px \wedge {\sim}Qx]$.

In closing this section, we note that there are other possible formulations of statements. For example, consider the statement "For all x, x is P or x is Q." Symbolized: $(x)[Px \vee Qx]$.

Exercises 7.3

In the following exercises: (*a*) Write a standard formulation for the statement. (*b*) Give a symbolic representation of the statement. (*c*) Using Venn diagrams, illustrate a true and a false instance of the statement.

1. All men are idealists.
2. Some people are rich.
3. No man is a fool.
4. There is at least one man who is practical.
5. There are people who are not rich.
6. There is a book which is not difficult.
7. Every man is a mortal.
8. Not all books are difficult.

In the following exercises, interpret the symbolic representations and write a "smooth" sentence for the expressions.

9. $(x)[Px \wedge {\sim}Qx]$.   10. $(x)Px$.
11. $(\exists x) \sim Qx$.   12. ${\sim}(x)[Px \rightarrow Qx]$.
13. $(\exists x)[Px \vee Qx]$.   14. ${\sim}(x)[{\sim}Px \wedge {\sim}Qx]$.
15. $(x)[{\sim}Px \rightarrow Qx]$.   16. ${\sim}(\exists x)[Px \wedge {\sim}Qx]$.

7.4 QUANTIFIED PROOFS

With the above brief discussion of the possible structuring and symbolization of quantified statements, we turn our attention to methods of proving quantified statements. In order to handle quantified statements, we must consider four fundamental quantified arguments.

7.4.1 Consider the quantified statement "For all x, x is P." If this statement is true, all elements x must be contained in P, that is, have the property P. It seems reasonable to say that if every element is in P, then a particular element, say, a, must also be in P. For example, in the classic Socrates Argument:

All men are mortal.

Socrates is a man.
_____

Therefore, Socrates is mortal.

which can be symbolically represented by:

$(x)[Hx \rightarrow Mx]$

Hs
_____

$\therefore Ms$

we have the problem of making the transition from the quantified to the specific singular proposition. This difficulty can be overcome by enunciating the following argument which will be assumed valid. We will call the argument a **Universal Specification**.

Universal Specification:

$(x)Px$
_____

$\therefore Pa$

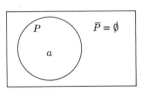

FIGURE 26.

With the Universal Specification argument available, we can easily justify the validity of the Socrates Argument.

Proof. 1. $(x)[Hx \rightarrow Mx]$ premise.

    2. Hs premise.

    3. $Hs \rightarrow Ms$ 1, Univ. Spec.

    4. $\therefore Ms$ 2, 3, mod. pon.

7.4.2 Now consider the argument:

No human is infallible.

All teachers are human.
_____

Therefore, no teacher is infallible.

The argument can be symbolically represented by:

$$(x)[Hx \to \sim Ix]$$
$$(x)[Tx \to Hx]$$
$$\therefore\ (x)[Tx \to \sim Ix].$$

Using Universal Specification, we can proceed as follows:

1. $(x)[Hx \to \sim Ix]$ premise.
2. $(x)[Tx \to Hx]$ premise.
3. $Ha \to \sim Ia$ 1, Univ. Spec.
4. $Ta \to Ha$ 2, Univ. Spec.
5. $Ta \to \sim Ia$ 3, 4, hyp. syll.
6. $\therefore\ (x)[Tx \to \sim Ix]$ 5, (?).

An adequate justification for the last concluding statement is lacking. In proceeding we selected an *arbitrary* element a in the implied universal set of x's. This was done to obtain statements which are true or false so that our normal logical rules would apply.

Now we ask whether we can justify the final generalization to the universally quantified concluding statement. We might argue that since the element a was perfectly arbitrary and since any arbitrary specific element would have sufficed to carry out the argument, the generalization must be justified. We should note, however, that our reference to an arbitrary element a is restricted to the set of x's. Also the same element a must be used uniformly throughout the instances where the universal quantification has been "dropped."

To formalize this argument, we state the following argument which will be assumed valid. We name the argument **Universal Generalization**.

Universal Generalization:

If a is an arbitrary element in a
set $x \in P$, then:

$$\frac{Pa}{\therefore\ (x)Px}$$

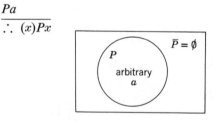

FIGURE 27.

Now we can eliminate the question mark in our previous example by writing "Univ. Gen." which justifies the conclusion.

7.4.3 Universal Specification and Universal Generalization lead us to consider Existential arguments which are similar in the sense that they will enable us to proceed with a specific element and then revert to the general element. For example, if we consider the existentially quantified statement $(\exists x)Px$, we note that the statement will be true if and only if there is in fact some element, say, a, in the set X such that Pa is true. Since in a proof we assume the premises to be true, it seems reasonable to assert that if $(\exists x)Px$ is a premise, then there must be an element, a specific but possibly unknown element, say, a, such that Pa is true.

Similarly, if $a \in X$ is an element such that Pa is true, we conclude that the statement $(\exists x)Px$ must be true. Note, however, that the element a which we mention with respect to existential quantification is restricted to a specific, possibly unknown, element in the set X.

Now we state the following arguments which we will assume valid without further justification.

Existential Specification:

$(\exists x)Px$
_____
$\therefore\ Pa$ for some $a \in X$.

Existential Generalization:

Pa for some $a \in X$.
_____
$\therefore\ (\exists x)Px$

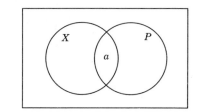

FIGURE 28.

EXAMPLE. Some men are practical.

All practical men are rich.
_____
Therefore, some men are rich.

Proof:
1. $(\exists x)[Mx \wedge Px]$ premise.
2. $(x)[Px \rightarrow Rx]$ premise.
3. $Ma \wedge Pa$ 1, Exist. Spec.
4. $Pa \rightarrow Ra$ 2, Univ. Spec.
5. Pa 3, simpl.
6. Ra 4, 5, mod. pon.
7. Ma 3, simpl.
8. $Ma \wedge Ra$ 6, 7, conj.
9. $\therefore\ (\exists x)[Mx \wedge Rx]$ 8, Exist. Gen.

Exercises 7.4

Assuming the premises true, prove the conclusions of the following arguments.

1. All men are fools.

Joe is a man.

Therefore, Joe is a fool.

2. Some problems are difficult.

Mathematical problems are not difficult.

Therefore, there are problems which are not mathematical.

3. All students study or fail.

There are students who do not study.

Therefore, some students fail.

4. People who inhale while smoking shorten their lives by ten years.

I will not shorten my life by ten years.

Therefore, I will not inhale while smoking.

Exercises 7

1. Sketch Venn diagrams and shade the truth set corresponding to the following compound statements:

(a) $\sim[p \wedge (q \vee \sim p)]$ (b) $(p \vee q) \to \sim q$ (c) $\sim[\sim p \vee (p \wedge \sim q)]$

2. Do as in exercise 1 with:

(a) $(p \wedge q) \leftrightarrow r$ (b) $\sim p \vee (q \to \sim r)$ (c) $\sim[\sim p \wedge (\sim q \vee r)]$

3. The shaded portions of the following Venn diagrams represent truth sets. Write symbolic representations of the corresponding compound statement forms.

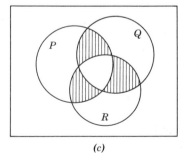

(a)

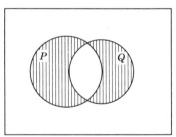

(b)

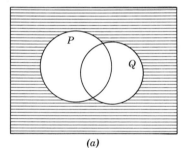

(c)

(d)

4. Test the validity of the following arguments, using truth sets and Venn diagrams.

(a) $\sim(P \wedge Q)$
$\underline{\quad P \quad}$
$\therefore \ \sim Q$

(b) $P \rightarrow (P \wedge Q)$
$\underline{\quad \sim Q \quad}$
$\therefore \ \sim P$

(c) $P \leftrightarrow \sim Q$
$\overline{\therefore \ \sim P \vee Q}$

5. Do as in exercise 4 with:

(a) $P \vee (\sim Q \wedge R)$
$\underline{Q \wedge (P \rightarrow \sim R)}$
$\therefore \ \sim R$

(b) $(P \wedge Q) \rightarrow R$
$\underline{\quad \sim R \quad}$
$\therefore \ \sim P$

(c) $(P \wedge Q) \vee (\sim P \wedge R)$
$\underline{\quad \sim Q \quad}$
$\therefore \ R$

6. Write quantified symbolic representations for the following statements.

(a) Some boys are stronger than men.

(b) All women are fickle.

(c) Some girls are not friendly.

(d) Not all students are dumb.

(e) There are no loafers in this class.

(f) All difficult books are not worth reading.

7. Using Venn diagrams, illustrate a true and a false instance for each of the statements of exercise 6.

8. Assuming the premises true, prove the conclusions of the following arguments.

(a) Not all students who study get good grades.
Students on the honor role get good grades.
Therefore, there are students who study who are not on the honor role.

(b) Some drivers of automobiles are aggressive drivers.
Defensive drivers are not aggressive.
All drivers are defensive or dangerous.
Therefore, there are dangerous drivers of automobiles.

9. Do as in Problem 8.

(a) Dogs are man's best friends.
No vicious animal could be man's best friend.
Therefore, dogs are not vicious animals.

(b) Some who attended the play left during the intermission.
Everyone who left during the intermission missed the excitement of the last act.
Therefore, some who attended the play missed the excitement of the last act.

10. Do as in Problem 8.

(a) All college freshmen study mathematics or English.
Therefore, all freshmen who do not study mathematics study English.

(b) All women are fickle.
Some women are friendly.
Therefore, some friendly people are fickle.

8

THE STRUCTURE
OF SETS

8.1. ELEMENTS IN SETS

Up to this point, we have not concerned ourselves with the relations between elements within a set. The elements within a set may be distinguishable one from another or not.

For example, consider a set of marbles of the same size, color, and texture. Although the set consists of separate physical objects, it might be quite difficult to distinguish between the marbles. On the other hand, a set consisting of objects of different shapes and sizes would have elements which are easily distinguishable. Of course, even with the set of marbles, we might, by marking or measuring them carefully, distinguish between the elements in the set.

In terms of symbolizing sets, we might describe two sets as follows: $C = \{n, n, n, n, n, n, n, n, n, n\}$ and $N = \{0, 1, 2, 3, 4, 5, 6, 7, 8, 9\}$. The set C has indistinguishable elements, whereas the set N has distinguishable elements. In this chapter, we will consider the latter type of sets with distinguishable elements.

8.1.1 In discussing the elements in sets, we may wish to name a specific element in a set. In this case, if we know the proper name of the element, all we need do is mention the name. For example, $1 \in N$ and $5 \in N$. When we explicitly state the proper name of an element in a set, we refer to it as a **constant**. That is, 2 is a constant.

If the proper name of a constant is unknown or irrelevant to a discussion, we often use a small letter from the first part of the alphabet or a letter with a subscript. For example, $a \in N$ refers to some specific but unknown element of the set N. We may also write $x_0 \in N$, meaning the same thing, that is, a specific but unknown constant. An element named in this way is called a **relative constant**. A relative constant is used to refer to a *fixed* element throughout a given discussion.

The distinction to be made between constants and relative constants is that a constant explicitly gives the proper name of an element, whereas a relative constant implies a constant whose proper name is unknown or irrelevant to the discussion.

8.1.1.1 Definition: By a **constant** we mean a fixed element of a set whose proper name is given. We often refer to the proper name of an element in a set as a constant.

8.1.1.2 Definition: By a **relative constant** we mean a fixed element of a set whose proper name is not given. We often refer to the "alias" of an element in a set as a relative constant.

8.1.2 In discussing sets, we have also described them in terms of the general property possessed by the elements.

For example, $B = \{x$ is a book$\}$ and $C = \{x \in B / x$ is about mathematics$\}$. The symbol x used in describing the sets B and C is quite different from a constant or a relative constant. In describing the set B, the x refers to a general or arbitrary element in the set. The x used in describing the set C refers to those elements which are in the set B and which are about mathematics. In either case, the x denotes elements whose names are unknown but relevant to the discussion.

In examining problems and situations, the naming of elements whose proper names are unknown but relevant to the discussion is very important. As in the above examples, the symbolizing of a "general" or "arbitrary" element, as well as the naming of unknown elements, reminds us and enables us to focus on and discuss the properties of the unknown elements. Conventionally, we denote these unknown and "arbitrary" elements with small letters from the end of the alphabet. An element named in this way is called a **variable**. That is, x, y, and z are called variables.

8.1.2.1 Definition: By a **variable** we mean an element which can be any one element of a set or which can be in turn different elements of a set or which can be a particular unknown element of a set or successively different unknown elements of a set.

We may think of a variable as being a "place-holder" or a "blank" for the name of an element. The symbols used to refer to statements in the tables of valid arguments and logical equivalences as well as those used to state the general rules for set relations are variables.

Exercises 8.1

1. Give examples of sets encountered in everyday activities which have distinguishable and indistinguishable elements.

2. Which of the elements in the following statements are constants, which relative constants, and which variables?

(a) $3 + 5 = 8$ (b) $x + y = y + x$ (c) $x = 5b$
(d) $ax + xy + by = 1001$ (e) $E = \{x \in W/x = 3a\}$

8.2 BINARY OPERATIONS

In order to proceed with the examination of the relationships possible between elements in a set, let us consider a simple but instructive example.

Suppose that we have a square which is pivoted at the center so that it can be rotated around the pivot. As an aid to our intuition, we might refer to Figure 29.

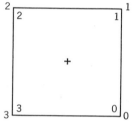

FIGURE 29.

The square has four vertices or corners. Let us name these vertices "0," "1," "2," "3,". We will also refer to the position of these vertices as being "0," "1," "2,", and "3." Now we define the set $V = \{0, 1, 2, 3\}$.

Let us imagine that the square is rotated around the pivot in a counterclockwise direction. Suppose the vertex 0 is moved to the position 1. We

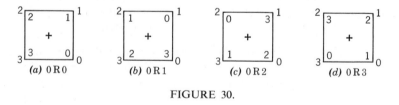

(a) 0 R 0   (b) 0 R 1   (c) 0 R 2   (d) 0 R 3

FIGURE 30.

can describe this action symbolically as "0 R 1." In a similar manner, the vertex 0 might be rotated to the position 2, 3, or even left unchanged. Let us denote these rotations by 0 R 1, 0 R 2, 0 R 3, and 0 R 0. The symbolism suggests that we define the set of rotations as $R = \{0\ R\ 0,\ 0\ R\ 1,\ 0\ R\ 2,$ 0 R 3} or more simply as $R = \{0, 1, 2, 3\}$.

What occurs to the other elements of V "under" the rotations as described above? We might list the results of an examination of this question.

TABLE 33

Rotation:	0 R 0	0 R 1	0 R 2	0 R 3
Vertex: 0	0	1	2	3
1	1	2	3	0
2	2	3	0	1
3	3	0	1	2

In the listing in Table 33, the top row indicates elements of R and the rows below, elements of V. If we select an element of V and an element of R, the listing tells us that the result will be an element of V. In our interpretation, however, we can identify the elements of R with the elements of V. That is, we can denote both the vertices and their positions with the names "0," "1," "2," and "3." Thus we can write $R = V$.

TABLE 34

R	0	1	2	3
0	0	1	2	3
1	1	2	3	0
2	2	3	0	1
3	3	0	1	2

If x and y are any two elements of V, we can now write x R y to indicate that the vertex x is rotated "under" the rotation denoted by y. Note that the meaning of x R y is not the same as y R x. That is, y R x means that the vertex y is rotated by x. For example, 2 R 1 means that the vertex 2 is rotated by the rotation 1 and from the table the result is the vertex 3. The statement 1 R 2 means the vertex 1 is rotated by the rotation 2 and the result is the vertex 3.

We are now in a position to describe many properties of the elements of the derived set V.

1. The set V has four distinct elements related in a "successive" order: 0, 1, 2, 3, 0, 1, 2, 3, $\cdots$.
2. For any two elements of V, we have defined a relationship which we call rotation, R.
3. If x and y are any two elements of V, they are related by R so that x R $y = z$ where z is again an element of V.
4. If x and y are any two elements of V, they are related by R so that x R $y = y$ R x (e.g., 1 R 3 = 3 R 1 = 0).

5. If x, y, and z are any three elements of V, we have x R $(y$ R $z) =$ $(x$ R $y)$ R z (e.g., 1 R (3 R 1) = (1 R 3) R 1 = 1).

Our example illustrates a type of set with properties which are of importance in the study of the relationships between elements in a set. Despite the work of Euclid over two thousand years ago, it was not recognized that an abstract axiomatic treatment of the structure revealed would result in logical knowledge which could be applied to *all* particular situations with the properties assumed in the axiomatic structure. George Peacock (1791–1858) in his *Treatise on Algebra* (1830) was perhaps the first to recognize the possibilities in a structuring of the elements in a set.

By the middle of the nineteenth century an Irish mathematician, William Rowan Hamilton (1805–1865), and the German mathematician, Hermann Gunther Grassman (1809–1877), had published results which opened the way for the study of many different structures of elements in sets.

8.2.1 In what follows, let us assume that there is an appropriate set with distinguishable elements. Our first step is to define what is meant by an **ordered pair** of elements. In our ordinary language, the word *pair* is usually thought of as referring to a set consisting of two elements: $P =$ $\{a, b\}$ where $a \neq b$. In addition to this, we wish to introduce the notion of "order." That is, we wish to specify which of two elements come first and which second. We will use a conventional notation, (a,b), to denote an ordered pair. The following examples should help to clarify the notion of ordered pairs.

1. A couple on a date, the male being named first:
   (Bill, Dot); (Sam, Sue).
2. For the set $B = \{a, b\}$: (a,b); (a,a); (b,a); (b,b).
3. For the sets $B = \{a, b\}$ and $C = \{c, d, e\}$ where we consider all possible ordered pairs formed by choosing an element from the set B for the first element and an element from the set C for the second element: (a,c); (a,d); (a,e); (b,c); (b,d); (b,e).

8.2.1.1 Definition: By an **ordered pair** we mean an element (x,y) formed by an element x from a set and an element y from a set such that x is "first" and y is "second."

The definition does not specify that the elements forming the ordered pairs need come from the same or different sets. The elements in an ordered pair need not be different, nor must they occur only once. The same element may be the first element in one ordered pair and the second element in another. The order may or may not be essential to a situation.

An ordered pair is not a set, because in a set the order of the elements is completely immaterial: $\{a, b\} = \{b, a\}$. That is, an ordered pair has the additional property of **order**. The ordered pair (a,b) is to be distinguished from the ordered pair (b,a) if $a \neq b$. Ordered pairs (a,b) and (c,d) are said to be equal, $(a,b) = (c,d)$, if and only if $a = c$ and $b = d$.

Since an ordered pair is an "object" of interest, we are led to consider the collections of ordered pairs formed in various ways. For example, if $B = \{a, b\}$ and $C = \{c, d, e\}$, we can form the set of *all* ordered pairs (x,y) where $x \in B$ and $y \in C$. This set of ordered pairs is denoted by $B \times C$. The set $B \times C = \{(a,c), (a,d), (a,e), (b,c), (b,d), (b,e)\}$. If (x,y) is an ordered pair formed by taking $x \in D$ and $y \in R$, then the set of *all* ordered pairs which can be formed in this way is called the **cartesian product set** of the sets D and R.

> 8.2.1.2 Definition: By the **cartesian product set** of two sets D and R we mean the set of *all* ordered pairs (x, y) such that $x \in D$ and $y \in R$. We write $D \times R = \{(x,y) \mid x \in D$ and $y \in R\}$.

The definition of a cartesian product set does *not* specify that the sets used in forming the "product" set need be the same or different. For example:

1. If M is the set of all male students in a particular college and W the set of all female students, then $M \times W$ is the set of all possible couples which can be formed by selecting a male student, then a co-ed. If Bill is a male student and Shirley a co-ed, then (Bill, Shirley) is an element of $M \times W$.
2. If $A = \{1, 2, 3\}$ and $B = \{a, b\}$, then
   (a) $A \times B = \{(1,a), (1,b), (2,a), (2,b), (3,a), (3,b)\}$.
   (b) $B \times A = \{(a,1), (a,2), (a,3), (b,1), (b,2), (b,3)\}$.
   (c) $A \times A = \{(1,1), (1,2), (1,3), (2,1), (2,2), (2,3), (3,1), (3,2), (3,3)\}$.
   (d) $B \times B = \{(a,a), (a,b), (b,a), (b,b)\}$.
3. Consider our introductory illustration with the square, the primary set considered was the set of vertices $V = \{0, 1, 2, 3\}$. The secondary set was $R = V$. $V \times V = \{(0,0), (0,1), (0,2), (0,3), (1,0), (1,1), (1,2), (1,3), (2,0), (2,1), (2,2), (2,3), (3,0), (3,1), (3,2), (3,3)\}$.

8.2.2 Recalling the illustrative example with the square, we note that an element of $V \times V$ can be interpreted as denoting a particular rotation of a vertex of the square. That is, the ordered pair $(2,1)$ can be interpreted as $2\ R\ 1$. The result of this rotation was an element of V, 3. We wrote $2\ R\ 1 = 3$.

Abstracting the notion from the concrete example, we consider any ordered pair obtained by selecting two elements from a given set and associating to this ordered pair another element from the set. That is, we note that it is possible to consider, for any set, the derived cartesian product set of the set with itself and a rule whereby an element in the given set is associated to each ordered pair of the cartesian product set. When this occurs, we say that a **binary operation** has been defined on the set. For the illustrative example with the square, Table 34 defines a binary operation on *V*.

> 8.2.2.1 Definition: By a **binary operation** on any set *A* we mean a rule whereby, for any two elements in *A*, we obtain a unique resulting element in *A*. A **binary operation** is thus a rule which selects a unique $x \in A$ for every element $(y,z) \in A \times A$.

Ordinary addition, subtraction, multiplication, and division are excellent examples of binary operations on a set. An operation on a set amounts to a selection process where we select a member of the set for every ordered pair in the cartesian product set of the set with itself. An operation assumes that we have at our disposal the entire set for each of the elements selected. For example, in ordinary addition of numbers, we write $2 + 2 = 4$ and $3 + 0 = 3$. In the notation of cartesian product sets, we would write $(2,2) = 4$ and $(3,0) = 3$.

Nothing in the definition of a binary operation specifies that the set on which the operation is defined must be a particular kind of set. We can define a binary operation on any set whatever. The definition does require that we specify an element for every possible ordered pair. That is, the operation must specify an element of the set for each ordered pair in the cartesian product set. However, there need not be any particular arrangement in the specification of the resulting elements of an operation.

For example, consider the set $B = \{a, b\}$. We form $B \times B = \{(a,a), (a,b), (b,a), (b,b)\}$. To obtain an operation, we must specify an $x \in B$ for every $(y,z) \in B \times B$. Arbitrarily, let us assign a to (a,a), a to (a,b), b to (b,a), and b to (b,b). This assignment of elements of B to elements of $B \times B$ defines an operation on *B*. There are other possible operations which might be constructed on *B*.

It is customary to designate an operation on a set by some distinctive symbol. For example, we might designate the operation defined above on *B* by the symbol @. We could then write: $a @ a = a, a @ b = a, b @ a = b$,

TABLE 35

@	a	b
a	a	a
b	b	b

and $b @ b = b$. A useful device is to construct a table to display the operation. The operation symbol is indicated at the upper left hand corner of the table. The marginal entries on the left hand column indicate the first elements of ordered pairs. The top row marginal entries indicate the second elements of ordered pairs. The entries in the body of the table specify the resulting element of the set under the indicated operation. Table 35 exhibits the operation @ on the set B. Table 36 exhibits further possible operations on B.

TABLE 36

(i) ø	a	b		(ii) ⊕	a	b		(iii) *	a	b
a	a	b		a	a	b		a	a	a
b	a	a		b	b	a		b	a	b

8.2.3 Going back again to the example of the rotation of the vertices of a square, we note that the concluding description of the properties of the elements of the set V included remarks concerning properties of the operation of rotation. For example, $x \mathrm{R} y = y \mathrm{R} x$ and $x \mathrm{R} (y \mathrm{R} z) = (x \mathrm{R} y) \mathrm{R} z$.

The properties of an operation determine to a great extent the usefulness of the operation. Operations with a few properties often lead to extensive structures of relationships between elements in a set. Certain common properties of binary operations are given proper descriptive names. In the following paragraphs, we will briefly examine these properties and name them.

As a preliminary remark, we note that a binary operation may not be completely defined on a set. That is, there may be ordered pairs for which no elements are assigned. In this case, we say that the operation is **not closed**. If the operation is well defined in the sense that every ordered pair in the cartesian product set has an element of the set assigned to it, then we say that the operation is **closed**.

8.2.3.1 Definition: A binary operation is said to be **closed** if, for each ordered pair in the cartesian product set, there is assigned an element of the set.

If a binary operation is defined and closed on a set, two immediate properties of the binary operation which are of interest are those called **commutative** and **associative** properties of the operation. These properties are illustrated in the example of the square as $x \mathrm{R} y = y \mathrm{R} x$ and $x \mathrm{R} (y \mathrm{R} z) = (x \mathrm{R} y) \mathrm{R} z$. In ordinary arithmetic, for addition we express these properties as "the sum of addends will be the same regardless of the order of addition."

8.2.3.2 Definition: We say that a binary operation, o, on a set S is **commutative** if $x \circ y = y \circ x$ for all $x \in S$ and $y \in S$.

8.2.3.3 Definition: We say that a binary operation, o, on a set S is **associative** if $x \text{ o } (y \text{ o } z) = (x \text{ o } y) \text{ o } z$ for all $x \in S$, $y \in S$, and $z \in S$.

Not all binary operations on sets are commutative or associative. For example, the operation @ on B given by Table 35 is not commutative. For this operation, we have $a \text{ @ } b = a$ and $b \text{ @ } a = b$ so that $a \text{ @ } b \neq b \text{ @ } a$. The operation is, however, associative. To test this property of the operation, we must check all eight possible situations which might occur. One possible situation is illustrated as follows: $a \text{ @ } (b \text{ @ } a) = a \text{ @ } b = a$ and $(a \text{ @ } b) \text{ @ } a = a \text{ @ } a = a$.

The operation (i) of Table 36 denoted by ø is not commutative and not associative. The operation is not commutative since $a \text{ ø } b = b$ while $b \text{ ø } a = a$. The operation is not associative since $b \text{ ø } (a \text{ ø } b) = b \text{ ø } b = a$ while $(b \text{ ø } a) \text{ ø } b = a \text{ ø } b = b$ so that $b \text{ ø } (a \text{ ø } b) \neq (b \text{ ø } a) \text{ ø } b$. Note that a single case in which the property does not hold true is sufficient to establish the denial of the general property.

Lest the reader feel that operations are not commutative and associative in general, we note that the operation (ii) of Table 36 denoted by $\oplus$ is both commutative and associative. The operation R in our illustration of the rotation of the vertices of a square was also both commutative and associative. In order to show that an operation is commutative and associative, we must show that the properties hold in every possible case. We illustrate the procedure for the operation $\oplus$ with one case and leave the remaining cases for the reader to verify.

Since $a \oplus b = b$ and $b \oplus a = b$, we have $a \oplus b = b \oplus a$. Since $a \oplus (b \oplus a) = a \oplus b = b$ and $(a \oplus b) \oplus a = b \oplus a = b$, we have $a \oplus (b \oplus a) = (a \oplus b) \oplus a$.

We have noted that more than one binary operation may be defined on a set. For example, in arithmetic we have addition, subtraction, multiplication, and division. We ask whether there is a common property which connects two operations. From ordinary arithmetic we have meaningful statements such as $3 \times (5 + 2) = 3 \times 7 = 21$. Note also that we might have done the arithmetic as follows: $3 \times (5 + 2) = (3 \times 5) + (3 \times 2) = 15 + 6 = 21$! The property above which connects the operations of addition and multiplication is called the **distributive** property of the two operations. That is, we say that ordinary multiplication is **distributive** over ordinary addition of numbers.

8.2.3.4 Definition: We say that a binary operation, o, is **distributive** with respect to a second binary operation, *, on a set S if $x \text{ o } (y * z) = (x \text{ o } y) * (x \text{ o } z)$ for all $x \in S$, $y \in S$, and $z \in S$.

As an example, consider the operations $\oplus$ and $*$ on the set $B = \{a, b\}$ given by (ii) and (iii) of Table 36. There are two possible situations: $\oplus$ distributive with respect to $*$, and $*$ distributive with respect to $\oplus$. For each situation, there are eight possible cases to check.

We show that $\oplus$ is not distributive with respect to $*$ by showing that it is false for $b \oplus (b * a) = (b \oplus b) * (b \oplus a)$. Since $b \oplus (b * a) = b \oplus a = b$ and $(b \oplus b) * (b \oplus a) = a * b = a$ by successive use of the tables, $\oplus$ is not distributive with respect to $*$.

The operation $*$ is distributive with respect to $\oplus$. For one case, we have $b * (b \oplus a) = b * b = b$ and $(b * b) \oplus (b * a) = b \oplus a = b$. Verification of the seven other cases will establish the property.

Exercises 8.2

1. For the example of the square, Figure 29, consider the operation defined as a "reflection" as follows: 0 F 1 consists of turning the square "over" on a horizontal axis, 0 F 2 consists of turning the square over on a diagonal connecting 1 and 3, 0 F 3 consists of turning the square over on a vertical axis, and 0 F 0 consists of turning the square on the diagonal through 0 and 2.

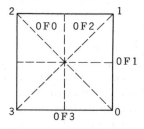

FIGURE 31.

   (a) Construct a table similar to Table 34 for this operation of reflection on V.
   (b) How many elements are there in $V \times V$?
   (c) Is the operation F above closed, commutative, associative? Illustrate.
   (d) If R is the rotation operation, is R distributive with respect to F? Is F distributive with respect to R? Illustrate.
2. Given $A = \{a, b, c\}$ and $B = \{p, q, r\}$, then list the elements of the cartesian product sets $A \times A$, $A \times B$, and $B \times A$.
3. Given $A = \{1, 2, 3, 4\}$, form the set of all subsets of A. Consider the relation of union of sets in the set of subsets of A. Does the relation of union define a binary operation? If so, describe the operation and discuss its properties.
4. Let U be the universal set of all statements with components P or Q. Does the logical connective called a conjunction define a binary operation on U? Does the disjunction define a binary operation on U? If so, discuss the properties of the operations.

5. Given $S = \{1, 2, 3, 4\}$, construct binary operations on S which satisfy the following:

(a) The operation is neither commutative nor associative.

(b) The operation is commutative but not associative.

(c) The operation is both commutative and associative.

(d) Two of the binary operations considered are not distributive one with respect to the other. Specify.

(e) The two binary operations considered are distributive one with respect to the other. Specify.

8.3 GROUPS, RINGS, AND FIELDS

Now that we have considered some of the possible properties of relations between elements in a set, the question arises as to whether there are particular kinds of sets which can be categorized by the properties of their elements. The answer is yes; over 200 different types of structures have been studied by modern mathematicians.

The reader may ask: "Of what earthly use is it?" Many answers might be given, not the least being that it satisfies the esthetic and inquisitive needs of a person. More practically, knowledge of types of structures will save much work and labor in the examination of the many varied problems which occur in concrete situations. Furthermore, the question of "why?" posed by the Greeks and the search for a "unity in nature," which led Leibniz to such great heights, push us forward. The study is further justified by its results, which include our modern technology, standard of living, and scientific achievements that speak for themselves.

With this, we turn to the examination and description of the three most useful and common types of structures of elements in a set.

8.3.1 The concept of a **group** describes one of the simplest structures of significance. The idea is due to a young Frenchman, Evariste Galois, who was twice refused admission to the École Polytechnique and after entering the École Normale was dismissed. In writing to a friend concerning his theories, he referred to his paper as "all this mess." "This mess" contained a key to the subject now called modern algebra.

It is convenient to describe the structure of a group axiomatically as follows:

There are two primitive notions described as

P_1: There exists a set G with elements $a, b, c, \cdots$

P_2: A binary operation o is defined on G.

The following axioms describe the properties necessary to a group.

A_1: For all $x, y \in G$, $x \text{ o } y \in G$. That is, the operation must be **closed**.

A_2: For all $x, y, z \in G$, $(x \text{ o } y) \text{ o } z = x \text{ o } (y \text{ o } z)$. That is, the operation must be **associative**.

A_3: There is an element $e \in G$ such that, for all $x \in G$, $x \circ e = x$. The element e is called an **identity** element of G.

A_4: If $x \in G$, then there is an element $y \in G$ such that $x \circ y = e$. The element y is called an **inverse** element of x and is often written x^{-1}.

If the operation on G is commutative, we say that the group G is **commutative** or **abelian**. The group will then satisfy the following additional axiom:

A_5: If $x, y \in G$, then $x \circ y = y \circ x$. That is, the operation is **commutative**.

8.3.1.1 Definition: By a **group** we mean any set G with elements $a, b, c, \cdots$ and a binary operation $\circ$ defined on G such that axioms A_1 through A_4 are satisfied.

8.3.1.2 Definition: By a **commutative** or **abelian group** we mean a group which satisfies A_5.

The identity and inverse elements mentioned in the axioms deserve attention. An *identity* element is an element which causes the other element in an operation to remain "stationary" under the operation. For example, in the ordinary addition of whole numbers, the number zero, 0, is an identity element. In multiplication, the number one, 1, is an identity. A natural question to ask is whether a group can have more than one identity element (see theorem T_4 which follows).

An *inverse* is an element which "reduces" a given element to the identity element under the operation. For example, in ordinary arithmetic, the negative of a number is the inverse of the number under the operation of addition. In multiplication, we have the reciprocals of numbers for inverses.

Examples of groups are relatively common. A few are described as follows:

1. The ordinary whole numbers, including the negative numbers, with the operation of addition form a group.
   (*a*) We can add any two whole numbers together and the result is a whole number.
   (*b*) The order in which we add whole numbers is immaterial so that the operation is associative.
   (*c*) The whole number 0 is the identity element for addition.
   (*d*) The negative of any number is the inverse of the number.
   (*e*) The group is also abelian by our comment in (*b*).
2. The example of the vertices of a square under rotation forms a group.

(a) Table 34 defines the operation and indicates that the operation is closed.

(b) Our previous discussion established the associative property of the operation R.

(c) The element denoted by 0 is the identity element. That is, $0 \text{ R } 0 = = 0$, $1 \text{ R } 0 = 1$, $2 \text{ R } 0 = 2$, $3 \text{ R } 0 = 3$.

(d) The inverse for each element is listed as follows:

$$\text{(element) R (inverse)} = 0$$

0	0
1	3
2	2
3	1

(e) In addition, the group is abelian since $x \text{ R } y = y \text{ R } x$.

3. The set $B = \{a, b\}$ with the operation $\oplus$ shown in Table 36(ii) forms a group with a as the identity and an element as its own inverse.

The general axiomatic structure of groups is quite elaborate. Assuming the material of previous chapters, we prove three theorems concerning groups and state a few further results for the reader to verify.

T_1: If $a, b, c \in G$ and $a = b$, then $a \circ c = b \circ c$ and $a \circ c \in G$.

> *Proof:* 1. $a \circ c = a \circ c, a \circ c \in G$ $a, c, \in G$ and o closed, A_1.
> 2. $a = b$ premise.
> 3. $\therefore\ a \circ c = b \circ c$ and   1,2, substitution.
> $a \circ c \in G$

T_2: If $a, b, c \in G$ and $a \circ c = b \circ c$, then $a = b$.

> *Proof:* 1. $a \circ c = b \circ c, a \circ c \in G$ premise, A_1.
> 2. $(a \circ c) \circ c^{-1} = (b \circ c) \circ c^{-1}$ 1, $c^{-1} \in G$, A_4, T_1.
> 3. $a \circ (c \circ c^{-1}) = b \circ (c \circ c^{-1})$ 2, A_2.
> 4. $a \circ e = b \circ e$ 3, A_4.
> 5. $\therefore\ a = b$ 4, A_3.

T_3: For all $x \in G$, $x \circ e = e \circ x$ where e is the identity element.

> *Proof:* 1. $x \circ e = x$ premise and A_3.
> 2. $e \circ x \in G$ A_3, A_1.
> 3. $(e \circ x) \circ x^{-1} = e \circ (x \circ x^{-1})$ A_4, A_1, A_2.
> 4. $(e \circ x) \circ x^{-1} = e \circ e = e$ 3, A_4, A_3.
> 5. $(e \circ x) \circ x^{-1} = x \circ x^{-1}$ 4, A_4.
> 6. $e \circ x = x$ 5, T_2.
> 7. $\therefore\ x \circ e = e \circ x$ 1,6, substitution

T_4: The identity e is unique in G. That is, a group G has only one unique identity.

> *Hint:* Use an indirect proof by assuming e and e'.

T_5: If $x \in G$, then $x \mathbin{\mathrm{o}} x^{-1} = x^{-1} \mathbin{\mathrm{o}} x$.
   Hint: Proof similar to T_3.

T_6: For each $x \in G$, x^{-1} is unique in G.

T_7: If $x \in G$, $(x^{-1})^{-1} = x$. That is, the inverse of the inverse of an element is again the element.

T_8: If $a, b \in G$, then there is a unique element $x \in G$ such that $a \mathbin{\mathrm{o}} x = b$.
   Hint: First show that x exists $(x = a^{-1} \mathbin{\mathrm{o}} b)$, then show that this element satisfies $a \mathbin{\mathrm{o}} x = b$.

T_9: If $a, x \in G$ and $a \mathbin{\mathrm{o}} x = a$, then $x = e$ the identity element.

T_{10}: If $e \in G$ is the identity, then $e^{-1} = e$.

8.3.2 The importance of groups lies in the fact that many significant structures contain the group structure within them as substructures. We have noted that the integers under addition have the structure of a group. In ordinary arithmetic, however, we are concerned with a second binary operation, multiplication.

An intermediate structure in which a second binary operation is available is called a **ring**. Informally, a ring is a set of elements with two binary operations which form a group and a part of a group connected by the distributive property.

8.3.2.1 Definition: By a **ring** we mean any set R with two binary operations o and * defined on R such that:
   1. R is an **abelian group** with respect to the operation o.
   2. The operation * is **closed** and **associative** on R.
   3. The operation * is **distributive** with respect to o on R.

A ring may also be called a **system**. The most common example of a ring is the set of integers with the operations of addition and multiplication. If the second operation * of a ring has an identity element, the identity for * is called a **unit element**. The identity element for the operation o is then called a **zero**. If both operations of a ring are commutative, the ring is called an **integral domain**.

Note that the second operation * on a ring R does not form a group even when extended to an integral domain. It seems natural to extend the structure of sets to form two complete groups on the set. When this is accomplished, we obtain one of the most important and useful types of structures of elements in sets. The structure is called a **field**.

The traditional subject of elementary algebra as taught in schools consists primarily of a study of the properties of a field. The primitive notions and axioms for a field can thus be used to develop elementary algebra.

Although this would be an elegant and esthetically satisfying undertaking, it would also be a tedious and extremely abstract development.

We first give a concise definition of a field, then describe it axiomatically.

8.3.2.2 Definition: By a **field** we mean any set F which is an integral domain such that every nonzero element has an inverse with respect to the second operation $*$.

P_1: There exists a set F with elements $a, b, c, \cdots$.

P_2: Two binary operations o and $*$ are defined on F. The first operation o is often written $+$ and called addition. The second is often called multiplication and if $a, b \in F$ is written ab or $(a)(b)$.

A_1: For all $x, y \in F$, $x \text{ o } y \in F$ and $x * y \in F$. (**closure**)

A_2: For all $x, y \in F$, $x \text{ o } y = y \text{ o } x$ and $x * y = y * x$. (**commutativity**)

A_3: For all $x, y, z \in F$, $(x \text{ o } y) \text{ o } z = x \text{ o } (y \text{ o } z)$ and $(x * y) * z = x * (y * z)$. (**associativity**)

A_4: There is an element $e \in F$ such that, for all $x \in F$, $x \text{ o } e = x$. (**zero** element)

A_5: There is an element $i \in F$ such that, for all $x \in F$, $x * i = x$. (**unit** element)

A_6: For all $x, y, z \in F$, $x * (y \text{ o } z) = (x * y) \text{ o } (x * z)$. ($*$ **distributive** with respect to o)

A_7 If $x \in F$, then there is an element $-x \in F$ such that $x \text{ o } (-x) = e$. (**additive inverse**)

A_8 If $x \in F$ and $x \neq e$, then there is an element $x^{-1} \in F$ such that $x * x^{-1} = i$. (**multiplicative inverse**)

If in addition to the above axioms we have the following two axioms, then the field is called an **ordered field**. An ordered field is often referred to as a **real number system**.

A_9: There is a subset P of F, $P \subset F$, such that for all $x \in F$ and $x \neq e$, we have one and only one of x and $-x$ in P.

A_{10}: For all $x, y \in P$, $x \text{ o } y \in P$ and $x * y \in P$.

8.3.2.3 Definition: The elements of P are called the **positive** elements of F. All other elements $x \in F$ and $x \neq e$ are called the **negative** elements of F.

8.3.2.4 Definition: If $x, y \in F$ and if $[x \text{ o } (-y)] \in P$, then we say, "**x is greater than y**" and write $x > y$. For the same situation, we may write $y < x$ and read it, "**y is less than x.**"

The ordinary numbers of school arithmetic, including the fractions, form an ordered field. Arithmetic is thus the study of a particular interpretation of the theorems of an ordered field. Ordinary addition, multiplication, subtraction, and division are, consequently, often called the four field operations.

The set $B = \{a, b\}$ with the operations $\oplus$ and $*$, as defined in Table 36 (ii) and (iii), form a field. We leave it for the reader to verify that axioms A_1 through A_8 are satisfied.

Many of the theorems for groups can be "carried over" into the structure of fields. Note, however, that axiom A_8 requires that the zero element e be excepted when considering the inverse x^{-1} of an element x under the operation $*$. The theorems for groups, T_1 through T_{10}, can be rewritten as field theorems (*note:* in these theorems we wrote x^{-1} for the inverse under the operation o, whereas in the field axioms this appears as $-x$ and the inverse x^{-1} applies to the operation $*$). For each group theorem there will be two field theorems, one for each operation.

In addition to the theorems which arise because of the group structure within a field, there are many theorems which involve both the operations o and $*$ defined in a field. The following theorems illustrate some important results.

T_{11}: For all $x \in F$, $x * e = e$.
    Proof: 1. $e = e \circ e$ A_4.
               2. $x * e = x * (e \circ e)$ 1, A_1.
               3. $x * e = (x * e) \circ (x * e)$ 2, A_6.
               4. $(x * e) \circ e = (x * e) \circ (x * e)$ 3, A_4.
               5. $e \circ (x * e) = (x * e) \circ (x * e)$ 4, A_2.
               6. $\therefore$ $e = x * e$ 5, T_2.

T_{12}: For all $x, y \in F$, $x * (-y) = -(x * y)$.
T_{13}: For all $x, y \in F$, $(-x) * (-y) = x * y$.
T_{14}: If $a, b \in F$ and $a * b = e$, then $a = e$ or $b = e$.
T_{15}: If $a \in F$ and $a \neq e$, then $e * a^{-1} = e$.
T_{16}: If $a, b \in F$ and $b \neq e$ and $a * b^{-1} = e$, then $a = e$.

If F is an ordered field, the following theorems on the order properties of the elements can be deduced.

T_{17}: If $x, y \in F$, then exactly one of the following is true: $x < y$, $x = y$, $x > y$.
T_{18}: If $a, b, c \in F$ and $a < b$ and $b < c$, then $a < c$.
T_{19}: If $a, b, c \in F$ and $a < b$, then $a \circ c < b \circ c$.
T_{20}: If $a, b, c \in F$ and $a < b$ and $e < c$, then $a * c < b * c$.
T_{21}: If $a\,b, c, d \in F$ and $a < b$ and $c < d$, then $a \circ c < b \circ d$.
T_{22}: If $a \in F$ and $a < e$, then $-a > e$.

In concluding this chapter, we note that the structure of elements in a set can be categorized and that our study can be reduced to the study of kinds of sets rather than the study of particular sets occurring in specific situations. In the next chapter, we will consider probably the most important kinds of sets which occur, that is, number sets.

Exercises 8.3
1. Consider the example of the square, Figures 29 and 31, exercise 1 of 8.2:
    (a) Does the reflection operation on $V \times V$ form a group?
    (b) Do the two operations of rotation and reflection form a ring? An integral domain? A field?
2. Given $T = \{0, 1, 2\}$:
    (a) Define an operation on T which will make T an abelian group.
    (b) Define a second operation on T which will make T a field.
3. Prove the theorems for groups numbered T_4 through T_{10} in 8.3.1.
4. Show that $B = \{a, b\}$ does not form a group with either of the operations @ of Table 35 or ø of Table 36(i).
5. Verify that the set $B = \{a, b\}$, with the operations $\oplus$ and $*$ as defined in Table 36(ii) and (iii), form a field.

Exercises 8
1. Given an equilateral triangle (Figure 32):

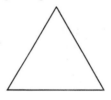

FIGURE 32.

   (a) Name and list the elements of the set $V = \{x$ is a vertex of the triangle$\}$.
   (b) Define operations on V analogous to the rotations and reflections of a square.
   (c) Do the separate operations of rotation and reflection form groups?
   (d) Do the operations together form a ring? A field?
2. Given that G is a group with the operation o, prove the following theorems:
    (a) If $a, b, c, d \in G$ and $a = b$ and $c = d$, then $a \circ c = b \circ d$ and $a \circ c^{-1} = b \circ d^{-1}$ ($c^{-1} = -c$ and $d^{-1} = -d$ in the notation for fields).
    (b) If $x, y \in G$, then $(x \circ y)^{-1} = x^{-1} \circ y^{-1}$.
    (c) If $x \in G$, then $x \circ e^{-1} = x$.
3. Given $S = \{0, 1, 2, 3, 4\}$ and the two operations $+$ and $\times$ as defined in Table 37, determine whether the operations define a field.
4. Prove that axiom A_5 ($x \circ y = y \circ x$) for groups is independent of the other axioms. (*Hint:* give an example of a structure in which all the other axioms are satisfied, whereas the axiom A_5 is not.)
5. Prove the theorems for fields numbered T_{12} through T_{16} in 8.3.2.

TABLE 37

+	0	1	2	3	4		×	0	1	2	3	4
0	0	1	2	3	4		0	0	0	0	0	0
1	1	2	3	4	0		1	0	1	2	3	4
2	2	3	4	0	1		2	0	2	4	1	3
3	3	4	0	1	2		3	0	3	1	4	2
4	4	0	1	2	3		4	0	4	3	2	1

6. Prove the theorems for ordered fields numbered T_{17} through T_{22} in 8.3.2.

7. State the group theorems T_1 through T_{10} as field theorems in pairs, that is, for the two operations o and *.

8. Recall your school arithmetic and state at least ten rules of arithmetic which are a result of field theorems.

9. Consider the hours as indicated on a clock. Define an "addition" of hours and show that the set of hours on a clock with this operation specifies a group.

10. A room has a sofa, a chair, and a table. Consider the set of elements which can be described as rearrangements of the furniture. Define the operation described as "successive" rearrangements of the furniture. Form a table for this operation and determine whether the set with this operation forms a group.

9
NUMBER SETS

9.1 NATURAL NUMBERS

We have seen how extremely useful sets could be in the study of arguments and proofs. Our consideration of the structure of sets in the last chapter suggests that there may be particular sets with elements following rules which would be useful in clarifying and simplifying many problems.

We have mentioned the natural origins of counting numbers. These are the familiar numbers 1, 2, 3, 4, $\cdots$. The need for distinguishing different quantities must have arisen very early among primitive men. A herdsman, wishing to make sure he had all his cattle, had them driven past him while he counted them. For convenience, he might have used markers. Later he could compare his markers with new countings to see whether he had the proper number of cattle.

An astute observer of the counting would notice that there are actually two distinct concepts of number occurring. The herdsman is measuring the size of his herd or is counting the order in which the cattle are arranged.

9.1.1 Since we are interested in the structure and nature of concepts, let us abstract from this typical situation a symbolic representation. We begin by assuming that we can count the number of elements in many sets. That is, if S is the name of a set and n is the number of elements in the set, we assume that we can denote by $S(n)$ the name of the set according to the number of elements in the set. For example, the sets:

$A = \{a, b, c\}$ will have the name $A(3)$.
$B = \{\text{Bill, Sam}\}$ will have the name $B(2)$.
$D = \{2, 4, 9, 12\}$ will have the name $D(4)$.
$E = \{\text{Bill}, b, 5\}$ will have the name $E(3)$.

Every set for which we can count the numbers of elements will now have a name according to the number of elements in the set. Form new sets according to the number n appearing in the parentheses: $S = \{x = S(n)/n$ is a given fixed counting number\}. We will have all those sets with $n = 1$ as elements in one set, those sets with $n = 2$ as elements in another set, those with $n = 3$ as elements in a third set, etc. Let us name the new sets $S_1, S_2, S_3, \cdots$. These latter sets, sets whose elements are all sets with the same number of elements, are called the **cardinal classes** of sets. Each class has associated with it a **cardinal name** symbolized by the same numerals which we used in counting the elements. For example, the sets A and E above are members of the set called "three," symbolized by "3." The set D belongs to the set called "four." This procedure defines a classification of all sets which have an intuitively countable number of elements.

Every intuitively countable set determines its own cardinal class. We can think of the cardinal name of a class as representing a property of every element in the class. "Two" is thus the name of a property of the set consisting of a pair of shoes. A property of the set consisting of a basketball team is represented by the cardinal name "five." This property of each member of a cardinal class is called the **cardinal number** property of the member. To the herdsman counting his cattle, the cardinal number of his herd measures the size of his herd of cattle. If the herdsman used markers, they formed a convenient representation of an element of the cardinal class for comparison with later countings, or with other herds.

TABLE 38
Cardinal Numbers

Cardinal Name	Symbol n	Description of an Element	Example of an Element
One	1	Set with one element.	$\{1\}$
Two	2	Set with two elements.	$\{1, 2\}$
Three	3	Set with three elements.	$\{1, 2, 3\}$
Four	4	Set with four elements.	$\{1, 2, 3, 4\}$
Five	5	Set with five elements.	$\{1, 2, 3, 4, 5\}$
$\cdots$	$\cdot$	$\cdots\cdots\cdots\cdots\cdots$	$\cdots\cdots$

In comparing sets in the above manner, we encounter sets with different numbers of elements in them. We can now arrange the cardinal names of sets in a "successive" order. If m and n are cardinal names, we say that m **precedes** n, or m **comes before** n, and write $m < n$, if, for arbitrary elements in m and n, the element of m has the same cardinal name as a proper subset of the element of n. That is, our herdsman in comparing his herd of cattle with another herd can determine whether the measure of his herd comes before the other herd or not by determining whether the cardinal name of his herd is the same as the cardinal name of a proper subset of the other herd or not.

If we compare the cardinal numbers, we obtain an ordering of the numbers: $1 < 2 < 3 < 4 < 5 < \cdots$. The *first* cardinal number is denoted by 1, *second* comes 2, then *third* comes 3, etc. The ordering leads to another interpretation for the arrangement of sets. They can be arranged in an **order** of before and after, or of preceding and succeeding. The order class or position of a set with respect to order is denoted by an ordinal name: first, second, third, etc. The ordinal name indicates the **ordinal number** property of a set. The ordinal numbers are represented by the same symbols as were used for the cardinals. This suggests, correctly, that the concepts of cardinal and ordinal numbers are closely related.

9.1.2 Let us continue our search for sets with elements following systematic rules. The problem is to describe, without direct reference to concrete situations, a set of entities following natural rules which will be useful as a model of idealized situations.

The following description is due to an Italian mathematician and logician named G. Peano (1858–1932). As primitive notions, Peano chose the concepts: (1) number set, N; (2) successor, s; and (3) the number denoted by 1. He asserted the following axioms:

A_1: $1 \in N$ and $1sx$ is false for all $x \in N$.
A_2: If $x \in N$, then there is exactly one $y \in N$ such that ysx.
A_3: If $x, y, z \in N$ such that ysx and ysz, then $x = z$.
A_4: If $M \subset N$ such that:
    (i) $1 \in M$ and
    (ii) whenever $x \in M$ and ysx, then $y \in M$,
    then $M = N$.

Since the set N follows rules which we would expect naturally, the set is called the set of **natural numbers**. Other more conventional descriptions of the natural numbers are possible. For convenience, the symbols for the numbers themselves often are referred to as the natural numbers. Note that the elements are ordered with the notion called succession.

    9.1.2.1 Definition: Any set which satisfies Peano's primitive notions and axioms is called a set of **natural numbers**.

Many sets would satisfy Peano's primitive notions without being of the kind which we call natural numbers. It is the axioms A_1 through A_4 which assert the distinctive properties of the set of elements.

A_1 asserts that there is a "first" or "initial" element, 1, in the set of natural numbers. The second axiom asserts that every element has an immediate successor. If we start with 1, there is exactly one element which is its successor, 2. There is exactly one successor to 2, that is, 3. The elements of the set can be arranged like a chain with a first link, a second link, etc. The third axiom, A_3, asserts that there is exactly one "predecessor" to each element except 1. That is, the chain (of numbers) does not "divide," "loop," or "split."

A_4 is an extremely important and interesting axiom. It describes the notion called the **principle of induction**. The axiom asserts that the natural numbers are like dominoes placed in a standing line so that pushing one over causes the next to fall over. Pushing the first dominoe over will then cause all of the dominoes to fall over.

In ordinary language we might express the principle of induction loosely as similar to the use of "etc." or "and so on." More practically, this principle enables us conveniently to discuss the counting or description of sets with an indefinite number of elements.

Consider a set such that an assertion is defined for every natural number n. Suppose the assertion defined for $n = 1$ is true, and that whenever the assertion defined for a natural number k is true, the assertion for the succeeding number $k + 1$, is true. Then, by the principle of induction, we can assert that every assertion defined for the natural numbers is true.

THEOREM 1. Let $P(n)$ be an assertion defined for *every* natural number n. If $P(1)$ is true, and if $P(k + 1)$ is true, whenever $P(k)$ is true [*Note:* $(k + 1)$ is the successor of (k)], then $P(n)$ is true for *all* the natural numbers n.

Can we count the number of elements in the set of natural numbers? No. We can go on indefinitely without end. In a general way, sets can be separated into two categories called **finite** and **infinite**. Informally, by a finite set we mean that the number of elements in the set can be determined uniquely, that is, the counting ends. An infinite set is a set which is not finite.

The natural number set is the simplest of the infinite classes of cardinals and is given the name "aleph null" $\aleph_0$. Representative members of this cardinal class or subsets of such members are said to be **countable** or **denumerable**. The set of natural numbers and its subsets form an important collection of representative sets which are useful as models for counting.

9.1.3 A convenient representation of number sets is suggested by the ordering property of the numbers. If we add to the idea of Venn diagrams the notion of ordering, we can construct diagrams for number sets which reveal many interesting properties of the sets. For example, instead of representing the set $N = \{1, 2, 3, 4, 5, 6, \cdots\}$ in the conventional way, we arrange the elements along a line to form a new diagram.

The elements in the number set are associated to points on a line to describe visually the ordering properties of the elements. When a number set is represented by a set of points, we call the representation a **point set representation** of the number set.

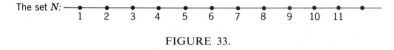

FIGURE 33.

A point set representation of the natural numbers shows the order, the discreteness, and the arrangement of the elements in the set. Note that there is a first "left-hand" member of the set but no last "right-hand" member of the set. The notion of succession can be described as a "jump" to the right.

Our concepts of addition and multiplication are easily represented on a point set. We can think of addition as a "jumping" of a given number of successors to the right. For example, $2 + 4 = 6$ is shown in Figure 34. We start at the element 2 and "jump" 4 successors to the right.

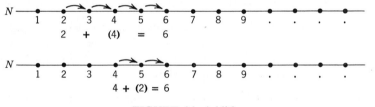

FIGURE 34. Addition.

If we interpret multiplication to mean a "repeated" addition of a number with itself, we can represent this notion as follows: $4 \times 2 = [(2 + 2) + 2] + 2 = 8$.

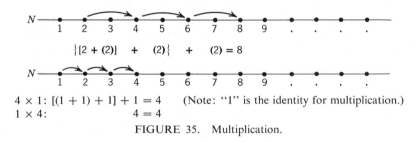

FIGURE 35. Multiplication.

The interpretation of multiplication suggests the forming of various subsets of the natural numbers. For example, $E = \{x \in N/x = n \times 2 \text{ for}$

all $n \in N\} = \{2, 4, 6, 8, \cdots\}$. The set E is called the set of **even** numbers. $\bar{E} = \{1, 3, 5, 7, 9, \cdots\}$ is called the set of **odd** numbers. In general, if k is any fixed natural number, then the set of elements defined by $K = \{x \in N/ x = n \times k$ for all $n \in N\}$ is called the set of **multiples** of k. The elements of the set K are said to be **divisible** by the fixed number k, and k is called a **factor** of any element of the set K.

Exercises 9.1

1. Find the cardinal number of each of the following sets.
   (a) $L = \{x$ is a letter in the English alphabet$\}$.
   (b) $M = \{x$ is a moon (satellite) of the planet Saturn$\}$.
   (c) $K = \{x$ is a member of your immediate family$\}$.
   (d) $Y = \{x$ is a day in the year 1960$\}$.
2. Describe how the ordinal number concept might be applied to the elements of each of the sets in exercise 1.
3. Imagine a "foreign" people who use only the symbols 1, 2, 3, 4, 5, and 0 as counting symbols. In counting they write: 0, 1, 2, 3, 4, 5, 10, 11, 12, 13, 14, 15, 20, 21, $\cdots$.
   (a) Associate our conventional "decimal" numerals to the "foreign" symbols. How would we write our conventional numbers 14, 20, 21, and 25 in this "foreign" symbolism? If 14, 20, 21, and 25 are numbers in the "foreign" symbols, how would we write them in our conventional "decimal" symbols?
   (b) Construct addition and multiplication tables for the "foreign" system which would correspond to our conventional tables.
4. The natural numbers do not form a group. Explain why this is so.
5. Although the natural numbers do not form a group, addition and multiplication as well as an ordering are well-defined in the set. State at least five theorems which can be proved for the natural numbers.
6. The inductive property of the natural numbers enables us to write definitions which include an infinite number of statements. Definitions of this type are called **recursive** or **inductive** definitions. For example:

   9.1.2.2 Definition: If a and n are any two natural numbers, by the **power** a^n we mean
   (i) $a^1 = a$
   (ii) $a^{n+1} = a^n a$.
   The number a is called the **base** and the number n the **exponent** of the power a^n.

   (a) If $a = 2$, then find the power a^n for $n = 3$, $n = 6$.
   (b) State the power, the base, and the exponent for each of the following: 3^4, $(10)^3$, 6^2.
   (c) If $a = 2$, $b = 3$, $n = 3$, and $m = 4$, then find
   (i) $a^n b^m$ (ii) a^{mn} (iii) $(ab)^n$ (iv) $b^m b^n$
   (v) a^{m+n} (vi) $a^n b^n$ (vii) $(a^m)^n$ (viii) $a^n a^m$

7. Given: 6, 9, 15, 19, 24, 30, 35, 42.

(*a*) Which of the numbers are multiples of 3? Of 5? Of 6?

(*b*) Which of the numbers are divisible by 2? By 3? By 7?

(*c*) For which numbers is 4 a factor?, 6?, 7?

(*d*) Find a set of factors of 35 and 42.

9.2 INTEGERS

The concept of "place position" occurs in records dating as far back as the Babylonians (c. 1600 B.C.). However, the usefulness of the idea was not capitalized on until the development of the Hindu-Arabic numerals about A.D. 700. Even though the "place position" idea was known, it was necessary to develop a symbol to indicate the "absence of a numeral." The invention of the Hindu-Arabic system with a symbol for "zero" was thus of great importance in the development of abstract number sets.

In writing numbers the position of a digit indicates the number of units of a given "magnitude." For example, in writing 42, the digit 4 stands for four tens and 2 for two units. In 24, the digit 2 stands for two tens and the 4 for four units. In 204, the 2 stands for two hundreds, the 0 for no tens, and 4 for four units. In 2400, 2 stands for two thousands, 4 for four hundreds, and the 0's for no tens and no units.

In discussing cardinal and ordinal classes we omitted any consideration of the null or empty set $\emptyset$. If we include this set and denote it by the cardinal name 0, we will have a "natural" inclusion of 0 among the cardinal and ordinal numbers. Furthermore, following a desire for completeness, we might introduce the symbol 0 as the identity element for addition in the natural numbers. That is, we assume the existence of a natural number 0 such that $0 + n = n + 0 = n$ and $0 \times n = n \times 0 = 0$ for any natural number n.

9.2.1 Now we ask a question which was called "absurd" by the famous mathematician Diophantus of Alexandria (c. 275). If a and b are natural numbers, is there always a natural number x which will make $a + x = b$ true? For example, if $a = 5$ and $b = 3$, what can we write for x? The answer is that there is no natural number x such that $5 + x = 3$. As recently as 1225, the mathematician Fibonacci (known also as Leonardo of Pisa, c. 1170–1250) interpreted this problem by saying, " I will show this question cannot be solved unless it be conceded that the man might be in debt."

Since we would like to have a set of numbers which will always enable us to answer the question, we are led to an extension of our natural numbers. That is, we create new numbers which will permit us to *always* answer the question: If $a + x = b$, then $x = $? The resulting extended set is called the **integers** which we denote by I.

The new number symbols are constructed by introducing a prefix symbol called a **negative** or **minus** sign. When the sign is prefixed to a natural number, we obtain a symbol for the *inverse* of the number under addition. The new numbers are called the **negative integers** and the natural numbers are called the **positive integers**. The entire set of integers then consists of the positive integers, the negative integers, and zero. Intuitively, it should be clear that the integers extend indefinitely in either direction along a point set representation. Given any integer, we are able to specify the integer which comes immediately "before" and "after" the given integer. If we are given any two integers, a and b, we can now find an *integer x* such that $a + x = b$.

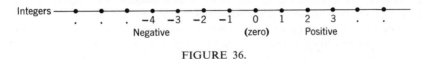

FIGURE 36.

The binary operations of addition and multiplication can be carried out in the integers just as in the natural numbers. We should be careful to note that the "direction" of an operation may appear reversed on a point set representation when the inverse elements are involved. For example, note that $6 + (-3) = 3$ suggests a "reverse" or inverse operation.

FIGURE 37.

9.2.1.1 Definition: By **subtraction** we mean that for any $a, b \in I$ we have $b + x = a$, written $x = a - b$. We read $a - b$ as "a minus b" or "b subtracted from a." The element x is called the **difference** of b subtracted from a.

The operation of subtraction is closed in the integers, whereas it is not in the natural numbers. Subtraction is not commutative or associative. With the definition of subtraction, the negative sign takes on an apparently dual meaning. It not only is a prefix symbol denoting a negative number, but it also appears as an operational symbol. However, the definition only facilitates and clarifies the use of the symbol to indicate the inverse of an element under addition.

9.2.2 We now have a set of elements called the **integers**. The operation of addition is closed, associative, and now with the introduction of zero and the negative integers there are an additive identity and inverses for every element. Furthermore the operation is commutative. Thus the integers form an **abelian group** under addition. Since the integers satisfy all the requirements of an abelian group, all the theorems for abelian groups hold in the set of integers under addition.

The operation of multiplication can also be carried out in the integers. With the operations of addition and multiplication, do the integers form a ring, an integral domain, or a field? The integers do in fact form an **integral domain**. However, the integers do not quite attain a field in structure.

Exercises 9.2

1. Give explicit examples of group theorems as applied to the integers.
2. Justify the conclusion that the integers form an integral domain.
3. State the properties of the integers which make the following statements true.
   (a) A positive integer times a negative integer is a negative integer: If $x > 0$ and $y < 0$, then $xy < 0$.
   (b) The product of two negative integers is a positive integer: If $x < 0$ and $y < 0$, then $xy > 0$.
4. Why is it that the integers do not form a field?
5. An integer can be represented as the difference, $m - n$, of two natural numbers. If $m > n$, the integer is positive. If $m = n$, the integer is 0. If $m < n$, the integer is negative. Thus we can define the integers in terms of pairs of natural numbers using the concept of difference as assumed. Let $(m - n) = (m,n)$, an ordered pair of natural numbers, denote an integer. Using the properties of the natural numbers:
   (a) find ordered pairs of natural numbers which represent the integers -7, -2, 0, 5, and 13.
   (b) and the ordered pair notation, define addition and multiplication of integers in terms of ordered pairs.
   (c) show that
      (i) $(a, b) = (c, d)$ if and only if $a + d = b + c$.
      (ii) $(a, b) = (m, m)$ if and only if $a = b$.
      (iii) $(x, y) + (m, m) = (x, y)$ and $(x, y)(m, m) = (m, m)$ for any integer (x, y).

9.3 RATIONAL NUMBERS

In forming the integers, we focused primarily on the addition of natural numbers. Let us now consider the multiplication operation. We can always say that if a and b are integers, then $ab = x$ is an integer. Can we say that x is always defined in the integers if $ax = b$, where a and b are integers?

For some integers a and b we can find an integer x such that $ax = b$. For other pairs of integers a and b, we cannot find an integer x which makes the statement $ax = b$ true. For example:

(a) If $a = 3$ and $b = 9$, then clearly $3x = 9$ has the answer $x = 3$.

(b) If $a = 6$ and $b = 12$, then $x = 2$ makes $6x = 12$ true.

(c) If $a = 4$ and $b = 9$, then there is no integer x which will satisfy $4x = 9$. Experimenting will show that 2 is too small while 3 is too large. Since there are no integers between 2 and 3, we must conclude that there is no integer x satisfying $4x = 9$.

If we note that the quantity x depends on the integers a and b, we might define a new set of numbers (a, b) of ordered pairs of integers. We could then proceed to a formal development of these new numbers.

However, for the sake of familiarity and convention, we define the element x in $ax = b$ as $x = \dfrac{b}{a}$.

9.3.0.1 Definition: If a and b are integers with $a \neq 0$, then by a **rational number** we mean an element x such that $ax = b$. We write $x = \dfrac{b}{a}$.

9.3.0.2 Definition: We say that $\dfrac{b}{a}$ and $\dfrac{c}{d}$ are **equal** if an only if $bd = ac$.

The definition of equality is a natural consequence of the properties of the integers. For example, we have $\dfrac{3}{4} = \dfrac{6}{8}$ when $(3)(8) = (4)(6) = 24$.

The definition leads us to enunciate an important theorem concerning the rational numbers.

THEOREM 1. If $\dfrac{b}{a}$ and $\dfrac{bc}{ac}$ are rational numbers, then $\dfrac{b}{a} = \dfrac{bc}{ac}$.

The definition of the rational numbers is equivalent to defining an inverse operation for multiplication. That is, the inverse exists for each element in the new set called the rational numbers. The inverse operation to multiplication is called **division** and the resulting element is called the **quotient**. That is, we write $x = \dfrac{b}{a}$ and read "b divided by a is x." The quotient of two integers is often not an integer. Thus division is not closed in the integers. A rational number is often described as the quotient of two integers.

Historically, the rational numbers were introduced as measuring numbers. The symbolism of the rational numbers is very convenient for indicating measurements and, in fact, most measurements are made by using the rational numbers.

9.3.1 A point set representation of the rational numbers can be constructed by noting that in $ax = b$, if a and b are equal to 1, then $x = 1$. Also if $a = 1$ and $b = 0$, then $x = 0$. That is, we can associate the rational number $\dfrac{1}{1}$ to the integer 1 and the rational number $\dfrac{0}{1}$ to the integer 0. The "distance" between these two points on a point set representation is called a **unit of length** for the representation.

Using the unit of length as determined above, we can mark off units to the right and left along the line. Now for $a = 2$ and $b = 1$, we have $x = \dfrac{1}{2}$. For this point we divide the unit of length into two equal parts to obtain a location for $\dfrac{1}{2}$. The distance $\dfrac{0}{1}$ to $\dfrac{1}{2}$ is called a half-unit length. Using this half-unit length, we mark off the half-units to the right and left. Next, for $a = 3$, we divide the unit length into three equal parts. This is called a one-third unit of length. Using this one-third unit of length, we mark off the "thirds." This process can be continued indefinitely to obtain a point set representation of the rational numbers.

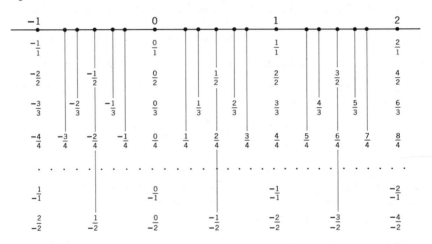

FIGURE 38.   A partial point set representation of the rational numbers.

Our interpretation of the rational numbers as an extension of the integers leads us to the following assertions:

T_2: If both a and b are positive (or negative) integers, then the rational number $x = \dfrac{b}{a}$ is positive.

T_3: If a and b are integers such that one is positive and the other negative, then the rational number $x = \dfrac{b}{a}$ is negative.

Although we have defined equality of two rational numbers so that, say, $\frac{1}{2} = \frac{2}{4}$, the elements, strictly speaking, are not identical. They *refer* to the same point on the representation of Figure 38. Formally, if we form the cartesian product set of the integers with themselves, we can consider subsets $E = \{(x,y) \in I \times I / x \neq 0, \; y \neq 0, \; \text{and} \; ax = by\}$ where a and b are nonzero integers. These sets along with the set $Z = \{(x, y) \in I \times I / x = 0, \; y \neq 0\}$ are called the equivalence classes of the rational numbers. Each of the classes is given a representative name. These names are called the '**reduced**' rational numbers. On Figure 38, the reduced rationals appear as the top names in each vertical column. The reduced names appearing are: $-1, -\frac{3}{4}, -\frac{2}{3}, -\frac{1}{2}, -\frac{1}{3}, -\frac{1}{4}, 0, \frac{1}{4}, \frac{1}{3}, \frac{1}{2}, \frac{2}{3}, \frac{3}{4}, 1, \frac{5}{4}, \frac{4}{3}, \frac{3}{2}, \frac{5}{3}, \frac{7}{4}, 2.$

The need for distinguishing the number zero from the other numbers is shown by the following informal argument. If the integer a in $x = \frac{b}{a}$ were allowed to be zero, we would have $x = \frac{b}{0}$. Now, we must also have $(0)(x) = b$ by the definition of x. This is a contradiction which is easily shown for example, by letting $b = 6$. Then we have $x = \frac{6}{0}$, meaning $(0)(x) = 6$ by the definition. But $(0)(x) = 0$! Thus, we arrive at $6 = 0$ a contradiction.

Unlike the natural numbers and integers, the rational numbers are such that we cannot name successive elements. If x and y are rational numbers such that $x \neq y$, then we can always find a third distinct rational number z such that z is between the numbers x and y. On a point set representation this means that for any two distinct rational points there is always another distinct rational point between the two given points.

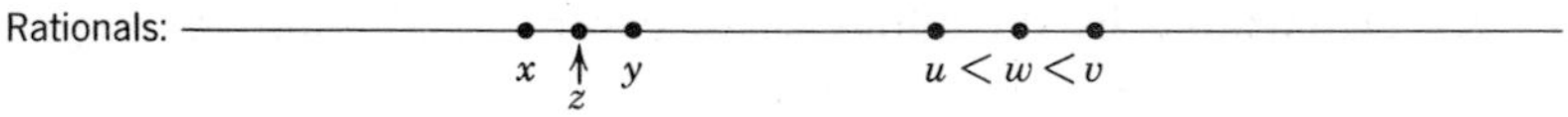

FIGURE 39.

The notion of between is symbolized as $x < z < y$ and is read "z is between x and y." The symbol $<$ is called an **inequality sign**. We have already used this symbol to denote **order**. For any two rational numbers x and y, we have $x < y$, $x = y$, or $x > y$. For convenience, we also refer to the *sense* of an inequality. We say that $x < y$ and $u < v$ have the same sense. Also $x > y$ and $u > v$ have the same sense. The inequalities $x < y$ and $u > v$ are said to have opposite senses.

To illustrate this property of the rational numbers consider the rational numbers $\frac{3}{5}$ and $\frac{2}{3}$. We can write that $\frac{3}{5} = \frac{18}{30}$ and $\frac{2}{3} = \frac{20}{30}$. Now it is clear that $\frac{19}{30}$ is a rational number between $\frac{3}{5}$ and $\frac{2}{3}$. For any two rational numbers, we can always find an element in the equivalence classes such that the a integer in $x = \frac{b}{a}$ is the same. Then for the distinct third rational number, we can select the b integer between the two given b integers. This property of the rational numbers is called a **denseness** property of the rationals.

*9.3.1.1 Definition: A set may be said to be **dense in itself** if for any two distinct arbitrary elements in the set, there is a third distinct element between the two given elements.

9.3.2 The denseness of the rational numbers guarantees that we can express any measurement to as close a degree of accuracy as we wish. Thus the rational numbers are sufficient for most calculations. We can add, subtract, multiply, and divide any rational number by any other rational number (division by zero excepted) and obtain a rational number. That is, the rational numbers are closed under these four operations. Ordinary school arithmetic usually consists of a study of the manipulations of the rational numbers. For $\frac{a}{b}$ and $\frac{c}{d}$ rational numbers, we can define the four operations as follows:

9.3.2.1 Definition: By the **sum** of two rational numbers we mean

$$\frac{a}{b} + \frac{c}{d} = \frac{ad + bc}{bd}.$$

EXAMPLE. $\frac{2}{3} + \frac{5}{6} = \frac{(2)(6) + (3)(5)}{(3)(6)} = \frac{12 + 15}{18} = \frac{27}{18} = \frac{3}{2}$

9.3.2.2 Definition: By the **difference** of two rational numbers we mean

$$\frac{a}{b} - \frac{c}{d} = \frac{ad - bc}{bd}.$$

EXAMPLE. $\frac{1}{3} - \frac{3}{4} = \frac{4 - 9}{12} = \frac{-5}{12}$

9.3.2.3 Definition: By the **product** of two rational numbers we mean

$$\left(\frac{a}{b}\right)\left(\frac{c}{d}\right) = \frac{ac}{bd}.$$

---

* This is a simplified definition of the technical meaning of a set being dense in itself.

EXAMPLE. $\left(\dfrac{5}{6}\right)\left(\dfrac{1}{2}\right) = \dfrac{5}{12}$

9.3.2.4 Definition: By the **quotient** of two rational numbers we mean

$$\frac{\dfrac{a}{b}}{\dfrac{c}{d}} = \frac{ad}{bc} \text{ where } c \neq 0.$$

EXAMPLE. $\dfrac{\dfrac{3}{5}}{\dfrac{2}{3}} = \dfrac{(3)(3)}{(5)(2)} = \dfrac{9}{10}$

Using the fact that the integers form an integral domain and that the rational operations are defined in terms of the integers, it is a relatively simple problem to show that the rational numbers form an **ordered field** under addition and multiplication.

In summary, we have proceeded from the concrete counting of a primitive herdsman's cattle to an abstraction of the notions of cardinal and ordinal numbers. Using these notions, we described the abstract, **axiomatically formed** set of objects called the natural numbers. The natural numbers can be thought of as an "idealized" model of counting. An important property of the natural numbers was the notion described as the **principle of induction**. A consideration of the structure of sets led us to an **extension** of the natural numbers into a new set called the integers. This led to the definition of subtraction and the **creation** of negative numbers. With the integers we realized a set with the properties of an integral domain. Our success led us to a further extension of the integers to obtain a **closure** with the inverses under multiplication. The rational numbers, we note, can be completely described in terms of pairs of integers. A new property was noted, that of **denseness**. The rational numbers with their property of denseness furnish us with an idealized model set which can be used to describe and focus on the notions of "as accurate as you wish" or "as close as you please." The rational numbers form an idealized model of an **ordered field** of elements. Thus, in the space of a few pages, we have covered the development of over 2000 years of effort.

Exercises 9.3

1. Given the definition: By a rational number we mean an ordered pair of integers (m,n) such that $n \neq 0$.
   (a) Define (i) equality, (ii) the sum, (iii) the product of rational numbers in terms of ordered pairs of integers.

(*b*) Give an explicit example of each of the four definitions, using the integers between -10 and 10.

2. Find the reduced rational number which names the equivalence class for each of the following rational numbers: $\dfrac{8}{4}, \dfrac{15}{30}, \dfrac{-35}{7}, \dfrac{-6}{9}, \dfrac{-12}{-4}, \dfrac{9}{27}, \dfrac{36}{-54}$,

3. Order the following rational numbers from smallest to largest: $\dfrac{5}{21}, \dfrac{3}{7}, \dfrac{2}{6}, \dfrac{1}{2},$ $\dfrac{4}{14}, \dfrac{2}{3}, \dfrac{25}{42}.$

4. (*a*) Find two distinct rational numbers between $\dfrac{2}{3}$ and $\dfrac{7}{12}$.

   (*b*) Find a distinct rational number between the two found in part (*a*).

5. Show that the rational numbers under addition and multiplication satisfy all the axioms for an ordered field.

6. Prove theorem 1 of 9.3: If $\dfrac{b}{a}$ and $\dfrac{bc}{ac}$ are rational numbers, then $\dfrac{b}{a} = \dfrac{bc}{ac}$.

9.4 REAL NUMBERS

Although the rational numbers are used extensively in measurement, it was discovered long ago that the rational numbers could not measure all lengths **exactly**. That is, if we conceive of a rational number as a unit which is obtained by "breaking" a unit length into small equal parts, we still cannot measure all lengths perfectly. For example, the diagonal of a square of unit length side cannot be measured and symbolized exactly by a rational number. On a point set representation, this is equivalent to saying that there is a point that has no rational name.

It is said that a Pythagorean named Hippasus was drowned by his fellows for revealing that there were measurements without rational names. The Greeks also studied the ratio (quotient) between the circumference of a circle and its diameter, using the name "quadrature of the circle" to describe the problem. Not until 1761 was it shown, by Johann Heinrich Lambert (1728–1777), that this ratio was not a rational number. This number is now denoted by π. This Greek letter was first used to mean the circumference or periphery of a circle, but in 1707 W. Jones gave the symbol its present meaning. Euler's adoption of π in 1736 brought it into general use as denoting this ratio.

In the works of Menelaus (c. 100) and the astronomer Ptolemy (c. 150), there is also reference to the ratios (quotients) of the sides of various triangles. These ratios, closely related to the properties of a circle, often lead to quantities which cannot be expressed as rational numbers. These are called "trigonometric ratios."

In the study of compound interest laws during the seventeenth and eighteenth centuries, it was discovered that there was another quantity which could not be written exactly as a rational number. This quantity was given the name "e." It has played an important role in modern science in describing not only physical phenomena but also relationships resulting from organic growth.

The knowledge of the existence of nonrational or **irrational** quantities leads to the consideration of this new set as a number set. The name "irrational" numbers is not meant to imply that the quantities are "un-reasonable" (although in our study of these quantities we might feel that this is so). The name is used to describe those numbers which cannot be expressed in a "ratio-like " manner.

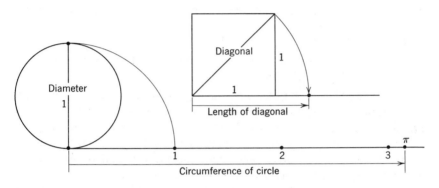

FIGURE 40.

Before proceeding to a study of irrational numbers, a simple example can be given for the existence of such quantities. In multiplication, we write that $a^2 = (a)(a) = b$. Now suppose we pose the question, for what number a is $b = 2$? The answer is that there is no rational number a such that $a^2 = 2$. Let us state and informally prove this assertion.

For $a^2 = 2$, a is not a rational number.

Proof: 1. Suppose $a = \dfrac{p}{q}$ where $\dfrac{p}{q}$ is a reduced rational number. This is a premise for indirect proof and we use the fact that every rational number can be expressed as a reduced rational number.

2. $a^2 = \left(\dfrac{p}{q}\right)^2 = \dfrac{p^2}{q^2} = 2$. From step 1, the premise, and a theorem concerning powers (see Exercises 9.1 problem 6).

3. $p^2 = 2q^2$. Step 2, definition.

4. p^2 is an even integer. Step 3, definition of an even number (see 9.1.3).

5. p is even. Step 4, and a theorem (If p^2 is even, then p is even.).

6. $p = 2n$. Step 5.

7. $(2n)^2 = 2q^2$. Steps 3 and 6.

8. $4n^2 = 2q^2$. Step 7 and theorem on powers.

9. $2n^2 = q^2$ and q is even. Step 8 and using the same argument as steps 3 through 5.

10. $q = 2m$. Step 9.

11. thus $\dfrac{p}{q} = \dfrac{2n}{2m}$. Steps 6 and 10.

12. but $\dfrac{p}{q}$ is a reduced rational number by step 1.

13. thus, by the contradiction of steps 11 and 12, we have that

$$a \neq \frac{p}{q}.$$

14. Therefore, a is not a rational number. We denote this number by $\sqrt{2}$.

9.4.1 The problem of describing the irrational numbers by an extension of the rational numbers is probably the most difficult step which we have faced. Various procedures have been devised to accomplish this step. We will proceed informally using a method devised by Richard Dedekind (1831–1916). The method depends upon the notion that if all the points on a line are separated or divided into two sets, such that every point in the first set lies to the left of every point in the second set, then there is one and only one point on the line which separates these two sets.

9.4.1.1 Definition: By a **Dedekind cut**, denoted by $(A \mid B)$, in the set of rational numbers we mean a separation or partitioning of the rational numbers into two sets A and B such that:

(1) Every rational number is in A or in B. ($A \cup B = R$ the rationals.)

(2) Each set contains at least one rational number. ($A \neq \emptyset$ and $B \neq \emptyset$.)

(3) Every element of A is less than every element of B. (If $x \in A$ and $y \in B$, then $x < y$.)

The definition appears to allow for four possible types of "cuts."

(a) The set A has a largest element, say, a, and the set B has no smallest element.

(b) The set A has no largest element but the set B does have a smallest element, say, b.

(c) The set A has a largest element, say, a, and the set B has a smallest element, say, b.

(*d*) The set *A* has no largest element and the set *B* has no smallest element.

Comparing these situations with the definition, we immediately note that type (*c*) is not possible since, by (3) of the definition, the sets must be disjoint. If so, then $a \neq b$ and by the density property of the rational numbers there must be a rational number, say, *c*, such that $a < c < b$ and $c \notin A$ and $c \notin B$. But this contradicts (1) of the definition.

We can assist our intuition by using point set representations of the rational numbers to illustrate various situations. If a point set is dense and we wish to indicate a subset consisting of *every* element in a segment, we use parentheses and brackets to describe whether there is or is not a first or last element in the subset. A parentheses is used to indicate that the "end" (the first or last) element is to be *excluded* from the set and a bracket is used to indicate that the "end" element is to be *included* in the set. If the "ends" are included in a set, the set is said to be **closed**. If the "ends" are excluded from a set, the set is said to be **open**. Sets may be **half-open** and **half-closed**.

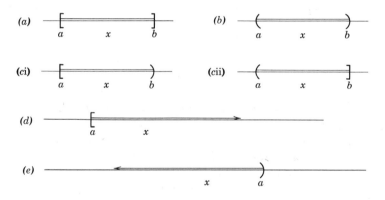

FIGURE 41.   Open and closed intervals.

(*a*) Closed at both ends: $a \leq x \leq b$
(*b*) Open at both ends: $a \leq x < b$
(*c*) Half-open or half-closed:
    (*i*) Closed on the left and open on the right. $a \leq x < b$
    (*ii*) Open on the left and closed on the right. $a < x < b$
(*d*) Closed on the left and extending to the right. $x \geq a$
(*e*) Open on the right and extending to the left. $x < a$.

The three possible types of Dedekind cuts can now be illustrated using point sets as in (*d*) and (*e*) of Figure 41. The first type of cut is illustrated by letting $A = \{x \leq 2\}$ and $B = \{x > 2\}$. *A* has a largest element "2." *B* has no smallest element. If *B* had a smallest element, say, *b*, then $2 < b$. But then there would be an element, say, *c*, such that $2 < c < b$ by the density property of the rational numbers. Then, since $c > 2$, we would have $c \in B$. But this would contradict the assertion that b was the smallest element in B. The second type of cut is illustrated by letting $A = \{x < 2\}$ and $B = \{x \geq 2\}$. The last type of cut where A has no largest element and B has no smallest is illustrated by considering $A = \{x < a$ where $a > 0$ and $a^2 = 2\}$ and $B = \{x > a$ where $a > 0$ and $a^2 = 2\}$. This last "cut" defines a unique element which we have denoted by $\sqrt{2}$.

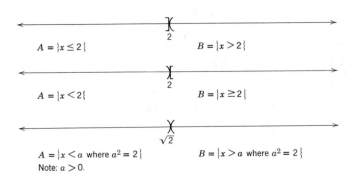

$A = \{x \leq 2\}$ $B = \{x > 2\}$

$A = \{x < 2\}$ $B = \{x \geq 2\}$

$A = \{x < a$ where $a^2 = 2\}$ $B = \{x > a$ where $a^2 = 2\}$

Note: $a > 0$.

FIGURE 42.

Each Dedekind cut defines an element in our new set. That is, the set of all Dedekind cuts defines a new set. Note that the cuts in our first two illustrations resulted in the same single rational element, 2. Cuts of this type are called **rational cuts** and can be identified with the set of rational numbers. For convenience, we consider only one of these two types of cuts, $(A \mid B)$ such that A has no largest and B has a smallest element. Dedekind cuts of the last type are called **irrational cuts**. The set of irrational cuts can be described as the complement of the set of rational cuts in the set of Dedekind cuts.

9.4.1.2 Definition: Two Dedekind cuts $(A \mid B)$ and $(C \mid D)$ are said to be **equal** if and only if the sets A and C are equal.

9.4.1.3 Definition: By the **real numbers** we mean a set which can be represented by the set of Dedekind cuts of a set of rational numbers.

By the definition, we can call the set of Dedekind cuts a set of real numbers. The real numbers name every point on a line and thus are often referred to as a **linear continuum**. The point set representation of a set of real numbers is often called a **number line**. Informally, the real numbers can be described as a "simply" ordered set C such that:

(1) C is a dense set.

(2) C has no first element or last element.

(3) If C is separated into two nonempty sets L and R such that:

    (*a*) If $x \in L$ and $y \in R$, then $x < y$

    (*b*) $L \cup R = C$

        then L has a largest element or R has a smallest element.

The real numbers include as subsets the natural numbers, the integers, the rational numbers, and the irrational numbers. The real numbers and the four subsets mentioned above constitute the most commonly used number sets.

9.4.2 In the structural description of the real numbers we did not concern ourselves with the problems of adequate symbolism to handle the manipulations and calculations which might be necessary in the applications of the real numbers to problems.

Although the Hindu-Arabic numerals which we commonly use originated about A.D. 700, the notation was not completely extended until the sixteenth century. Simon Stevin (1548–1620), a native of the Netherlands, through his efforts to develop the place value idea of the Hindu-Arabic numerals, introduced the method of **decimal notation**.

We have noted (9.2) that the position of a digit indicates the numbers of units of a given "magnitude." For example, the number 546 means that we have 5 hundreds, 4 tens, and 6 units. On a point set representation, the number 546 is located by first moving to the right to 500, then to 40 on the scale from 500 to 600, and finally to 6 on the scale from 540 to 550. That is, we move a given number of units on each scale of divisions successively from the largest to the smallest division.

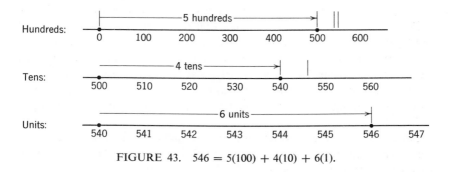

FIGURE 43. $546 = 5(100) + 4(10) + 6(1)$.

If we start with a given scale, our conventional decimal notation takes 10 units on the given scale to form one unit on the next larger scale. To obtain the next finer scale, we divide the given scale so that each unit on the scale will be 10 units on the finer scale. The digits in a decimal representation of a number then indicate the number of scale units of every scale unit considered.

If we mark the "unit length" position in some way, we would be able to continue the place value notation for even finer scales. In writing a number decimally, we can indicate larger scales to the left and finer scales to the right of the mark. The "indicator" or "mark" which is used is called a **decimal point** and is placed at the right foot of the digit which indicates the number of "unit lengths" in the given number. For example, in 32.41 we have 3 tens, 2 units, 4 tenths, and 1 hundredth. The number can also be written as:

$$32.41 = 3(10) + 2(1) + 4\left(\frac{1}{10}\right) + 1\left(\frac{1}{100}\right)$$

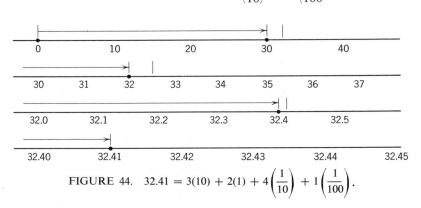

FIGURE 44. $32.41 = 3(10) + 2(1) + 4\left(\frac{1}{10}\right) + 1\left(\frac{1}{100}\right)$.

Every decimal representation of a number consists of all zeroes or there is a first nonzero digit on the left. When writing a number, we conventionally start with the first nonzero digit on the left or with a zero in the units position of the decimal representation. For example, 546.21 and 0.061. If there is a last nonzero digit on the right, we terminate the decimal representation with this digit. Nonzero digits may continue to the right by repeating in "groups" or in some irregular manner. When repeating in groups, we write the repetition once and indicate the group of digits which repeat by placing a small dot over each repeating digit. For example, 1.732̇73̇2̇.

Let us examine the decimal representations of numbers with respect to the number sets which we have discussed. First, all decimal representations which have no nonzero digits to the right of the decimal point and which are not prefixed with a negative sign represent natural numbers. For example: 51.0, 50.0, 1500.0, etc. When prefixed by a negative sign, these represent the negative integers: -51.0, -50.0, -1500.0, etc. Thus the integers can all be represented in decimal form.

All decimal representations which have nonzero digits to the right of the decimal point can be classed into two types: (1) decimal representations which terminate or which repeat in "groups" and (2) decimal representations which do not terminate or repeat. The first type (1) can always be converted into a rational form. The second type (2) represent irrational numbers. For example:

(a) $1.73273\dot{2} = N$ $1000N = 1732.73273\dot{2}$
$$N = 1.73273\dot{2}$$
$$999N = 1731.0$$

$$\text{Thus } N = \frac{1731}{999}$$

(b) $0.125 = N$ $1000N = 125.0$ $\text{Thus } N = \frac{125}{1000} = \frac{1}{8}$

(c) $\sqrt{2} = 1.414214 \cdots$ where the dots to the right indicate a continuing succession of digits.

(d) $\pi = 3.1415926536 \cdots$

(e) $e = 2.7182818285 \cdots$

It can be shown that the decimal representation of numbers enables us to represent all real numbers. That is, we can associate a point on the real line to each decimal, and to each decimal there corresponds a point on the line. We note, however, that we can only approximate an irrational number to as close a unit of measure as we wish. In practice, therefore, measurements are all done in the rational number set. It is in theoretical and idealized situations that we use and speak of exact and irrational quantities.

In practical applications and problems, the four operations of addition, multiplication, subtraction, and division can be carried out just as in the rational number set. In theoretical work, the operations with irrational quantities must often be left as an indicated operation. However, the operations can be well-defined for the set of Dedekind cuts on the set of rational numbers such that all the properties are retained. Thus the real numbers also form a well ordered field.

Exercises 9.4

1. The irrational number phi (ϕ) is not well known, but it expresses a fundamental ratio which appears often when least expected. The ancient Greeks were familiar with this quantity which they called the "golden ratio." Its decimal expansion is $\phi \simeq 1.61803398 \cdots$. An interesting article on the number ϕ appears in the *Scientific American* magazine dated August 1959. Read, then write a short commentary on the article.

2. The number e can be approximated by the expression $\left(1 + \dfrac{1}{n}\right)^n$ where n is a natural number. Let $n = 1, 2, 3, 4$ and find the value of this expression for each n. What do you observe in relation to the approximations and the number e as approximated by $2.7182818285 \cdots$?

3. Specify the sets A and B which define the Dedekind cuts for the numbers $-2, \frac{2}{3}, \sqrt{5}, -\sqrt{3}$.

4. Illustrate the set relationship between the natural numbers, the integers, the rationals, and the real numbers by giving an example of each kind of number such that each successive number does not belong to the previous set.

5. Write the following number as the sum of numbers of various scale "magnitudes" and construct a point set representation for it: 203.826.

6. Write the following decimal representation as the quotient of integers: $-23.015\hat{0}1\hat{5}$.

Exercises 9

1. Give examples of sets with the cardinal names 11, 9, 6, 20.

2. Chickens in a flock are often said to have a "pecking order." Is this related to the concept of ordinal numbers? If so, describe the relationship.

3. The power a^n was defined in exercise 6 of 9.1. Prove the following theorems concerning powers of a natural number, using Theorem 1 of the natural numbers stated in 9.1.2.

   If a, b, n, and m are natural numbers, then:
   (a) $(ab)^n = a^n b^n$
   (b) $a^m a^n = a^{m+n}$
   (c) $(a^m)^n = a^{mn}$

4. If N is the set of natural numbers, then the set P defined as $P = \{x \in N/x$ is not divisible by any $n \in N$ except 1 and $x\}$ is called the set of **positive prime numbers.**
   (a) Find the first ten distinct members of P.
   (b) Every natural number can be expressed as a product of prime numbers. For example, $3850 = 2 \times 5 \times 5 \times 7 \times 11$. Express the natural numbers 126 and 2860 as products of elements of P.

5. If a and b are integers, then $a - b = a + (-b)$. Note that the negative sign on the left of the equality indicates an operation, whereas the negative sign on the right denotes the negative of b, that is, the inverse of b under addition. A proof of the assertion might proceed as follows:
   1. $a - b = x$ means $b + x = a$
   2. $b + [a + (-b)] = [a + (-b)] + b$
   3. $b + [a + (-b)] = a + [(-b) + b]$
   4. $b + [a + (-b)] = a + 0$
   5. $b + [a + (-b)] = a$
   6. $\therefore\ a + (-b) = a - b$
   Furnish a formal justification for each step of the proof.

6. The smallest positive integer which is a multiple of each number in a set of

positive integers is called the **lowest common multiple** of the given set of integers. For example, for 4, 6, 12, and 28 the lowest common multiple is 84. Find the lowest common multiple of each of the following sets of positive integers:

(a) 5, 15, 21, and 9   (b) 3, 8, 12, and 18

7. If a and b are positive integers such that $a < b$, we are often interested in finding the greatest multiple of a such that it is less than or equal to b. For example, if $a = 13$ and $b = 68$, then the greatest multiple of a less than b is $5(13) = 65$. The difference between b and $5a$ is 3. We can write $b = 5a + 3$, or $68 = 5(13) + 3$. In general, if $a < b$ and we write $b = qa + r$, then q is called the **quotient** and r the **remainder** in the **division** of b by a.

(a) Find the greatest multiple of the first integer which is less than or equal to the second:

(i) 7 and 65   (ii) 12 and 113   (iii) 17 and 239

(b) For each part of (a) write the result in the form $b = qa + r$ by finding r for each pair of integers.

8. List at least five elements in each of the following equivalence classes of rationals:

(a) $\dfrac{3}{8}$ (b) $-\dfrac{2}{3}$ (c) $\dfrac{9}{5}$

9. In the following, do the indicated operations and express the result as a reduced rational number.

(a) $\dfrac{5}{3} + \dfrac{1}{6}$ (b) $\dfrac{7}{12} + \dfrac{4}{15}$ (c) $\left(\dfrac{1}{2} + \dfrac{2}{3}\right) + \dfrac{3}{4}$

(d) $\dfrac{7}{6} - \dfrac{3}{5}$ (e) $\dfrac{9}{4} - \dfrac{11}{3}$ (f) $\left(\dfrac{5}{4} - \dfrac{4}{3}\right) + \dfrac{2}{5}$

(g) $\dfrac{5}{4} - \left(\dfrac{4}{3} + \dfrac{2}{5}\right)$ (h) $\dfrac{5}{4} + \left(\dfrac{4}{3} - \dfrac{2}{5}\right)$ (i) $\dfrac{5}{4} - \left(\dfrac{4}{3} - \dfrac{2}{5}\right)$

(j) $\dfrac{\frac{2}{3}}{\frac{2}{5}}$ (k) $\dfrac{\frac{5}{6}}{\frac{3}{2}}$ (l) $\left(\dfrac{7}{3}\right)\left(\dfrac{5}{2}\right)$

(m) $\left(\dfrac{27}{8}\right)\left(\dfrac{4}{9}\right)$

10. Write the following rational numbers as decimals, using "ordinary" long division.

(a) $\dfrac{17}{12}$ (b) $\dfrac{4}{9}$ (c) $\dfrac{17}{20}$ (d) $\dfrac{93}{40}$

11. Give an informal proof to show that there is no rational number a such that $a^2 = 3$.

12. In making measurements, we often approximate irrational numbers with
rational numbers. For example, we can approximate $\sqrt{7}$ by using the
definition that if $\sqrt{7} = a$, then $a^2 = 7$. We first "guess" a value of a to be
between 2 and 3, say, 2.5 in decimal form. Noting that $a = \dfrac{7}{a}$, we can
divide 7 by our first "guess" to obtain an a value for the left side of the
equality. Now we note that the exact value of a must be between 2.5 and 2.8,
$2.5 < a < 2.8$. We make a second "guess" between the two values, say, an
"average" of the two: $a \cong \dfrac{(2.5 + 2.8)}{2} = 2.65$. We divide 2.65 into 7 to
obtain another value for a, 2.64. Now we know that a must be between 2.64
and 2.65, say, 2.645 which can be taken as still another "guess." The process
can be continued indefinitely to obtain closer and closer approximations to
the exact value of a.

Using the above method, approximate $\sqrt{19}$ and $\sqrt{52}$ to within an "error"
of not more than 0.001. That is, the exact value should differ from the
approximation by less than 0.001.

13. The equation $b = qa + r$ describes the ordinary process of division (see
problem 7). The quantity a is called the divisor and b the dividend.

We are often interested in finding the **greatest common divisor** of two
positive integers with remainders equal to zero. For example, if $m = 24$ and
$n = 60$, then $d = 12$ is the largest integer which divides both m and n
without a remainder. That is, $24 = 2(12)$ and $60 = 5(12)$ and the quotients
2 and 5 have no common divisor.

Find the greatest common divisors of:
(a) 132 and 51   (b) 72 and 56   (c) 42 and 140

14. If a and b are positive integers with no common divisors, and if a divides an
integer m, and b divides m with no remainders, then show that the product
ab divides m with no remainder.

15. Show that one of any three consecutive integers is divisible by 3.

10
CONDITIONS ON SETS

10.1 THE SET BUILDER

We now return to the question of specifying sets. A set can be described by stating the conditions under which elements are in the set. If U is a specified universal set, then we can describe a subset of U as $S = \{x \in U/Fx\}$. The set S is then understood to consist of those elements and only those elements such that $x \in U$ and Fx. If we conceive of the condition F

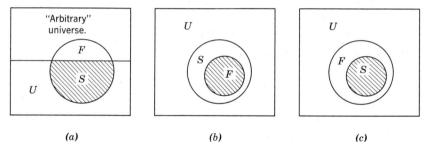

| (a) | (b) | (c) |

FIGURE 45.
(a) $x \in U$. (b) Necessary: $F \subset S$. (c) Sufficient: $S \subset F$.

on arbitrary elements x as defining a set, then $S = \{x \in U/Fx\}$ asserts that $F \subset S$ and $S \subset F$ in U so that $S = F$ in U. These latter assertions are often called the necessary and sufficient conditions for defining the set S.

The form $\{x \in U/Fx\}$ is often called a **set builder** since it enables us to build a set from elements in a given universal set. The set builder defines two sets in the given universal set U: the truth set for Fx and its complement. That is, the set S is the **truth set** of F in U. The condition Fx describing a set is often neither true nor false in itself. A specific substitution must be made from the universal set to form a statement which is either true or false. If the substitution of an element makes the statement true, then the element belongs to the set. Otherwise, it does not.

For example:

(a) $Q = \{x \in C/x^2 - 2x + 1 = 0\}$
    If $x = 1$, then $(1)^2 - 2(1) + 1 = 0$ so that $1 \in Q$.
    If $x = -1$, then $(-1)^2 - 2(-1) + 1 \neq 0$ so that $-1 \notin Q$.
(b) $N_0 = \{x \in N/x = 2n - 1$ for $n = 1, 2, 3, \cdots\}$
    $1, 3, 5, \cdots$ are in N_0 since $1 = 2n - 1$ for $n = 1$, $3 = 2n - 1$ for $n = 2$, $5 = 2n - 1$ for $n = 3$, etc.
    $2, 4, 6, \cdots$ are not in N_0 since $2n - 1$ cannot equal $2, 4, 6, \cdots$ for any natural numbers n.
(c) $L = \{x \in R/2 \leq x < 4\}$
    The condition $2 \leq x < 4$ divides the set of rationals into L and the complement of L. L consists of all the rational numbers between 2 and 4 and includes 2 but excludes 4. $\frac{5}{2} \in L$ but $\frac{3}{2} \notin L$.

We say that **Fx is a condition on x**, meaning that when an element of the universal set is substituted in Fx, the statement becomes true or false. If, when an element c of the universal set is substituted in Fx, the statement Fc is true, then we say that c **satisfies** the condition Fx. That is, $c \in S$ implies a condition on c since c must form a true substitution instance of Fx. The statements "c satisfies Fx" and "Fc is true" are thus equivalent.

10.1.0.1 Definition: Two conditions Fx and Gx are said to be **equivalent** in a universal set U, if and only if $\{x \in U/Fx\} = \{x \in U/Gx\}$.

For example, for Fx and Gx take $x < 10$ and $0 < x < 10$. If U is the set of natural numbers:

$\{x \in N/x < 10\} = \{x \in N/0 < x < 10\} = \{1, 2, 3, 4, 5, 6, 7, 8, 9\}$

If U is the set of integers:

$\{x \in I/x < 10\} = \{\cdots -4, -3, -2, -1, 0, 1, 2, \cdots, 9\}$
$\{x \in I/0 < x < 10\} = \{1, 2, 3, 4, 5, 6, 7, 8, 9\}$

Thus Fx and Gx *are* equivalent in the universal set of natural numbers but are *not* equivalent in the integers.

Since conditions specify sets, it is important to understand the structure of conditions. For convenience we will consider conditions on number sets. Traditionally, the study of elementary conditions on sets is found in *elementary algebra* courses in the secondary schools. Space will not permit more than a very brief exposition of three of the more important beginning topics.

10.1.1 The Egyptians appear to have known some rudimentary rules for manipulating conditions. In Plato's writings, verbal conditions are mentioned as a popular subject of discourse. Diophantus of Alexandria presented a collection of conditions in his *Arithmetica*. However, the name *algebra* did not occur until the Arab writer Mohammed ibn Músa al-Khowárizmi had written his treatise *al-jabr w'al muqábalah*. Although interesting rules, such as the Rule of False Position and the Rule of Three, were known before the Renaissance, it was not until adequate symbolism was developed that a systematic structuring of conditions became available.

For convenience in describing and studying conditions we use special terminology. Understanding the terminology is thus a first step in the study of conditions. For brevity, we list a few of the most important terms followed by a brief informal definition and an illustration or two.

(1) **Expression:** An expression is any symbolic form: $x - y$, $2x$, $ab + 3$, $x^2 + 2bx - c$.

(2) **Term:** A term is a quantity or member of an expression. In $x^2 - 5x + 2$, the terms are x^2, $-5x$, and 2. In $ax^2 + (a + 1)x - c$, the terms are ax^2, $(a + 1)x$, and $-c$.

(3) **Factor:** A factor is a quantity which divides another given quantity. 2 and 3 are factors of 6. 4 and a are factors of $4a$. x is a factor of x^2. (Also see 9.1.3.)

(4) **Power, exponent,** and **base:** (See definition 9.1.2.2 of problem 6, Exercises 9.1.)

(5) **Evaluation:** Evaluation is the process of finding the numerical value of a given expression for given values of the quantities involved. If $a = 3$, $b = 7$, and $x = 5$, then $3x - 2ab = 3(5) - 2(3)(7) = -27$.

(6) **Simplify:** To simplify means to do in the correct order all operations that are indicated in a symbolic statement.
$$\frac{6 + 9}{7 - 4} = \frac{15}{3} = 5; \qquad \frac{x^2 - 1}{x + 1} = x - 1.$$

(7) **Coefficient:** A coefficient is the product of all the factors of a term except one, of which the product is said to be the coefficient. 2 is the coefficient of x in $2x$. $2ay$ is the coefficient of x^2 in $2ax^2y$, whereas $2a$ is the coefficient of x^2y and 2 is the *numerical* coefficient of the term.

Terms and expressions are formed by applying the operations of addition, subtraction, multiplication, and division to successive pairs of quantities. The following examples illustrate a few situations which might arise.

(*a*) The associative and commutative laws allow us to omit parentheses in addition (and multiplication).
$$3 + (4 + 1) = (3 + 4) + 1 = 4 + (1 + 3) = 4 + 3 + 1 = 8.$$
$$a + (b + c) = b + (a + c) = a + b + c.$$

(*b*) In subtraction we must be careful in the use of parentheses.
$$4 + (3 - 7) = 4 + 3 - 7 = 0 \text{ while } 4 - (3 - 7) = 4 - 3 + 7 = 8 \text{ and } 4 - (3 + 7) = 4 - 3 - 7 = -6.$$
$$a - b = -b + a = -(b - a).$$

(c) When elements are enclosed in parentheses, they are to be treated as if they were one quantity. When a quantity in parentheses is multiplied by another element, the distributive law may be applied.

$$8 - (2 + 3) = 8 - 5 = 3; \qquad 2(5 + 3) = 2(8) = 16.$$
$$2(a + b) = 2a + 2b; \qquad a(3 + 5) = 3a + 5a = 8a.$$

(d) In division, the "bar" serves the same purpose as parentheses.

$$\frac{8 - 5}{4 - 1} = \frac{3}{3} = 1 \text{ while } \frac{8}{4} - \frac{5}{1} = 2 - 5 = -3.$$

(e) In manipulating expressions, multiplication and division take "precedence" over addition and subtraction (by convention).

$$2 + (5)(3) = 2 + 15 = 17; \qquad (not \ 2 + (5)(3) = (7)(3) = 21.)$$

(f) The quotient of two quantities may often be reduced by applying the fundamental theorem that $\dfrac{ac}{bc} = \dfrac{a}{b}$.

$$\frac{4ax^2}{2x} = 2ax; \qquad \frac{3m^2n^3}{9m^4n} = \frac{n^2}{3m^2}; \qquad \left(\text{but } not \ \frac{a+2}{ab} = \frac{2}{b} \ !\right).$$

Terms and expressions may be combined to form further terms and expressions. If there are different terms, operations are indicated in the expression. If there are two or more **similar** terms, the expressions may be simplified. For example:

(i) $3a + 2b - c + b + 2a - 3 + 5c + 2 = 5a + 3b + 4c - 1.$

(ii) $(2m - n) + (3m - 2n) = 5m - 3n.$

(iii) $(3a + 2b) - (b - a) = 4a + b.$

(iv) $(3a^2)(-4a) = -12a^3.$

(v) $5ab(2a + 1) = 10a^2b + 5ab.$

(vi) $(3x + 5)(4x - 7) = 12x^2 - x - 35.$

(vii) $\dfrac{x^2 + 6x + 8}{x + 2} = \dfrac{(x + 4)(x + 2)}{(x + 2)} = x + 4.$

Two common types of problems occur in the **simplification** of expressions. The first is the removal of more than one set of parentheses. When one set of parentheses is enclosed by another, the technique is to remove one set at a time, beginning with the innermost set of parentheses. For example:

(s.i) $2x - [x - (3x + 4) - 1] = 2x - [x - 3x - 4 - 1] = 2x - x + 3x + 4 + 1 = 4x + 5.$

(s.ii) $x - [2x^2 - \{3x^2 + (5x - x^2) + x\}] = x - [2x^2 - \{3x^2 + 5x - x^2 + x\}] = x - [2x^2 - 3x^2 - 5x + x^2 - x] = x - 2x^2 + 3x^2 + 5x - x^2 + x = 7x.$

(s.iii) $-[a + b - a(b + a - 1)] = -[a + b - ab - a^2 + a] = -a - b + ab + a^2 - a = a^2 - 2a + ab - b.$

The second type of problem is referred to as **factoring**. This process depends mainly on recognizing certain special products. The most common forms are illustrated in the following examples.

(f.i) *Common factors:* $ab + ac = a(b + c)$; $2mx - 6m = 2m(x - 3)$.

(f.ii) *Difference of two squares:* $x^2 - 4 = (x + 2)(x - 2)$; $4m^3 - m = m(2m + 1)(2m - 1)$; $6a^2b^2 - 24b^2 = 6b^2(a + 2)(a - 2)$.

(f.iii) *Trinomials:* $x^2 + (a + b)x + ab = (x + a)(x + b)$; $x^2 + 5x + 6 = (x + 2)(x + 3)$; $a^2 - 3a - 10 = (a + 2)(a - 5)$; $x^2 - 6x + 8 = (x - 4)(x - 2)$; $6x^2 + 23x + 20 = (3x + 4)(2x + 5)$; $15x^2 - 2x - 8 = (3x + 2)(5x - 4)$.

(f.iv) *Squares:* $b^2 + 2bc + c^2 = (b + c)^2$; $z^2 + 10z + 25 = (z + 5)^2$; $a^2 - 24a + 144 = (a - 12)^2$; $1 + 4y + 4y^2 = (1 + 2y)^2$.

For more detailed development of these important "skill" and "forming" topics, the reader is referred to any standard *elementary algebra* text.

Exercises 10.1

1. If $a = 2$, $b = -3$, $c = 5$, $d = -\frac{1}{2}$, and $x = \frac{5}{2}$, then evaluate the following expressions.

   (i) $3a - 2bc$

   (ii) $\dfrac{6ad}{5b}$

   (iii) $\dfrac{a + 3b}{x - 2d}$

   (iv) $(ax^2 + 5d)^2 - ac^2$

   (v) $2b(x - c)$

   (vi) $3a - (b + c)$

   (vii) $\dfrac{x + a}{b + c} + \dfrac{a - d}{x - d}$

2. Simplify by carrying out the indicated operations and combining like terms where possible.

   (i) $3a + 4b - 2 + 7b - 6a + 5$

   (ii) $6(3a - 5) - 7(2a - 6)$

   (iii) $3(5m + 2) - (6m - 4)$

   (iv) $(x - b)(x + b) - 2(x + b)^2$

   (v) $3a(3 - 5b) + 7(a + b - 5)$

   (vi) $\dfrac{(x + a)^2 - 2a(x + a)}{(x - a)}$

3. Factor the following expressions:

   (i) $x^2 + 7x + 12$

   (ii) $m^2 - 5m - 24$

   (iii) $4x^3 - 9x$

   (iv) $3x^2 - 6x + 3$

   (v) $1 - 16a + 64a^2$

   (vi) $25y^2 - 4x^2$

10.2 EQUATIONS, INEQUALITIES

Symbolic statements Fx which specify the conditions under which elements are in a set are often in the form of **equations** or **inequalities**.

10.2.0.1 Definition: An **equation** is a symbolic statement of equality between two quantities.

10.2.0.2 Definition: An **inequality** is a symbolic statement that one quantity is less than or greater than another quantity.

Equations and inequalities are symbolic sentences which describe the conditions in a certain problem. Many problems can be solved by translating the situation into equations and/or inequality statements which specify the restrictions and conditions on the elements of some universal set. Once the conditions have been specified, we can proceed to search for the specific members of the truth set for the conditions.

For example, suppose we wish to cut a piece of sheet metal into a rectangle so that it is exactly 98 square inches in area and its length is twice its width. Now we wish to find its length and width. We proceed by noting that the universal set is "inches." If we name the width x, then the length must be $2x$. Now since the area of a rectangle is equal to the width times the length, we have $(x)(2x) = 98$. The truth set must be $S = \{x/2x^2 = 98\}$. The condition $2x^2 = 98$ can be simplified to $x^2 = 49$. Then we note that if x is set equal to 7, then the condition will be true. Also, -7 appears to satisfy the condition. Since this is a physical length, we note that the additional condition $x > 0$ must be included. Thus $S = \{x/2x^2 = 98 \text{ and } x \geq 0\}$ $= \{7\}$. Now, reinterpreting our results, we conclude that the width must be 7 inches and the length 14 inches. The area will then be, in fact, 98 square inches and the length twice the width.

We say that the numbers which make an equation or inequality true (the elements of the truth set) are the **solutions** for the equation or inequality. The process of finding the elements of the truth set is called **solving**. The development of the skills and methods for finding solutions of equations and inequalities (truth sets) forms an important part of the content of traditional elementary algebra courses.

The conditions specified in a problem are not always simple. Much ingenuity and careful thinking may be required to solve an equation or inequality. Like discovering a formal proof, the process of solving for the truth set satisfying given conditions Fx can be divided into short steps. Each step is justified by a valid argument, known property of the elements of the universal set, or by a definition.

To find the elements of a truth set or solution set, we search for an equivalent condition for the universal set which is simpler than the previous condition. We continue the process of simplification of the condition step by step until we obtain an explicit statement which specifies the elements in the truth set of the conditions. The process is directed by a few theorems which can be deduced from the structure of sets and the properties of the number sets discussed in the last chapter. For convenience, these theorems are assumed. They are commonly called the axioms of equality and inequality. These rules enable us to manipulate, in a well regulated manner, the conditions given, so that every step of the process can be followed and checked. The final solutions can be checked by substituting the elements in the given conditions to verify that they satisfy the conditions.

The following tables of rules refer to elements in the set of real or rational numbers. The given equations are general conditions such that the antecedent condition and the consequent conditions are equivalent in the sense that they have the same solution sets in the universal sets of real or rational numbers.

TABLE 39

Rules for Equations

I. If $x = y$, then $x + a = y + a$.

II. If $x = y$, then $x - a = y - a$.

III. If $x = y$ and $c \neq 0$, then $xc = yc$.

IV. If $x = y$ and $c \neq 0$, then $\dfrac{x}{c} = \dfrac{y}{c}$.

TABLE 40

Rules for Inequalities

I. If $x < y$, then $x + c < y + c$.

II. If $x < y$, then $x - c < y - c$.

III. If $x < y$ and $c > 0$, then $xc < yc$.

IV. If $x < y$ and $c < 0$, then $xc > yc$.

V. If $x < y$ and $c > 0$, then $\dfrac{x}{c} < \dfrac{y}{c}$.

VI. If $x < y$ and $c < 0$, then $\dfrac{x}{c} > \dfrac{y}{c}$.

10.2.1 We conclude this chapter with a few examples of sets defined by simple conditions and their solutions. The conditions are solved by applying the rules of equality and inequality from Tables 39 and 40. Usually this process will consist of looking for simpler equivalent conditions until a condition of the form $x = ($ ——— $)$ or $x < ($ ——— $)$ appears. For convenience, we will list the steps and justify them briefly in a way similar to the form used in proofs.

1. $S = \{x \in C / x - 3 = 7\}$.

    (a) $x - 3 = 7$ given condition.

    (b) $x = 10$ I.

    (c) $S = \{10\}$ solution.

2. $S = \{x \in C / x + 12 = 5\}$.

    (a) $x + 12 = 5$ given condition.

(b) $x = -7$ II.
(c) $S = \{-7\}$ solution.

3. $S = \left\{x \in C / \dfrac{x - 5}{3} = 11\right\}.$

   (a) $\dfrac{x - 5}{3} = 11$ given condition.

   (b) $x - 5 = 33$ III.
   (c) $x = 38$ I.
   (d) $S = \{38\}$ solution.

4. $S = \{x \in C / 7x + 4 = 18\}.$
   (a) $7x + 4 = 18$ given condition.
   (b) $7x = 14$ II.
   (c) $x = 2$ IV.
   (d) $S = \{2\}$ solution.

5. $S = \{x \in C / 2x + 3 = x - 2\}.$
   (a) $2x + 3 = x - 2$ given condition.
   (b) $2x = x - 5$ II.
   (c) $x = -5$ II.
   (d) $S = \{-5\}$ solution.

6. $S = \left\{x \in C / \dfrac{x + 5}{x + 2} = -2\right\}.$

   (a) $\dfrac{x + 5}{x + 2} = -2$ given condition.

   (b) $x + 5 = -2(x + 2)$ III.
   (c) $x + 5 = -2x - 4$ distributive.
   (d) $x = -2x - 9$ II.
   (e) $3x = -9$ I.
   (f) $x = -3$ IV.
   (g) $S = \{-3\}$ solution.

7. $S = \left\{x \in C / x + 3 = \dfrac{4}{x + 3}\right\}.$

   (a) $x + 3 = \dfrac{4}{x + 3}$ given condition.

   (b) $(x + 3)^2 = 4$ III.
   (c) $x + 3 = 2$ or $x + 3 = -2$ the "square root."
   (d) $x = -1$ or $x = -5$ II.
   (e) $S = \{-1, -5\}$ solution.

8. $S = \{x \in C / 3x^2 + 5 = 53\}.$
   (a) $3x^2 + 5 = 53$ given condition.
   (b) $3x^2 = 48$ II.

(c) $x^2 = 16$ IV.

(d) $x = 4$ or $x = -4$ the "square root."

(e) $S = \{4, -4\}$ solution.

9. $S = \{x \in C / 2x^2 - 5x = 3\}.$

(a) $2x^2 - 5x = 3$ given condition.

(b) $2x^2 - 5x - 3 = 0$ II.

(c) $(2x + 1)(x - 3) = 0$ factoring.

(d) $2x + 1 = 0$ or $x - 3 = 0$ theorem.

(e) $2x = -1$ or $x = 3$ I, II.

(f) $x = \dfrac{-1}{2}$ or $x = 3$ IV.

(g) $S = \left\{\dfrac{-1}{2}, 3\right\}$ solution.

10. $S = \{x \in C / x^2 + 3x + 2 = 0\}.$

(a) $x^2 + 3x + 2 = 0$ given condition.

(b) $x^2 + 3x + \dfrac{9}{4} = \dfrac{1}{4}$ I.

(c) $\left(x + \dfrac{3}{2}\right)^2 = \dfrac{1}{4}$ factoring.

(d) $x + \dfrac{3}{2} = \dfrac{1}{2}$ or $x + \dfrac{3}{2} = \dfrac{-1}{2}$ the "square root."

(e) $x = -1$ or $x = -2$ II.

(f) $S = \{-1, -2\}$ solution.

11. $S = \{x \in C / x - 3 < 7\}.$

(a) $x - 3 < 7$ given condition.

(b) $x < 10$ I.

(c) $S = \{x < 10\}$ solution.

   5   6   7   8   9 10 11 12 13 14   (C)

12. $S = \{x \in C / x + 5 > 8\}.$

(a) $x + 5 > 8$ given condition.

(b) $x > 3$ II.

(c) $S = \{x > 3\}$ solution.

   0   1   2   3   4   5   6   7   8   9   (C)

13. $S = \left\{x \in C / \dfrac{x - 2}{3} \leq 4\right\}.$

(a) $\dfrac{x - 2}{3} \leq 4$ given condition.

(b) $x - 2 \le 12$ III.
(c) $x \le 14$ I.
(d) $S = \{x \le 14\}$ solution.

11   12   13   14   15   16   17   ·18   19   (C)

14. $S = \{x \in C / 4x - 3 \ge 17\}$.
   (a) $4x - 3 \ge 17$ given condition.
   (b) $4x \ge 20$ I.
   (c) $x \ge 5$ V.
   (d) $S = \{x \ge 5\}$ solution.

2   3   4   5   6   7   8   9   10   11   12   (C)

15. $S = \{x \in C / 3 - 2x < 9\}$.
   (a) $3 - 2x < 9$ given condition.
   (b) $-2x < 6$ II.
   (c) $x > -3$ VI.
   (d) $S = \{x > -3\}$ solution.

−5   −4   −3   −2   −1   0   1   2   3   (C)

16. $S = \left\{ x \in C / \dfrac{x + 5}{x + 2} > 2 \right\}$.

   (a) $\dfrac{x + 5}{x + 2} > 2$ given condition.

   (b) $x + 2 > 0$, $x + 2 = 0$, or   theorem: $z > 0$, $z = 0$, or
      $x + 2 < 0$ $z < 0$.
   (c) If $x + 2 > 0$, then $x > -2$ (b), II.
   (d) $x + 5 > 2x + 4$ (a), (c), III.
   (e) $x + 1 > 2x$ II.
   (f) $x < 1$ II.
   (g) $-2 < x < 1$ (c), (f)
   (h) $x + 2 \ne 0$ (a), (b)
   (i) If $x + 2 < 0$, then $x < -2$ (b), II.
   (j) $x + 5 < 2x + 4$ (a), (i), IV.
   (k) $x + 1 < 2x$ II.
   (l) $x > 1$ II.
   (m) $x < -2$ and $x > 1$ (i), (l), contradiction.

−4   −3   −2   −1   0   1   2   3   4   (C)

(n) $x + 2 \not< 0$ (m).

(o) $S = \{-2 < x < 1\}$ solution.

17. $S = \left\{ x \in C / \dfrac{5}{x-2} \leq 1 \right\}.$

(a) $\dfrac{5}{x-2} \leq 1$ given condition.

(b) $x - 2 > 0$ or $x - 2 < 0$ but   theorem, (a).
$x - 2 \neq 0$

(c) If $x - 2 > 0$, then $x > 2$ (b), I.

(d) $5 \leq x - 2$ (a), (c), III.

(e) $7 \leq x$ I.

(f) $x > 2$ and $x \geq 7$ (c), (e).

(g) If $x - 2 < 0$, then $x < 2$ (b), I.

(h) $5 \geq x - 2$ (a), (g), IV.

(i) $7 \geq x$ I.

(j) $x < 2$ and $x \leq 7$ (g), (i).

(k) $x < 2$ or $7 \leq x$ (f), (j).

(l) $S = \{x < 2$ or $7 \leq x\}$ solution.

18. $S = \{x \in C / x^2 + 2 \leq 6\}.$

(a) $x^2 + 2 \leq 6$ given condition.

(b) $0 \leq x^2 \leq 4$ theorem: $z^2 \geq 0$, II.

(c) $-2 \leq x \leq 0$ or $0 \leq x \leq 2$ the "square root."

(d) $-2 \leq x \leq 2$ (c).

(e) $S = \{-2 \leq x \leq 2\}$ solution.

19. $S = \{x \in C / (x-1)(x+3) \leq 0\}.$

(a) $(x - 1)(x + 3) \leq 0$ given condition.

(b) $x - 1 \geq 0$ and $x + 3 \leq 0$ theorem: If $ab < 0$ then a
           or   and b alternate in sign.
$x - 1 \leq 0$ and $x + 3 \geq 0$

(c) If $x - 1 \geq 0$ and $x + 3 \leq 0$,   (b), I, II, contradiction.
then $x \geq 1$ and $x \leq -3$

(d) If $x - 1 \leq 0$ and $x + 3 \geq 0$,   (b), I, II.
then $x \leq 1$ and $x \geq -3$

(e) $-3 \leq x \leq 1$ (d).
(f) $S = \{-3 \leq x \leq 1\}$ solution.

Exercises 10.2

1. Given Fx in $S = \{x \in C/Fx\}$ as follows:
   (a) $2x - 3 = 7$ (b) $x + 4 = 2x - 3$
   (c) $\dfrac{x + 5}{2x - 7} = 1$ (d) $3(x - 1) = 6x$
   (e) $5x + (2x - 3) = 2(x + 6)$ (f) $x^2 + 2 = 11$
   solve for the set S and list the elements of S.
2. Do as in exercise 1 with:
   (a) $2x - 5 < x + 2$ (b) $x + 2 > 7$
   (c) $\dfrac{5x - 4}{3} < 2$ (d) $\dfrac{3}{x - 1} \geq 4$
   (e) $2x < \dfrac{1}{3 - x}$ (f) $\dfrac{x + 2}{2 - x} \leq 3$

Exercises 10

1. A condition is said to be *universally true in a set U* if it is satisfied by every element of U. The condition is said to be *universally false in U* if no element of U satisfies the condition. If $S = \{x \in U/Fx\}$ is
   (a) universally true, to what set does it correspond?
   (b) universally false to what set does it correspond?
2. If $F = \{x \in U/Fx\}$ and $G = \{x \in U/Gx\}$ and $H = \{x \in U/Hx\}$ and $F \subset G$ and $G \subset H$ then what is the logical relationship between Fx, Gx, and Hx?
3. If $a = 3$, $b = -1$, $c = \frac{2}{3}$, $d = -\frac{1}{2}$, and $x = 6$, then evaluate the following expressions.
   (a) $c - \dfrac{a}{b}$ (b) $a^2c^2 + (x - bd)$
   (c) $3d - \dfrac{2(x - a)}{2b + x}$ (d) $\dfrac{cx + 2b}{bcd}$
   (e) $\left(\dfrac{a^2 - b}{x + b}\right) + \left(\dfrac{x^2 - 3x - 5}{a - b}\right)$ (f) $3bx^2 + 2cx + a^2x + 5d$
4. Simplify the following expressions by carrying out the indicated operations and combining like terms where possible.
   (a) $(2x - 4) - (3x - [-7 + 4x] - 12)$
   (b) $3a(2 + 5a) - (a + 1)(a - 1) - 2a(7a + 3)$
   (c) $\dfrac{2}{2x - 1} - \dfrac{3}{3x + 1}$ (d) $4(x - y)^2 - 3(x + y)^2 + 14xy$
   (e) $\left(\dfrac{a^2 - b^2}{3a^2}\right)\left(\dfrac{18ab}{a + b}\right)$ (f) $\dfrac{\dfrac{b}{a} - \dfrac{a}{b}}{\dfrac{1}{a} + \dfrac{1}{b}}$

5. Factor the following expressions.

(a) $ac + bd + ad + bc$ (b) $12x^2 - 3a^2$

(c) $x^2 + x + \frac{1}{4}$ (d) $3 + 3x - 6x^2$

(e) $(a - 2)^2 - 2(a - 2) + 1$ (f) $4x^2 - 12x + 9$

6. Given Fx in $S = \{x \in C/Fx\}$ as follows:

(a) $3x + 1 = \frac{5}{2}$ (b) $\dfrac{x - 3}{2} = x - 2$

(c) $x^2 + 2x = -1$ (d) $5(2x - 3) = 3(x + 2)$

(e) $2(3x - 5) + 3(x + 1) = x + 9$ (f) $(x + 2)(x - 3) = x(x - 2)$

solve for the set S and list the elements of S.

7. Do as in exercise 6 with:

(a) $3x + 1 < 7 - x$ (b) $\dfrac{3 - 2x}{1 + x} \geq 3$

(c) $(x - 2)(2x + 1) < 0$ (d) $2(x - 3) \geq x$

(e) $\dfrac{15}{x^2 + 1} < 3$ (f) $2x - 1 \leq \dfrac{15}{x}$

8. A useful concept in specifying conditions is that of a **ratio**.

10.2.1.1 **Definition:** By the **ratio** of a number a to a number b we mean the quotient of the numbers $r = \dfrac{a}{b}$.

10.2.1.2 **Definition:** By a **proportion** we mean that two ratios $\dfrac{a}{b}$ and $\dfrac{c}{d}$ are equal. We write $\dfrac{a}{b} = \dfrac{c}{d}$. The numbers a, b, c, and d are called the **terms** of the proportion. The numbers a and d are called the **extremes**, b and c are called the **means**.

(a) Prove that in any proportion, the product of the means equals the product of the extremes.

(b) If $\dfrac{a}{b} = \dfrac{c}{d}$, then prove that $\dfrac{b}{a} = \dfrac{d}{c}$.

(c) Find the unknown term in each of the following proportions.

(i) $\dfrac{2}{x} = \dfrac{11}{6}$ (ii) $\dfrac{18}{4} = \dfrac{x}{6}$ (iii) $\dfrac{x - 1}{9} = \dfrac{x + 2}{8}$ (iv) $\dfrac{2}{x} = \dfrac{x}{8}$

9. An application of proportions is used in the proof of Pythagoras's theorem concerning the relationship between the sides of a right triangle. In order to illustrate this proof, we define still another useful concept, that of **similar** triangles.

10.2.1.3 **Definition:** Two triangles are said to be **similar**, if and only if their angles are equal to each other in pairs.

THEOREM. Similar triangles have the sides opposite their equal angles in the same ratio.

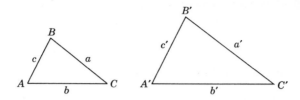

FIGURE 46.   Triangle ABC is similar to triangle $A'B'C'$.

THEOREM. $\dfrac{a}{a'} = \dfrac{b}{b'} = \dfrac{c}{c'}$.

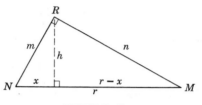

FIGURE 47.

Given the right triangle RMN (Figure 47) construct an *altitude* to the side opposite the *right angle* (the longest side called the *hypotenuse*), and call this h.

(a) Prove: $r^2 = m^2 + n^2$.

(b) Prove: $\dfrac{x}{h} = \dfrac{h}{r - x}$.

10. A useful manipulative device is called "completing the square" of an expression of the form: $ax^2 + bx + c$. For example:

1. $ax^2 + bx + c = a\left(x^2 + \dfrac{b}{a}x + \dfrac{c}{a}\right) = a\left(x^2 + \dfrac{b}{a}x + \dfrac{b^2}{4a^2} + \dfrac{c}{a} - \dfrac{b^2}{4a^2}\right)$

$$= a\left[\left(x + \dfrac{b}{2a}\right)^2 - \left(\dfrac{b^2}{4a^2} - \dfrac{c}{a}\right)\right]$$

$$= a\left[\left(x + \dfrac{b}{2a}\right)^2 - \left(\dfrac{b^2 - 4ac}{4a^2}\right)\right]$$

$$= a\left(x + \dfrac{b}{2a} + \dfrac{\sqrt{b^2 - 4ac}}{2a}\right)\left(x + \dfrac{b}{2a} - \dfrac{\sqrt{b^2 - 4ac}}{2a}\right)$$

$$= a\left(x + \dfrac{b + \sqrt{b^2 - 4ac}}{2a}\right)\left(x + \dfrac{b - \sqrt{b^2 - 4ac}}{2a}\right).$$

2. $3x^2 + 4x + 1 = 3(x^2 + \frac{4}{3}x + \frac{1}{3}) = 3(x^2 + \frac{4}{3}x + \frac{4}{9} + \frac{1}{3} - \frac{4}{9})$

$$= 3[(x + \frac{2}{3})^2 - \frac{1}{9}] = 3(x + \frac{2}{3})(x + 1)$$

$$= (3x + 1)(x + 1).$$

(a) Use the above technique of "completing the square" to factor:
  (i) $2x^2 + 13x - 7$; (ii) $6x^2 + x - 2$.
(b) (i) If $2x^2 + 13x - 7 = 0$, then find the truth set (solutions) for x.
  (ii) If $6x^2 + x - 2 \leq 0$, do as in (i).

11. In working with equations, it is often useful to be able to manipulate so that a particular unknown is isolated on one side of an equation. The isolated element is sometimes called the **subject** of the equation. For example, in $p = 2s + b$, p is the subject. We can manipulate the equation into the form $s = \dfrac{p - b}{2}$ so that now s is the subject of the equation.

Using the rules for equations, manipulate the given equations so that the indicated element is the subject in each case.
(a) $p = 2a + 2b$, b. (b) $F = \frac{9}{5}C + 32$, C.
(c) $A = p + prt$, r. (d) $A = p + prt$, p.
(e) $2S = n(a + k)$, n. (f) $2S = n(a + k)$, a.

12. Simplify the following expressions.
(a) $9(5y - 7x) + 4(-3x + 2y)$
(b) $(2m + 9)(3m - 7) - 6(m + 7)(m - 2)$

(c) $\dfrac{2}{a^2} + \dfrac{1}{b^2} - \dfrac{3}{a^2b^2}$
(d) $\dfrac{\left(\dfrac{m^2n}{ax^2}\right)\left(\dfrac{6x^3}{n}\right)}{\left(\dfrac{3mx}{2a}\right)}$

13. Factor the following expressions.
(a) $25x^2 + 10xy + 100y^2$ (b) $2ab - 2ac - bc + b^2$
(c) $4x^2 + 4x - 3$ (d) $4x^2 + 8ax + 4a^2 - 1$

14. Solve the following equations and inequalities.
(a) $\dfrac{3}{x} - 1 = \dfrac{2}{5x} - \dfrac{7}{3x}$ (b) $\dfrac{3x}{6 - x} = \dfrac{2 - 3x}{x}$
(c) $x^2 + 81 = 18x$ (d) $x^2 \leq 2x - 1$
(e) $\dfrac{x}{2 - x} \leq \dfrac{1}{x}$

15. Given that $x = \dfrac{5y - 4}{7}$ and $2y = 3x + 1$, find the truth set satisfying the conditions.

11
PROBLEM
SOLVING

11.1 PROBLEMS

Problem solving is very important in human affairs. Every decision, every prediction, every action represents a specific solution to some specific problem.

Even one-celled organisms must act in their immediate environment for survival. Primitive organisms solve survival problems automatically through the development of *biological mechanisms*. More complex organisms, such as animals, bring into play the factor of *memory*. Problems are attacked at random and success is based on a *trial and error* process. Although these problem solving processes may be adequate in a simple natural environment, they are woefully inadequate in the complex world of human society.

Man's modern civilization demands that the individual face and solve many difficult and perplexing problems. In order to find satisfactory solutions, the individual must learn the intellectual processes and principles which underly successful solutions as they have been slowly and painfully developed over the centuries. The distinct success which man has enjoyed has been due to his ability to communicate and transmit solutions and information concerning problems between individuals and between groups. In this way, the individual has had the advantage of having available a tremendous pooling of experience.

The distinctive quality of problem solving as practiced by man is in his use of symbolism and abstractions. For example, successful men, when aware of a particular problem, do not proceed at a biological or trial and error level. They hunt for specific data which can be abstracted from the problem situation. Data when available is interpreted and translated into meaningful symbolic expressions for solution. With the well regulated structures of symbols at his command, the expressions can be examined for symbolic solutions. When found, the solutions can be re-interpreted and applied as actions in the natural universe. In this intellectual problem-solving approach, there are three important elements: the natural universe, the symbol structure, and the interpreting organism called man.

In a simplified way we can detail the steps in a typical intellectual solution of a problem as follows:

(*a*) There is first an observation and awareness that a problem exists for the individual in the natural universe.

(*b*) Observations and measurements are made. Available records and data are collected.

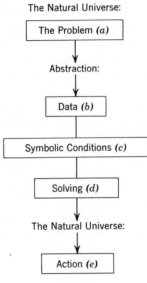

The Natural Universe:

The Problem (*a*)

Abstraction:

Data (*b*)

Symbolic Conditions (*c*)

Solving (*d*)

The Natural Universe:

Action (*e*)

FIGURE 48.

(*c*) The problem is formalized through interpretations. Symbolic expressions are formulated which describe the abstracted properties and characteristics of the problem.

(*d*) Now the symbolic "thinking tools" are brought into play. The symbolic expressions are solved to obtain symbolic solutions to the problem.

(*e*) Finally, the solutions are re-interpreted, tested, and verified. Appropriate actions are taken to eliminate the problem from the natural universe.

11.1.1 Mathematics as a language and reasoning tool is particularly well-suited for use in problem solving. It is a disciplined and exact process, concise and precise, with rules which, unlike the rules in most languages, are almost without exception. When a chain of reasoning is carried out mathematically, the reasoning can be sure and swift. In problem solving, mathematics is also an art characterized by its simplicity of form and expression. It is creative and imaginative, and as Bertrand Russell has remarked, "[it] possesses not only truth, but supreme beauty."

The eminent physicist, Lord Kelvin (1824–1907), asserted that "when you can measure what you are speaking about and express it in numbers, you know something about it."

The first step subsequent to becoming aware of a problem is to note that there are elements and objects which can be described in terms of their properties and characteristics. For example, a problem concerning people might be described by the physical characteristics, such as height, weight, age, etc., of the people involved, or by their qualitative characteristics, such as intelligence, social attitudes, personality, etc. In measurement, we are always referring to the measurement of properties and characteristics of objects and not to the objects themselves.

In order to abstract a numerical measurement of a property of an object, we must have available an **independent standard unit** of measurement of the property. For example, to measure the length of a pencil we might use a standard ruler with "inches" marked along its edge. A comparison of the marked property of the ruler with the property of length of the pencil enables us to abstract a numerical measure of the length of the pencil.

The origins of standard units of measure are deeply embedded in the cultural history of man. The common measurement of length called a "foot" possibly originated from the practice of using one's foot to measure the lengths of objects. The furlong possibly originated as the length of a furrow representing a half-day's work. Standard units of volume and of weight are ordinarily determined in terms of units of length and the volume of some common substance such as water. The need for uniformity and dependability of standard units led to standards such as the meter, originally defined as a ten-millionth of the distance from a pole of the earth to the equator. The metric system for lengths was then defined in terms of this standard meter length.

A uniform and dependable system of standard measurements in itself constitutes an important factor in the development of the culture and economy of a country. The increase in the effectiveness and power of the ancient Greeks may very well have been related to their adoption of uniform weights, measures, and money. Modern civilization is almost completely dependent upon accurate and precise measurements.

Although much has been done to attain accuracy, precision, and dependability in measurements, measurements are always subject to errors. By error we mean the difference between the numerical value of the measurement obtained and the "true" one. Errors are due to various causes which can conveniently be categorized into three types:

(A) By **systematic errors** we mean those errors due to:
    (1) the instrument used in making the measurement.
    (2) the unconscious habits of the person observing the measurement.
    (3) the conditions under which the measurement was made.
(B) By **random errors** we mean those errors due to:
    (1) the variations in an observer's estimate of the measurement.
    (2) the fluctuations in the physical environment.
    (3) the vagueness in the definitions of standard units.
(C) By **illegitimate errors** we mean those errors due to:
    (1) outright mistakes in observing instruments, making calculations, and in recording data.
    (2) the symbolic processes used in determining the numerical value of a measurement.
    (3) unreasonably poor conditions during the process of measurement.

Most, or even all, of the above kinds of errors are present in every measurement. When a measurement has small random errors, we say that the measurement is **precise** or has high precision. When a measurement has small systematic errors we say that the measurement is **accurate**. However, illegitimate errors are avoidable and should have no place in the statement of a measurement.

Although measurements are never "perfect" or "true," the abstracted numerical measures of the properties of objects in a problem represent the first step in the intellectual solution of a problem.

11.1.2 The usefulness of numerical measurements depends upon our ability to express and solve problems symbolically. Man in dealing with the natural universe has, through experiments and much observation, developed a large fund of knowledge concerning the relationships which hold in the universe. For example, Galileo, while at the University of Pisa in 1581, formulated the laws of the pendulum. It was Galileo who discovered the law of free falling bodies. There is also the story of the apple which fell on Isaac Newton's head and caused him to study the law of gravitation. Many of these discoveries and the relationships and rules which have been developed to describe them are available for use in the expression and solving of problems symbolically.

11.1.2.1 **Definition**: A **formula** is a rule, relation, or principle which is stated in mathematical symbols.

Frequently, solving problems becomes a relatively simple task when appropriate formulas are available. For convenience, a collection of the more commonly used formulas follow.

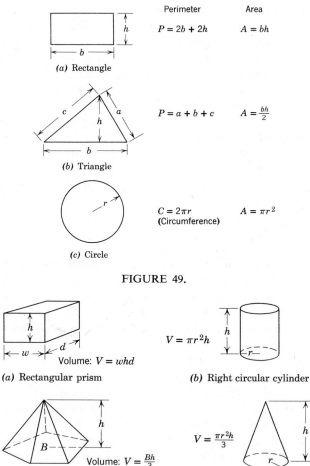

	Perimeter	Area
(a) Rectangle	$P = 2b + 2h$	$A = bh$
(b) Triangle	$P = a + b + c$	$A = \frac{bh}{2}$
(c) Circle	$C = 2\pi r$ (Circumference)	$A = \pi r^2$

FIGURE 49.

(a) Rectangular prism — Volume: $V = whd$

(b) Right circular cylinder — $V = \pi r^2 h$

(c) Pyramid — Volume: $V = \frac{Bh}{3}$

(d) Right circular cone — $V = \frac{\pi r^2 h}{3}$

FIGURE 50.

Formulas from physics:

(a) Ohm's law: $E = IR$ where E is the electromotive force in volts, I is the current in amperes, and R is the resistance in ohms.

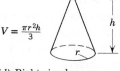

(b) Distance traveled: $d = rt$ where d is the distance, r is the rate, and t is the time. Note that the units may vary; e.g., miles, miles per hour, and hours; or feet, feet per second, and seconds.

(c) The lever principle: $w_1 d_1 = w_2 d_2$ where the distances are in the same units and the weights are in the same units.

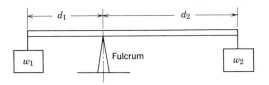

FIGURE 51.

(d) The focal length of a lens: $\dfrac{1}{f} = \dfrac{1}{p} + \dfrac{1}{q}$ where f is the focal length, p the object distance, and q the image distance.

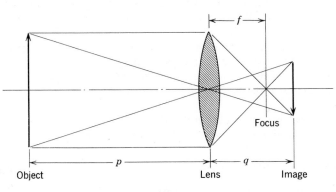

FIGURE 52.

(e) The gas laws: $\dfrac{V_1 P_1}{T_1} = \dfrac{V_2 P_2}{T_2}$ where V_1 and V_2 are the initial and terminal volumes, P_1 and P_2 are the initial and terminal pressures, and T_1 and T_2 are the initial and terminal temperatures.

(i) Charles' law (constant pressure): $\dfrac{V_1}{V_2} = \dfrac{T_1}{T_2}$

(ii) Boyle's law (constant temperature): $\dfrac{V_1}{V_2} = \dfrac{P_2}{P_1}$

Formulas from business and economics:

(a) Simple interest: $i = prt$ where i is the interest, p is the principal, r is the interest rate, and t is the time in years.

(b) The total amount available: $A = p + prt$ where the units are the same as in (a).

(c) Selling price: $S = c + p$ where c is the cost and p is the profit.

(d) The total amount available with interest compounded annually: $A = p(1 + r)^n$ where p is the principal, r is the interest rate, and n is the number of years.

Exercises 11.1

1. In the measurement of lengths, two common systems of units are used: the British and the metric.

(a) Construct tables describing the units used in each of these systems.

(b) Construct a table showing how to convert units in one system to units in the other.

2. Two important measurements are the measurement of the diameter or circumference of the earth and the velocity of light.

(a) The ancient Greeks measured the earth. Find reference sources describing these measurements and write a short essay on the methods used.

(b) Albert A. Michelson (1852–1931) used a revolving mirror to measure the velocity of light. Write a short essay on Michelson's method of measurement of the velocity of light.

3. Describe this text in terms of various measures of its properties and characteristics both physically and qualitatively.

4. Find and state formulas which describe the following:

(a) The distance a free-falling body falls due to the force of gravity in a given time.

(b) Newton's law of universal gravitation.

(c) The relationship between work, force, and distance.

11.2 SOLVING PROBLEMS

The most important single element in problem solving is the individual working on the problem. The secret of real success is the *confidence* and *desire* to succeed. One must try and try again, vary the methods and procedures, have brains and good luck. There are no infallible rules for solving problems.

Simple problems are often solved by recognition, recollection, or by an immediate insight into the problem. For more complex problems, it may be necessary to resort to lengthy study, planning, or discussion. Whatever the problem, the individual solving it gains in experience and has the satisfaction of discovery.

The individual's first step in solving a problem must be to get started, to determine what the problem is. As G. Polya states in his little volume *How To Solve It*, "It is foolish to answer a question that you do not understand. It is sad to work for an end that you do not desire." How do we start? Start by *reading* or *writing out* the problem. Explore and familiarize yourself with the problem. Visualize the problem. What are the parts? What data is given? What data is desired?

A useful habit is to *carefully organize* the problem. Neatness and clarity in our work will help us to focus on the problem. Give the problem a reference, a title. Build an outline of the problem with the given parts. Draw a diagram or figure, if possible. Symbolize the given data and restrictions. Give names to objects and their measurements. Introduce suitable notation. Good notation cannot be overemphasized; train yourself to symbolize carefully. Define your symbols. Proper notation should suggest the order and connections between the objects in the problem.

As an individual *develops a plan* for the solution of a problem, the need for additional data may suggest itself. Determine what is necessary for the solution of the problem. What calculations must be made? What formulas can be used? What constructions will be necessary? The way from understanding and organizing a problem to conceiving a plan for its solution may be a long and tortuous road. In fact, the main achievement may be to conceive the idea and to develop a plan for the solution of a problem. In developing a plan, we may repeatedly change our point of view, our way of looking at the problem. Our conceptions may be vague when we start, incomplete, confused. As progress is made, our outlook may change; we may progress from confusion to determination, from tentative hypotheses to definite actions and assertions, and finally from eagerness to jubilation and the satisfaction of solution and understanding.

The plan for solving a problem gives the general outlines for the calculations, procedures, and constructions necessary for the solving of the problem. We must now *carry out* the details of the plan. Examine each detail, put every item in its proper place. Do not forget our initial purpose: to specify the solution of the problem.

Once a solution has been obtained, we should *check* it, re-examine the method used in finding it. There is much more in our conception of a problem when we have solved it than when we began the problem. We should consolidate our gains, establish new insights, develop our ability to solve further problems.

11.2.1 In problem solving the individual should aim at mobilizing past experiences, formerly acquired knowledge. Good ideas and plans are based on past ideas, experiences, and recollection. However, memory alone is not enough. The "reasoning tools" must be used properly and effectively. We can do this by directing specific questions to ourselves. By using a well-structured procedure and careful organization in our work, we can minimize the chances of omissions and careless mistakes which may lead to illegitimate errors.

In simplified outline form, the following procedures suggest an individual's attack on any problem.

1. *Get started.* Become familiar with the problem.
   What are the parts?
   What is given?
   What is desired?
   What are the conditions?
   Are there restrictions?
   Can I find a formula?
   Can I draw a figure, a diagram?
2. *Organize. Develop a plan* for the solution of the problem.
   What type of problem is it?
   Is the available data suffiicent?
   Have I listed every item?
   Have I named all of the objects?
   Is the notation good?
   Do I understand all of the terms used?
   Can I combine parts?
   Can I simplify?
   What about supplementary data?
   Can I reorganize and restate the problem?
   Do I know a related problem?
   Can I divide the problem into two or more simpler problems?
   Can I generalize on the problem?
   Is there a special case for the problem?
3. *Act. Carry out* the plan.
   Be careful, patient.
   Work out the details.
   Check each step.
   Don't forget the plan.
   What is the solution?
   State and mark the solution to the problem.
4. *Check* the solution. Consolidate any gains in insight and experience.
   Good ideas are based on past ideas.
   Achievement grows with experience.
   Establish learning.

If we cannot solve a problem, we should not give up all hope. Failure can be a challenge. Begin with an easier problem. Build your strength in problem solving with practice and experience. Remember, success is not so much due to talent or opportunity as it is to concentration and perseverence. We build step by step, little by little, bit by bit to overcome

problems and obstacles. In the final analysis, one learns to solve problems by solving them.

11.2.2 Perhaps a few examples may help.

PROBLEM. The diameter of an automobile wheel is 32 inches. How
many revolutions does the wheel make in going 1 mile? If the auto is going
at a rate of 40 miles per hour, how many times does the wheel turn in 1
second?

Solution. What are the parts? What is given? What is desired? Can
we draw a figure? How many revolutions does the wheel make? In one
revolution, how far does the wheel travel? How "long" is a mile?

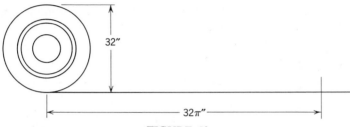

FIGURE 53.

Supplementary data, formulas:
$$C = 2\pi r$$
$$1 \text{ mile} = 5280 \text{ feet.}$$
$$1 \text{ foot} = 12 \text{ inches.}$$
$$1 \text{ hour} = 60 \text{ minutes.}$$
$$1 \text{ minute} = 60 \text{ seconds.}$$

Work. $C = 32\pi = 32\left(\dfrac{22}{7}\right) = 100.57'' = 8.38'$, approximately.   5280
divided by 8.38 is approximately 630. The wheel makes approximately
630 revolutions in one mile.

Work. 40 miles per hour is $\frac{2}{3}$ miles per minute or $\frac{2}{3}$(5280) feet per
minute. 3520 feet per minute is at the rate of 58.66 feet per second. 58.66
divided by 8.38 is 7. At 40 miles per hour the wheel turns 7 times in 1
second.

Answer. The wheel makes approximately *630 revolutions* in 1 mile. At
40 miles per hour the wheel turns *7 times* in 1 second.

Note the questions, the figure, the formulas, the work, the stating of the
solutions.

PROBLEM. If $\frac{4}{5}$ bushel of grain occupies 1 cubic foot, how many bushels
of grain can be stored in a bin 4 feet by 6 feet by 8 feet?

Solution. What is given? What is desired? What is the relation of the grain to the bin? How many cubic feet of volume does the bin have available?

Formula. $V = whd$

Work. $V = 4 \times 6 \times 8 = 192$ cubic feet. $(\frac{4}{5})(192) = 153.6$ bushels of grain will occupy the 192 cubic feet in the bin.

Answer. *153.6 bushels* of grain can be stored in the bin.

PROBLEM. A man who weighs 150 pounds wishes to balance himself and a rock weighing 500 pounds on an 8-foot long lever. If the man and the rock are at the extreme ends of the lever, where should the fulcrum of the lever be placed in order that the two are balanced?

Solution. What are the parts? How are they related? What is desired? What is the fulcrum? Can we draw a figure?

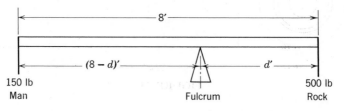

FIGURE 54.

A fulcrum is the support or point of support on which a lever turns in raising or moving something. When the lever is balanced, the lever equation must be true.

Formula. $w_1 d_1 = w_2 d_2$

Work. $(150)(8 - d) = (500)(d)$, $1200 - 150d = 500d$, and $d = 1.846$ approximately.

Answer. The fulcrum should be placed *1.846 feet* from the rock to balance the lever.

Check the solution again in the formula. Note the definition and the possible two choices of distances as answers. Does the figure help?

PROBLEM. A man invested part of $12,000 at 4% interest and the rest at 3% interest. The annual income from the 3% investment was $80 more than the income from the 4% investment. How much did he invest at each rate?

Solution. What are the parts? What is given? Will a table help? What are the relationships? What parts should we name?

Formula. $i = prt$ where p is investment, r is rate, i is income, and t equals 1 since this is an annual period.

TABLE 41

Investments		Rate	Income
First:	x	4%	y
Second:	$\$12{,}000 - x$	3%	$y + \$80$

Work. $4\% = .04$ and $3\% = .03$ so that $y = .04x$ and $y + 80 = .03(12{,}000 - x) = 360 - .03x$. Combining, we have $.04x + 80 = 360 - .03x$. Since $.07x = 280$, $x = 4{,}000$ and $12{,}000 - x = 8{,}000$.

Answer. The man invested *$4,000 at 4%* interest and *$8,000 at 3%* interest.

Check. $.04(4{,}000) = 160$ and $.03(8{,}000) = 240$. $4{,}000 + 8{,}000 = 12{,}000$.

Note the importance of proper naming of unknown quantities. The tabulation of information is very helpful as well.

PROBLEM. Two ships leave the same harbor 1 hour apart. The first ship steams due north at 10 miles per hour and the later ship moves due west at 15 miles per hour. How far apart will they be 3 hours after the second ship leaves the harbor?

Solution. Read the problem over and rephrase. There are two ships traveling at two rates and going in two directions. How far apart will they be? How far has each ship gone? How do we measure the distance between the ships? Can we form a table? Can we draw a figure?

TABLE 42

Ship	Rate	Direction	Distance	At $t = 3$
A	10	North	$d_1 = 10t + 10$	40
B	15	West	$d_2 = 15t$	45

Formulas. $d = rt$ for the distances the ships travel. $d^2 = d_1{}^2 + d_2{}^2$ for the distance between the two ships.

Figure 55 shows both the time and distances traveled by the two ships. The right triangle suggests Pythagoras's very useful formula.

Work. $d^2 = (40)^2 + (45)^2 = 1600 + 2025 = 3625$.

$$d = \sqrt{3625} = 60.21 \text{ approximately.}$$

Answer. Three hours after the second ship leaves the harbor, the ships will be approximately *60.21 miles apart.*

Review the problem. Check the answer.

PROBLEM. The sum of ten consecutive odd numbers is 220. Find the first and last members of the set.

Solution. What is the first number? Name it! Let n be the name of the first number. The second number must be $n + 2$. The third $n + 4$.

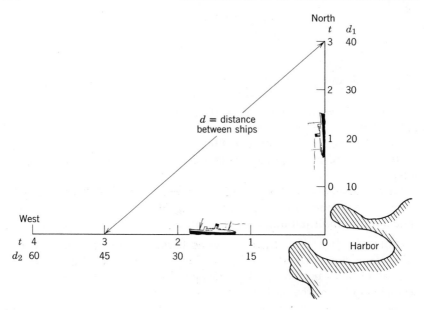

FIGURE 55.

Can we find a general name for the kth number in the set? How many two's must be added to the kth number? The second number has 1 two added. The third has 2 two's added. There must be $k - 1$ two's added to the kth number. Thus the kth number must be $n + 2(k - 1)$.

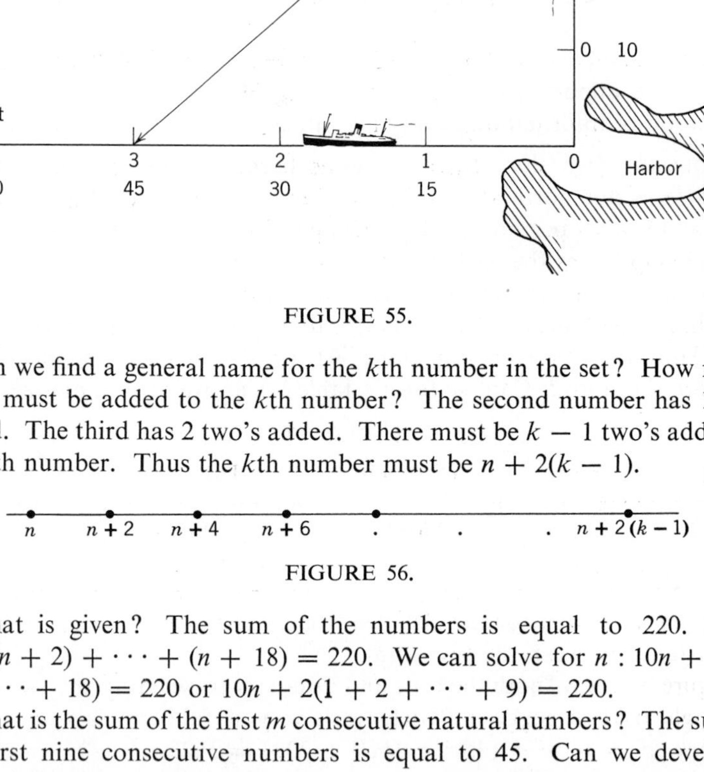

FIGURE 56.

What is given? The sum of the numbers is equal to 220. Then $n + (n + 2) + \cdots + (n + 18) = 220$. We can solve for n: $10n + (2 + 4 + \cdots + 18) = 220$ or $10n + 2(1 + 2 + \cdots + 9) = 220$.

What is the sum of the first m consecutive natural numbers? The sum of the first nine consecutive numbers is equal to 45. Can we develop a general formula for the sum of m consecutive natural numbers? What will the sum look like? "Turn" the sum "around."

$$S = 1 + 2 + 3 + 4 + \cdots + m.$$
$$S = m + (m - 1) + (m - 2) + \cdots + 1.$$

Look at the vertical arrangement of terms in the sums. The first pair of terms is equal to $m + 1$, the second $(m - 1) + 2$, the third $(m - 2) + 3$, etc. Each pair of terms has $m + 1$ as their sum. How many pairs are there? Adding, we have $2S = m(m + 1)$. The sum of the first m consecutive natural numbers is equal to $S = \dfrac{m(m + 1)}{2}$. For $m = 9$, we have $S = \dfrac{9(9 + 1)}{2} = 45$.

Returning to our problem, we have $10n + 2(45) = 220$, $10n = 130$, and $n = 13$.

Answer. The *first number* in the set is 13. The *tenth number* is $13 + 18 = 31$.

Checking. $13 + 15 + \cdots + 29 + 31 = 220$.

Review this problem. How many new ideas does it suggest? Note the notation. Is mathematical induction suggested in the proof of formulas? The auxiliary problem of finding the sum of the first m consecutive natural numbers is interesting. What variations to the problem are suggested? The problem might be written out briefly as follows:

PROBLEM RESTATED. The sum of ten consecutive odd numbers is 220. Find the first and last members of the set.

Work. Let n be the first number, then $n + (n + 2) + \cdots + (n + 18) = 220$.

$$10n + (2 + 4 + \cdots + 18) = 220.$$
$$10n + 90 = 220$$
$$10n \quad\;\; = 130$$
$$n \quad\;\; = 13$$

Answer. The first number is 13, the last 31.

Check. $13 + 15 + 17 + 19 + 21 + 23 + 25 + 27 + 29 + 31 = 220$ is true.

PROBLEM. Two gears have 48 and 15 teeth, respectively. If two particular teeth on the gears are meshed, how many complete revolutions must the smaller gear make before the same two teeth can mesh together again?

Solution. Draw a diagram. Visualize the gears turning, the teeth of the gears meshing. Give the parts names. Describe the action taking place.

As the gears turn, the teeth are mated by number. A complete revolution of the smaller gear is equivalent to "moving" through 15 numbered positions. The tooth numbered 0 or 15 on the small gear must be mated with the tooth numbered 0 or 48 on the large gear. That is, some exact number of revolutions, say n, of the small gear must result in an exact number of turns, say m, of the large gear. How can we describe this matching? We must set $15n = 48m$, where n and m are positive integers.

Can we form a table?

TABLE 43

n:	1	2	3	4	5	6	7	8	9
m:	$\frac{5}{16}$	$\frac{5}{8}$	$\frac{15}{16}$	$\frac{5}{4}$	$\frac{25}{16}$	$\frac{15}{8}$	$\frac{35}{16}$	$\frac{5}{2}$	$\frac{45}{16}$

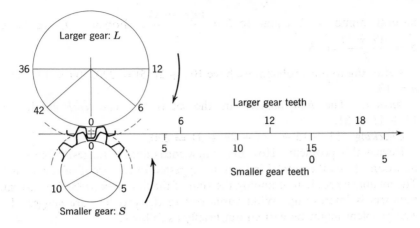

FIGURE 57.

We note that every 4 revolutions of the small gear results in $\frac{5}{4}$ revolutions of the large gear. Four of these groups of 4 revolutions of the small gear must then result in 5 revolutions of the large gear. That is, 16 revolutions of the small gear result in 5 revolutions of the large gear.

Note that $15n = 48m$ can be written $5n = 16m$. Since 5 and 16 have no common divisors, n must be a multiple of 16 and m a multiple of 5. The smallest such multiples are 16 and 5.

Answer. The small gear completes 16 *revolutions* and the large gear 5.
Check. $(15)(16) = (48)(5)$.

Is there a comparable situation in the rotation of the hour and minute hands of a clock? Is it possible to describe the relative positions of the planets in the above way? In an auto, if we were to mark the positions of a piston and a wheel, could we compare their relative positions to each other? Note the "cyclic" or repetitious nature of the numbers in the problem.

Exercises 11.2

Develop and solve the following problems, using the general four-step "self-questioning" method.

1. Find the cross sectional area of the I-beam shown in Figure 58.
2. If the beam of Figure 58 is 6 feet long and weighs 150 pounds per cubic foot, what is the total weight of the beam?
3. Electric power is measured in watts, $W = EI$ where E is the potential in volts and I the current in amperes. Find the resistance R in ohms of a 150-watt light bulb when connected to a constant 110-volt source.
4. A man starts walking directly away from point A at 2 miles per hour. A second person wishes to intercept the man by traveling along a semicircular route that has the first man's route as a diameter. How rapidly must the

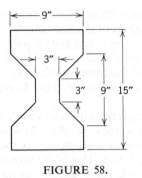

FIGURE 58.

second person walk the semicircular route? At what points can the second man intercept the first?

5. A man had a net income of $8,500 before taxes. The federal tax was 22% of the first $4,000 and 40% of the remainder, after state taxes had been deducted. The state tax was 16% of the remainder from $8,500 after the federal taxes were deducted. Find the federal and state taxes paid.

Exercises 11

1. A trapezoid is a plane figure that has four sides, two of which are parallel. Find formulas for the area and perimeter of a trapezoid.

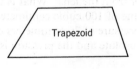

FIGURE 59.

2. A regular tetrahedron is a triangular pyramid whose faces are all equilateral triangles. If an edge of a regular tetrahedron is $2\sqrt{3}$ inches, find the volume and total surface area of the tetrahedron. If the tetrahedron is inscribed in a right circular cone, find the difference in their volumes. *Hint:* Look up the terms in an appropriate source.

3. An airplane on patrol can fly at 450 miles per hour for a maximum of 6 hours. What is the aircraft's extreme "radius of action," that is, the farthest it can fly and return to its base on a direct route? What is the total area of "coverage" of the aircraft on repeated patrols?

4. A rectangle is twice as long as it is wide. If the length and width of the rectangle are each increased by 2 inches, the area of the rectangle is increased by 52 square inches. Find the original dimensions of the rectangle.

5. An ant is located 2 feet from the end and 2 feet from the floor on the wall of a room 10 feet wide, 12 feet long, and with a ceiling 9 feet high. The ant

wishes to crawl along the walls and ceiling of the room to a point 1 foot from the other end and 2 feet from the floor on the opposite wall of the room. If the ant crawls in a "straight" line and his path includes part of the ceiling, what is the shortest path that he can crawl to reach the other point?

6. A 100-pound weight is 6 feet from the fulcrum of a lever. Another weight is 4 feet on the other side of the fulcrum. How heavy is the weight if the lever is balanced?

7. A 10-pound weight is 2 feet from the fulcrum of a lever. A 6-pound weight is 3 feet from the fulcrum on the other side. At what point on the lever must a 2-pound weight be placed in order to balance the lever?

8. A man made two investments. One of the investments was $600 more than the other. The two investments together amounted to $3,000. Find the amount of each investment.

9. A theater charged $1.50 for adults and $0.90 for students and children. A total of $385.50 was collected at a matinee performance for which 313 tickets were sold. How many adults attended the matinee?

10. Two resistances of 12 and 16 ohms, respectively, are connected in parallel in an electrical circuit. If the total resistance R is given by the formula $\frac{1}{R} = \frac{1}{R_1} + \frac{1}{R_2}$ for R_1 and R_2 resistances in parallel, find the total resistance of the electrical circuit.

11. A lens is placed at a distance of 3.2 feet from a burning candle, with the axis directed toward the candle. An image of the candle is produced on a screen at a distance of 8.5 feet from the lens. What is the focal length of the lens?

12. A gas occupies a volume of 100 cubic centimeters at a temperature of 273° absolute and under a pressure of 76 centimeters of mercury. If the temperature is raised to 373° absolute and the pressure is doubled, what volume will the gas occupy?

13. Find a formula for the sum of the squares of the first n natural numbers. *Hint:* form the ratio of the sum of squares to the sum of the first n natural numbers.

14. Prove that the sum of the first n cubes of the natural numbers is equal to the square of the sum of the first n natural numbers.

15. The second, minute, and hour hands of a clock almost coincide each hour. Find the time to within 1 second at which the hands almost coincide between 9:00 and 10:00 A.M. How long will it be before they "pass" each other again?

12
RELATIONS

12.1 RELATIONS

In Chapter 8 we defined the notions of **ordered pairs** and **cartesian product sets** (8.2.1). For our present purposes, we assume these notions. Along with the ideas of sets and elements, we will extend the applications of ordered pairs and cartesian product sets.

The use of the term "relation" to indicate a form of connection between two or more objects is common in our everyday vocabulary. For example, phrases such as "is above," "is the father of," "comes before," etc., all suggest the notion of a relation between things. In mathematics, the term "relation" is made precise; it is used to refer to subsets of ordered pairs.

If we form the cartesian product of two sets A and B, we can consider many subsets of $A \times B$. Such a subset defines a connection between the first elements from A and second elements from B. In mathematics, any such collection of ordered pairs is said to form a **relation**.

For example, consider the sets $A = \{a, b, c\}$ and $B = \{p, q, r\}$. Forming $A \times B = \{(a,p), (a,q), \cdots, (c,r)\}$ we can select a subset, say $R = \{(a,q), (b,p), (b,r), (c,q)\}$. The set R is then called a relation on $A \times B$. A point set representation can be drawn to illustrate and study the relation.

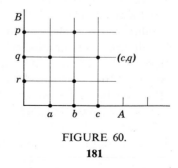

FIGURE 60.

12.1.0.1 Definition: If A and B are sets, then by a **relation** on the cartesian product set $A \times B$ we mean a condition R on $(x,y) \in A \times B$. A relation on $A \times B$ is thus a subset of $A \times B$.

12.1.1 Since point set representations or **graphs** of relations are useful and convenient in the study of relations, we will examine their construction in somewhat more detail. If A and B are given sets, we can construct their individual point set representations perpendicular to each other. If light guide lines are drawn through the points of the representations parallel to the given sets, their intersections form a "grid" of points. These points can be thought of as representing the ordered pairs belonging to the cartesian product set. Conventionally, the first elements of ordered pairs are taken to refer to the elements of the horizontal point set and the second elements to the vertical set. A relation is then displayed by darkening those points of intersection which belong to the relation.

For our example, the cartesian product set consists of the nine points of intersection of the guide lines. The relation is displayed by the darkened points of intersection. The ordered pair (c,q) represents the point such that $c \in A$ and $q \in B$; c is directly above $c \in A$ on the horizontal point set representation of A and q is directly across from $q \in B$.

If $A = \{1, 2, 3, 4, 5\}$ and $B = \{1, 2, 3, 4, 5\}$, various relations on $A \times B$ can be described as in Figure 61.

The elements of ordered pairs are called **coordinates**. For the ordered pair (2,5), $2 \in A$ is called the "A coordinate of the point (2,5)." Also $5 \in B$ is called the "B coordinate of (2,5)." The point set representations of the sets A and B are called the "**A and B axes.**"

12.1.2 Relations are defined by **conditions on ordered pairs.** Given a cartesian product set, relations are specified by using the set-builder notation $\{(x,y) \mid y \mathrel{R} x\}$ where $y \mathrel{R} x$ is a conditional statement in the two variables x and y. When the set $A \times B$ is clearly understood, we write the condition $y \mathrel{R} x$ by itself. The set R is formed by the set of ordered pairs which make $y \mathrel{R} x$ true. That is, R consists of those ordered pairs in $A \times B$ which **satisfy** $y \mathrel{R} x$. We say that the set R is the **solution set** for $y \mathrel{R} x$, that is, the truth set for the condition.

We often speak of a "**value of a variable**," meaning an element of the set to which the variable belongs. In examining relations and conditions we often list specific values of the variables involved. For example, for $R = \{(x,y) \mid x > y\}$ in Figure 61(d), we can check to see whether the ordered pair (5,3) is in R or not by noting whether $5 > 3$ is true or not. Since the condition is true, we conclude that $(5,3) \in R$. The ordered pair (3,5), however, is not in R since $3 > 5$ is false.

In constructing graphs of relations, the above technique can be used

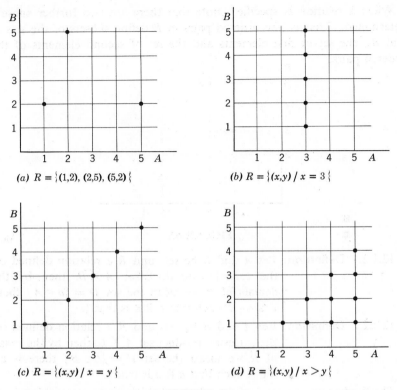

(a) $R = \{(1,2), (2,5), (5,2)\}$

(b) $R = \{(x,y) \mid x = 3\}$

(c) $R = \{(x,y) \mid x = y\}$

(d) $R = \{(x,y) \mid x > y\}$

FIGURE 61.

to form a table of ordered pairs which satisfy the conditions. We do this by selecting convenient values of x or of y and solve the resulting conditional statement for the other variable.

Suppose $A = B = \{1, 2, 3, 4, 5\}$ and we are given the relation $R = \{(x,y) \mid y = 2x - 1\}$ to graph. We can successively choose the values 1, 2, and 3 for x. These values result in 1, 3, and 5 for y, respectively. When we choose $x = 4$, we obtain $y = 7$ which is not in B. We might try $y = 2$, but then we obtain $x = \frac{3}{2}$ which is not in A. The three ordered pairs which we have found can be used to facilitate the construction of the graph of R.

TABLE 44

x	y
1	1
2	3
3	5
4	–

When a relation is specified, note that there are two further subsets determined. That is, the ordered pairs in R define subsets of the sets A and B: the set of first elements and the set of second elements of the ordered pairs.

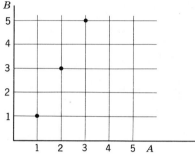

FIGURE 62.

12.1.2.1 Definition: Let A and B be sets and R a relation defined on the cartesian product set $A \times B$, then by the **domain of R** we mean the set $D = \{a \in A \mid$ there is a $b \in B$ such that $b \, R \, a$ is true.$\}$.

12.1.2.2 Definition: Let A and B be sets and R a relation defined on the cartesian product set $A \times B$, then by the **range of R** we mean the set $H = \{b \in B \mid$ there is an $a \in A$ such that $b \, R \, a$ is true.$\}$.

The domains and ranges of the relations which we have considered are noted as follows:

(i) Figure 60:	$D = \{a, b, c\}$,	$H = \{p, q, r\}$.
(ii) Figure 61(a):	$D = \{1, 2, 5\}$,	$H = \{2, 5\}$.
(iii) Figure 61(b):	$D = \{3\}$,	$H = \{1, 2, 3, 4, 5\}$.
(iv) Figure 61(c):	$D = \{1, 2, 3, 4, 5\}$,	$H = \{1, 2, 3, 4, 5\}$.
(v) Figure 61(d):	$D = \{2, 3, 4, 5\}$,	$H = \{1, 2, 3, 4\}$.
(vi) Figure 62:	$D = \{1, 2, 3\}$,	$H = \{1, 3, 5\}$.

12.1.3 Since relations on a cartesian product set $A \times B$ are subsets of $A \times B$, they have all the properties of subsets.

1. If R_1 and R_2 are relations on $A \times B$, then $R_1 \subset R_2$ means that whenever $b \, R_1 \, a$ then we have $b \, R_2 \, a$ for $a \in A$ and $b \in B$.
2. $R_1 \cup R_2$ is the relation containing the set of all ordered pairs in R_1 or R_2, that is, if $(a,b) \in R$ then $(a,b) \in R_1$ or $(a,b) \in R_2$.
3. $R_1 \cap R_2$ is the relation containing only those ordered pairs in both R_1 and R_2.
4. The complement of a relation R can be denoted by $\bar{R}$. $\bar{R}$ is the set of all ordered pairs in $A \times B$ and *not* in R.

Although relations always occur in connection with elements, we can consider the properties of relations independently of the elements. Recall our discussion of sets as compared to the structure of elements in sets. Among the set of all possible relations which can be defined on a given cartesian product set $A \times B$, there are certain special relations which should be noted.

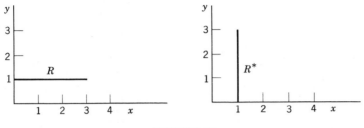

FIGURE 63.

The relation U consisting of all the ordered pairs in a cartesian product set $A \times B$ is called the **universal relation** on $A \times B$. The relation consisting of the empty subset of $A \times B$ is called the **empty** or **absurd relation** on $A \times B$. If $A = B$, the relation $E = \{(x,y) \mid x = y\}$ is called the **identity relation** on $A \times A$. For example, Figure 61(c) illustrates the identity relation for the set $A \times A$ where $A = \{1, 2, 3, 4, 5\}$.

If R is a relation on $A \times B$, we can form the subset of $B \times A$, consisting of those ordered pairs (b,a) such that $b\,R\,a$ is true. That is, if $R = \{(x,y) \mid y\,R\,x\}$, then we can form $R^* = \{(y,x) \mid y\,R\,x\}$. The relation R^* is called the **transpose** or **inverse relation** of R. For example, on the cartesian product set of real numbers to real numbers, the transpose of $R = \{y = 1 \text{ and } 0 \leq x \leq 3\}$ is $R^* = \{x = 1 \text{ and } 0 \leq y \leq 3\}$.

Three important and common properties of relations are described by the terms **symmetric**, **reflexive**, and **transitive**.

12.1.3.1 Definition: If a relation $R = R^*$, the transpose relation, then the relation is said to be **symmetric**.

12.1.3.2 Definition: If $A = B$ and R is a relation on $A \times A$, then we say that R is **reflexive** if the identity relation is a subset of R: $E \subset R$.

12.1.3.3 Definition: If R is a relation on $A \times A$, R is said to be **transitive** if whenever $b\,R\,a$ and $c\,R\,b$ we have $c\,R\,a$.

If a relation has all three of the above properties, it is said to be an **equivalence** or **congruence relation**. The identity relation is clearly an equivalence relation.

Exercises 12.1

1. Given the following graphs of relations:

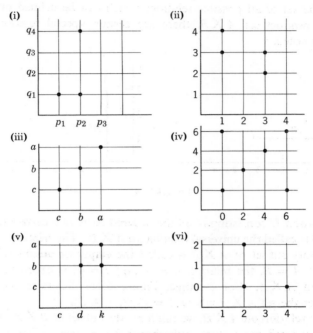

FIGURE 64.

(*a*) List the ordered pairs belonging to each relation.

(*b*) Specify the domain and range of each relation.

(*c*) If it applies, state whether each of the relations is symmetric, reflexive, and/or transitive.

2. If $A = \{1, 2, 3, 4, 5, 6\}$ and $B = \{1, 2, 3, 4, 5, 6\}$, then graph the relations specified by the following:

(*a*) $R_1 = \{(1,4), (2,3), (2,5), (4,1), (6,2)\}$.

(*b*) $R_2 = \{(1,4), (2,6), (3,2), (4,1), (5,2)\}$.

(*c*) $R_3 = \{y = 2x - 3\}$.

(*d*) $R_4 = \{y \leq x\}$.

(*e*) $R_5 = \{y = x \text{ or } y = 3\}$.

(*f*) $R_6 = \{y = 3 \text{ and } x > y\}$.

(*g*) $R_7 = R_1 \cup R_2$.

(*h*) $R_8 = R_1 \cap R_2$.

3. (*a*) Specify the domain and range of each of the relations of exercise 2 above.

(*b*) Discuss each of the relations of exercise 2 with respect to the symmetric, reflexive, and transitive properties of relations.

12.2   COORDINATE SYSTEM

The most common sets A and B which are used to define the cartesian product sets on which relations are specified are sets of real numbers. For what follows, we will, for convenience, understand that the underlying sets are sets of real numbers (unless otherwise indicated). Relations defined on cartesian product sets of reals to reals are called **real relations**.

12.2.1   Graphs of real relations are of special interest in mathematics. A graph first begins with the construction of two real number lines perpendicular to each other. The intersection of the number lines is used to indicate

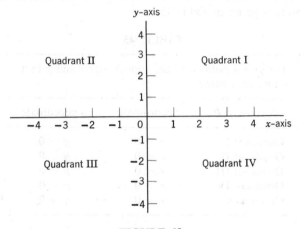

FIGURE 65.

a common "zero" point for the two sets. This "zero" point is called the **origin** of the graph. The set of first elements of ordered pairs is taken conventionally as referring to the set represented horizontally. This set is called the **x-axis** and values on this set are called "x values." The vertical set is called the **y-axis** and the values on this set are called "y values." The unit point on the x-axis is taken to the right and thus the positive numbers extend to the right and the negative numbers to the left. The unit point on the y-axis is taken above the origin with the positive values extending up the line. The two axes are called the **coordinate axes**. The coordinate axes divide the total plane area into four parts. These parts are called **quadrants**. The quadrants are numbered in counterclockwise order.

To every ordered pair (x,y) of real numbers we can associate a point in the plane. First locate the element x along the x-axis and construct a vertical guide line through this point. Next locate the y value along the

y-axis and construct a guide line horizontally through this point. The vertical and horizontal guide lines will intersect in a point, say P. The point P is then associated with the ordered pair (x,y).

The numbers x and y are called the **"x and y coordinates"** of the point P respectively. We write $P(x,y)$ meaning "the point P with the coordinates x and y." By reversing the above procedure, we can associate an ordered pair (x,y) to every point on the plane. This identification of points in the plane with ordered pairs of real numbers is said to define a **coordinate system** and the plane is then called a **coordinate plane**.

The set of all points in a coordinate plane can be conveniently separated into five disjoint subsets. The relationship of the coordinates in the disjoint subsets is given in Table 45.

TABLE 45

$P(x,y)$ is a point with the coordinates x and y in a coordinate plane.

Location of P	x coordinate		y coordinate
Quadrant I	$x > 0$		$y > 0$
Quadrant II	$x < 0$		$y > 0$
Quadrant III	$x < 0$		$y < 0$
Quadrant IV	$x > 0$		$y < 0$
On an axis	$x = 0$	*or*	$y = 0$

We speak of **the graph** of a point $P(x,y)$, meaning the point representing the ordered pair (x,y). We also speak of **graphing** a point $Q(x,y)$, meaning to construct and locate the point Q on a coordinate system.

The idea and use of coordinates dates back to the ancient Egyptians. The Greeks and Romans used coordinates in map making and surveying. However, the significance of the idea as associated with number sets was not realized until Descartes developed the concept during the seventeenth century. The importance of the interpretation of a coordinate system lies in the fact that it enables us to translate many geometric notions into algebraic statements and vice versa.

12.2.2 We have noted that the notion of length or distance is of fundamental importance in the measurement of objects in the natural universe. Using Pythagoras's relationship between the sides of a right triangle, we can establish a general formula for the numerical distance between two points on a coordinate plane.

Let $P(x_1,y_1)$ and $Q(x_2,y_2)$ be two given points on a (cartesian) coordinate plane. Construct perpendiculars to the axes from the points P and Q

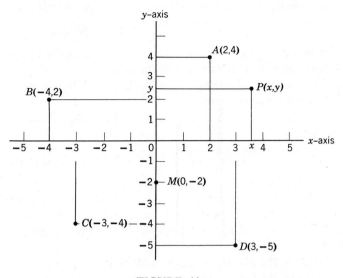

FIGURE 66.

so that a right triangle is formed with P, Q, and $R(x_2, y_1)$ as vertices. By comparing directly with the axes, we note that the numerical lengths of PR and QR can be described by the differences $x_2 - x_1$ and $y_2 - y_1$, respectively. For the moment, let us ignore the sign of the differences.

If we denote the length of PQ by d, we have:

$$d^2 = (x_2 - x_1)^2 + (y_2 - y_1)^2$$

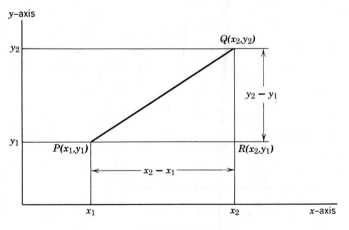

FIGURE 67.

We define the positive numerical length of the segment PQ to be equal to:

$$d = \sqrt{(x_2 - x_1)^2 + (y_2 - y_1)^2}$$

By convention, we can take the square root to mean the positive square root unless otherwise specified. Since the differences $x_2 - x_1$ and $y_2 - y_1$ are always squared, they appear as positive quantities irrespective of the sign of the original differences.

For example, if $A(4,3)$ and $B(-1,5)$, we can compute the numerical length of AB:

$$AB = \sqrt{(-1 - 4)^2 + (5 - 3)^2} = \sqrt{29} = 5.385 \text{ units approximately.}$$

Many problems can be described and solved by using the distance formula. For example, consider the points $A(4,3)$, $B(-1,5)$, $C(-3,-2)$, and $D(3,-2)$. The four points determine a four-sided figure called a quadrilateral. Let us find the perimeter of the quadrilateral $ABCD$ in Figure 68.

After labeling the given points, we note that the perimeter is the sum of the lengths of the sides. Applying the distance formula, we have:

$AB = 5.385$ units approximately.
$CD = 6.0$ units by direct comparison with the x-axis.
$BC = \sqrt{(-2)^2 + (-7)^2} = \sqrt{53} = 7.280$ units approximately.
$DA = \sqrt{(1)^2 + (5)^2} = \sqrt{26} = 5.099$ units approximately.

Adding the four lengths, we have: The perimeter is approximately *23.764 units.*

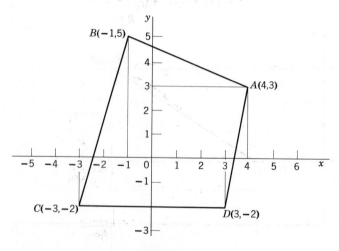

FIGURE 68.

Exercises 12.2

1. Given that the points $D(-4,0)$, $E(3,-3)$, and $F(5,4)$, determine a triangle on a coordinate system, sketch a figure of the triangle on the coordinate plane. Find its perimeter and area.

2. In Figure 68, the *midpoint* of side AB has the coordinates $K(\frac{3}{2},4)$. Find the midpoints L, M, and N of the sides BC, CD, and DA, respectively.

3. The midpoints K, L, M, and N of exercise 2, referring to Figure 68, form a quadrilateral $KLMN$. Describe this quadrilateral. Experiment with quadrilaterals formed in this way. Can you state and prove a general theorem for this situation?

4. Find a formula for the area of any triangle with vertices $A(x_1,y_1)$, $B(x_2,y_2)$, and $C(x_3,y_3)$ on a coordinate system.

12.3   EXAMPLES, LOCUS

Now that we have developed tools for the discussion of relations, let us examine some varied examples. We will list a few ordered pairs that satisfy the relation, specify the domain and range, and graph the relation. In addition, we will direct our attention to one or more of the interesting properties of the relation.

EXAMPLE 1. $R = \{(x,y) \mid y = 2 - x \text{ for } -1 \leq x \leq 3\}$.

Note that the relation specifies only certain values of x. Selecting values of x in the interval $-1 \leq x \leq 3$, we can obtain values of y such that

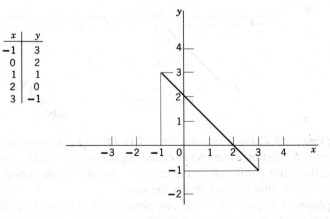

x	y
-1	3
0	2
1	1
2	0
3	-1

FIGURE 69.

$y = 2 - x$. Once we have a table of ordered pairs satisfying the relation, we can proceed to graph the points listed. When we have graphed a sufficient number of points to indicate a definite pattern, we can attempt to generalize the process and complete the graph. From our observations, we can then determine the domain and range of the relation.

The five points appear along a line segment. If we consider any value of x in the given interval, we find that the value of y will be such as to name a point on this segment joining $(-1,3)$ to $(3,-1)$. Since all of the possible values of x and y which satisfy the relation are included in the graph, the graph is complete and shows the entire set of ordered pairs satisfying the relation. By inspection, the domain is the closed interval $-1 \leq x \leq 3$ and the range is the closed interval $-1 \leq y \leq 3$. Finally, we note that this relation is symmetric.

EXAMPLE 2. $R = \{y = x\}$.

This is the identity relation which is symmetric, reflexive, and transitive. Constructing a table of ordered pairs, we can easily graph the relation.

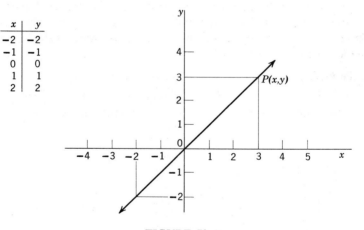

x	y
-2	-2
-1	-1
0	0
1	1
2	2

FIGURE 70.

The points fall along a straight line. Let $P(x,y)$ be a point on the line, then, since the distances to the axes are equal, we will have $y = x$. But if $y = x$, the point P will satisfy the relation. Similarly, any point in R will satisfy $y = x$ so that it must be on the line.

The graph of Figure 70 is not complete as in example (1). We could choose larger or smaller values of x and obtain ordered pairs which satisfy $y = x$ not shown on Figure 70. Since any value of x is permissible and results in a value of y, we conclude that the domain consists of the set of all real numbers. It is clear that the range set must also be a set of all real numbers.

EXAMPLE 3. $R = \{-1 \le y \le 1\}$.

The condition does not mention any restriction on x. That is, the x and y values are in a sense "free" of each other. In specifying relations, if either of the variables is not mentioned, it is conventionally understood to mean that the variable not mentioned may take on any real value. The domain of this relation is thus the set of all real numbers. The range is the closed interval $-1 \le y \le 1$. The graph appears as a solid "band"or "strip" which extends to the right and to the left. The relation is not symmetric, reflexive, or transitive.

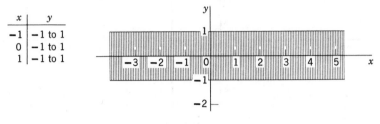

x	y
-1	-1 to 1
0	-1 to 1
1	-1 to 1

FIGURE 71.

EXAMPLE 4. $R = \{-2 \le y \le 2x - 1 \text{ and } -1 \le x \le 2\}$.

For $x = -1$ we have $-2 \le y \le -3$ which is impossible. Note that when $2x - 1 = -2$, the value of y must be -2. Solving for x in $2x - 1 = -2$, we obtain $x = -\frac{1}{2}$. For values of x between $-\frac{1}{2}$ and 2 we obtain intervals of y values. Graphing the relation, we note that the domain is the closed set $-\frac{1}{2} \le x \le 2$ and the range is $-2 \le y \le 3$. The relation is the set of all ordered pairs (points) in and on the boundary of the triangle.

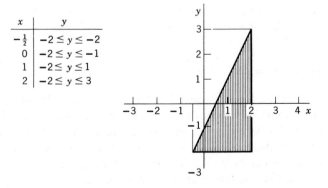

x	y
$-\frac{1}{2}$	$-2 \le y \le -2$
0	$-2 \le y \le -1$
1	$-2 \le y \le 1$
2	$-2 \le y \le 3$

FIGURE 72.

EXAMPLE 5. $R = \{y = 3 \text{ or } x = 2\}$.

Since the connective "or" is defined to mean that one or the other or both conditions are true, we have the two straight lines as shown on the graph. The domain and range sets are both sets of real numbers

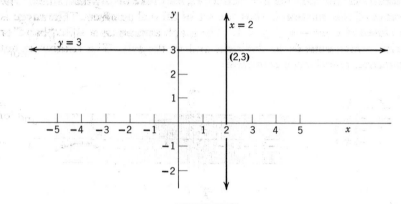

FIGURE 73.

Since a relation is a set, we can separate the relation into convenient subsets. Let $R = R_1 \cup R_2$ where $R_1 = \{y = 3\}$ and $R_2 = \{x = 2\}$. Note that we can form $R_1 \cap R_2 = \{(2,3)\}$. The intersection of two relations is often of interest and is referred to as a **"simultaneous solution"** of the given relations.

TABLE 46

Relation	Domain	Range
R_1	real numbers	3
R_2	2	real numbers
$R_1 \cup R_2$	real numbers	real numbers
$R_1 \cap R_2$	2	3

EXAMPLE 6. $R = \left\{ 0 \le y = \dfrac{1}{x} \right\}$.

Note that there are two special restrictions implied by the conditions. Both x and y must be greater than or equal to zero and $x \ne 0$. For $x = 1$, we have $y = 1$. As we select successively larger values of x, we obtain successively smaller values of y. As we select smaller values of x, we obtain larger values of y. The domain consists of the set of all positive real numbers, that is, the interval of positive real numbers open on the left and extending to the right. The range set is also a set of positive real numbers. In this relation we note that interchanging the range and domain sets results in the same relation again so that the relation is symmetric.

A natural extension of this relation might be to eliminate the restriction that $y \geq 0$. That is, consider $R_h = \left\{y = \dfrac{1}{x}\right\}$. The graph of R_h would

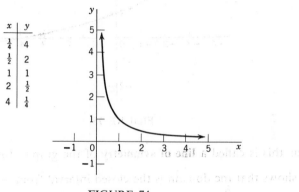

x	y
$\frac{1}{4}$	4
$\frac{1}{2}$	2
1	1
2	$\frac{1}{2}$
4	$\frac{1}{4}$

FIGURE 74.

appear in two distinct parts. The separate parts are called **branches** of the graph or relation.

EXAMPLE 7. $R = \{x = y^2 - 5y + 4\}$.

A table of ordered pairs is obtained by selecting values of x or y such that we can obtain "easy" values of y or x. For example, note that for $y = 0$, we have $x = 4$. We also note that we can write $y^2 - 5y + (4 - x) = 0$. Now if $4 - x$ were 0, 4, or 6 we could easily factor $y^2 - 5y + (4 - x)$ and solve for y in the equation. Successively setting $4 - x$ equal to 0, 4, and 6 we obtain six ordered pairs which satisfy the condition.

A useful device is to "complete the square."

$$x = y^2 - 5y + 4 = \left(y^2 - 5y + \frac{25}{4}\right) - \frac{9}{4} = \left(y - \frac{5}{2}\right)^2 - \frac{9}{4}$$

The quantity $\left(y - \dfrac{5}{2}\right)^2$ must always be greater than or equal to 0. When it is equal to 0, we have $y = \dfrac{5}{2}$ and $x = -\dfrac{9}{4}$. For all other values of y, $\left(y - \dfrac{5}{2}\right)^2$ is greater than zero and thus x must be more positive than $-\dfrac{9}{4}$.

Note that there is a value of x for every value of y. The values of y are arranged in pairs equally distant above and below the line $x = \dfrac{5}{2}$. A line

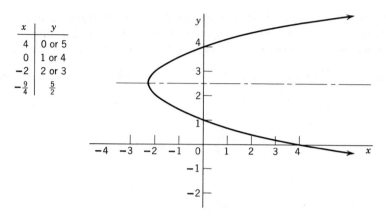

x	y
4	0 or 5
0	1 or 4
−2	2 or 3
−$\frac{9}{4}$	$\frac{5}{2}$

FIGURE 75.

such as this is called a **line of symmetry** of the graph. Inspection of our work shows that the domain is the closed interval from $-\frac{9}{4}$ extending to the right, $x \geq -\frac{9}{4}$. The range is the set of all real numbers. Graphs (or curves) of this type are called parabolas.

EXAMPLE 8. $R = \{x^2 + y^2 \leq 9\}$.

Examination shows that we can consider the two situations: $x^2 + y^2 = 9$ and $x^2 + y^2 < 9$. In either case, interchanging the roles of x and y or the

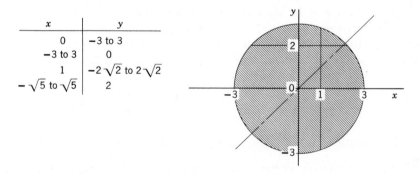

x	y
0	−3 to 3
−3 to 3	0
1	$-2\sqrt{2}$ to $2\sqrt{2}$
$-\sqrt{5}$ to $\sqrt{5}$	2

FIGURE 76.

sign of the variable does not change the condition, that is, the same values are obtained. The implication is that if we can find one ordered pair which satisfies the equation, we can immediately interchange the values of the variables or change their signs to obtain three more ordered pairs that satisfy the equation.

Considering the equation $x^2 + y^2 = 9$, note that the extreme values are 3 and -3. That is, if $x = 0$, $y = 3$ or -3. If $y = 0$, then $x = 3$ or -3. In the inequality $x^2 + y^2 < 9$, we have that: if $x = 0$, then $-3 < y < 3$. Also for $y = 0$, $-3 < x < 3$. For each value of either variable, within the extreme values, we obtain an interval of values for the other variable.

The domain and range of this relation consist of the closed interval from -3 to 3 of real numbers. Note that every line through the origin is a line of symmetry for this relation. Since the identity relation is also a line of symmetry for the relation, the relation is symmetric. (*Note:* the reader should check to see that this must be true.) In geometry, this relation is called a circle, including all the points interior to it (its area).

12.3.1 In many applications, relations are described geometrically. For example, where should we locate two posts for a fence along a given line so that they will be a certain distance from a given point? Problems of this kind can often be represented in terms of relations defined on a coordinate system.

For convenience, let us suppose that we have a map with a coordinate system on it. Suppose the above line were given by the relation $L = \{x = 10\}$ and the fixed point by $P(2,3)$. Now, we wish to find the location of posts such that they will be on L and, say, 12 units from P. The problem can then be stated concisely as:

Given a line $L = \{x = 10\}$ and a point $P(2,3)$, find the points (x,y) such that $R = \{(x,y) \mid x = 10$ and the distance to $P(2,3)$ is 12 units$\}$.

Solution.

1. We first sketch a figure and label the given parts.

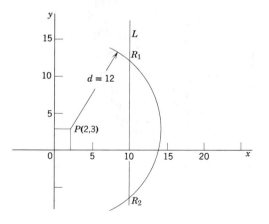

FIGURE 77.

2. There appear to be two points which satisfy the conditions of the problem. These points must lie on the intersection of the line and the relation consisting of all points 12 units from P. Thus, we must have:

(a) $x = 10$ and

(b) $12 = \sqrt{(x - 2)^2 + (y - 3)^2}$

3. Combining the conditions (a) and (b) we have:

$$12 = \sqrt{(8)^2 + (y - 3)^2}$$
$$144 = 64 + (y - 3)^2$$
$$80 = (y - 3)^2$$
$$4\sqrt{5} = y - 3 \quad \text{or} \quad 4\sqrt{5} = -(y - 3)$$
$$y = 3 + 4\sqrt{5} \quad \text{or} \quad y = 3 - 4\sqrt{5}$$

4. Thus, if R_1 and R_2 are the points, we have:

$$R_1(10, 3 + 4\sqrt{5}) \quad \text{and} \quad R_2(10, 3 - 4\sqrt{5})$$

5. After checking to see that these points do in fact satisfy the conditions of the problem, we can decimalize the irrational numbers involved and state the solution to the problem as: If L is the given line and P the given point, there are two points $R_1(10, 11.944)$ and $R_2(10, -5.944)$ such that the points are on L and 12 units from P.

The above illustrates a very useful and powerful technique in the application of coordinate systems and relations to problems. In essence, it is a problem-solving technique used to determine algebraic conditions for problems described geometrically. The algebraic conditions, once determined, can often be solved. The algebraic solutions may then be reinterpreted into the geometry of the problem to give explicit answers to the problem. The solution sets to problems of this type are often called **loci**.

12.3.1.1 Definition: A **locus** is any set of points, lines, or curves, and only those points, lines, or curves, which satisfy one or more given conditions.

If a set of points consists of all those points, and only those points, whose coordinates satisfy a given equation, then the set of points is said to be the **locus of the equation** and the equation is said to be the **equation of the locus**.

A definite procedure has been found to be useful in determining the equation of a locus. The steps in this procedure are described as follows:

(A) Sketch a figure of the given data on an appropriate coordinate system. Carefully label the relevant points, lines, and other significant parts.

(B) Examine the figure and select a *representative* point $P(x,y)$ which appears to satisfy the geometric requirements of the problem. Be careful not to select any special point as representative of the conditions.

(*C*) Now state the conditions on the point *P* algebraically. That is, express the conditions on *P* in terms of equations involving x and y.

(*D*) Simplify or solve the equations to obtain the equation of the locus or the specific points constituting the locus.

(*E*) Check your work and state the complete solution of the problem.

The following examples illustrate the above procedure.

EXAMPLE 1. Find the equation of the locus of all points such that the y coordinates of the points are always equal to the distance of the points to $F(4,3)$.

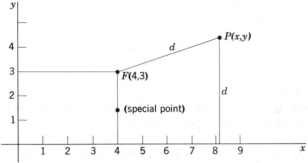

FIGURE 78.

Solution.
(*A*) and (*B*).
(*C*) $y = d$ and $d = \sqrt{(4 - x)^2 + (3 - y)^2}$ so that
$y^2 = (4 - x)^2 + (3 - y)^2$.
(*D*) $y^2 = (16 - 8x + x^2) + (9 - 6y + y^2)$ and

$6y - 9 = 16 - 8x + x^2$ or $y = \dfrac{x^2 - 8x + 25}{6}$.

(*E*) Check by graphing a few points which satisfy the equation. A conventional standard form for this type of equation is $(y - \frac{3}{2}) = \frac{1}{6}(x - 4)^2$. The special point indicated in Figure 78 has the coordinates $(4, \frac{3}{2})$. The locus is called a parabola.

Care should be taken in simplifying or solving in step (*D*) since multiplying and dividing by the variables x and y may effect the condition of the problem through the extension or restriction of the possible ordered pairs satisfying the condition.

EXAMPLE 2. Find the equation of the locus of all points equidistant from the lines $x = y$ and $y = 0$.

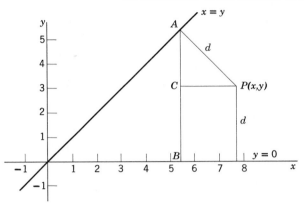

FIGURE 79.

Solution.

(*A*) and (*B*).

(*C*) The distance of *P* to the line $y = 0$ is equal to the y coordinate of *P*.

The distance *PA* is the perpendicular distance from *P* to the line. To determine this distance, after some experimentation, we draw *AB* and *PC* parallel to the axes. Note that the triangles *PAC* and *AOB* are similar (see 9 in Exercises 10).

For convenience, let the coordinates of point *A* be (x_0, y_0). We can then write the following conditions:

(i) $d = y$ given.

(ii) $x_0 = y_0$ given.

(iii) $d^2 = (x - x_0)^2 + (y - y_0)^2$ distance formula.

(iv) $\dfrac{x - x_0}{x_0} = \dfrac{y_0 - y}{y_0}$ geometry.

(*D*) Combining (ii) and (iv) and simplifying:

$$x - x_0 = x_0 - y \ \text{ or } \ 2x_0 = x + y \ \text{ or } \ x_0 = \frac{x + y}{2}$$

Now, using (iii):

$$d^2 = \left[x - \left(\frac{x + y}{2} \right) \right]^2 + \left[y - \left(\frac{x + y}{2} \right) \right]^2$$

$$= \left(\frac{x - y}{2} \right)^2 + \left(\frac{y - x}{2} \right)^2$$

$$= 2 \left(\frac{x - y}{2} \right)^2$$

$$= \frac{(x - y)^2}{2}$$

And from (i): $y^2 = \dfrac{(x-y)^2}{2}$

So that: $y = \dfrac{x-y}{\sqrt{2}}$ or $y = -\dfrac{x-y}{\sqrt{2}}$

And: $y\sqrt{2} = x - y$ or $y\sqrt{2} = y - x$

(E) Thus we conclude that the equations of the required locus are:

$$y = \frac{x}{1+\sqrt{2}} \text{ and } y = \frac{x}{1-\sqrt{2}}$$

In decimal form: $y = 0.41x$ and $y = -2.41x$

The equations describe two straight lines through the origin.

Note that geometric properties were used to determine the distance from P to the line $x = y$. Since the measurements of distances from points to lines is quite common, it would be useful to determine a formula for the computation of such distances.

EXAMPLE 3. Find the equation of the locus of all points 2 units farther from the point $F(0,2)$ than from the line $x = 2$.

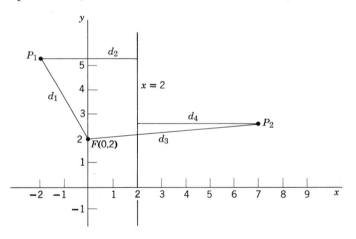

FIGURE 80.

Solution.

(A) and (B).

(C) There are two general possibilities: the points may be to the left or to the right of the line $x = 2$.

    (i) Let P_1 be to the left of $x = 2$:

        (a) $d_1 = d_2 + 2$,   (b) $d_1{}^2 = x^2 + (y-2)^2$,   (c) $d_2 = 2 - x$

    (ii) Let P_2 be to the right of $x = 2$:

        (a) $d_3 = d_4 + 2$,   (b) $d_3{}^2 = x^2 + (y-2)^2$,   (c) $d_4 = x - 2$

(D) For P_1: $x^2 + (y - 2)^2 = (2 - x)^2 + 4(2 - x) + 4$ and
$(y - 2)^2 = -8(x - 2)$
For P_2: $x^2 + (y - 2)^2 = (x - 2)^2 + 4(x - 2) + 4$ and
$(y - 2)^2 = 0$ so that $y = 2$.

(E) In this problem, we note that the locus consists of the union of the two loci defined by:
$$(y - 2)^2 = -8(x - 2) \text{ and } y = 2 \text{ for } x \geq 2.$$

Note that for P_1 the values of $x - 2$ must be negative so that $x \leq 2$. The reader should check by finding ordered pairs that satisfy the equations, and by graphing the pairs to see that they satisfy the original geometric conditions.

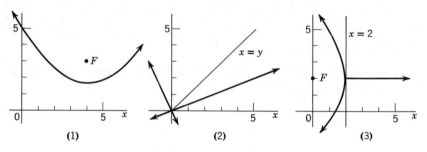

FIGURE 81. Graphs of loci for examples (1), (2), and (3).

Exercises 12.3

1. Discuss and graph the following relations:
  (a) $R = \{y \leq x\}$.
  (b) $R = \{y = 2x - 3 \text{ or } y = 2 - x\}$.
  (c) $R = \{0 \leq y \leq x \text{ and } 1 \leq x \leq 5\}$.
  (d) $R = \{xy - x = 1\}$.
  (e) $R = \{y = x^2 - 5x + 4\}$.
2. Find the equation of the set of all points such that the distance to the y-axis is always three more than twice the distance to the x-axis.
3. Find the equation of the locus of all points such that the sum of the distances to $F_1(-3,0)$ and $F_2(3,0)$ is always equal to 10 units.
4. Find the equation of the locus of all points which are closer to the point $F(4,0)$ than to the y-axis.
5. Find the equation of the locus of all points such that the sum of the squares of the distances to $A(0,2)$ and $B(6,2)$ will always equal the square of the distance between A and B.

Exercises 12

1. If $D = \{a, b\}$ where $a \neq b$, find the following:
  (a) all relations on $D \times D$.
  (b) all symmetric relations on $D \times D$.

(c) all reflexive relations on $D \times D$.

(d) all transitive relations on $D \times D$.

(e) all relations on $D \times D$ which are both symmetric and reflexive.

(f) the transpose or inverse relation for each relation on $D \times D$.

2. If N is the set of natural numbers, then graph the relations on $N \times N$ specified by:

(a) $R_1 = \{(n,m) \mid n$ is not divisible by m and $m \leq n \leq 20\}$.

(b) $R_2 = \{(n,m) \mid m = 2n - 1$ for $n \leq 10\}$.

(c) $R_3 = \{(n,m) \mid m + 1 \leq 3n - 1$ for $n \leq 4\}$.

(d) $R_4 = \{(n,m) \mid 2n - 1 \leq m \leq n + 8\}$.

(e) $R_5 = R_2^*$ (the transpose of R_2).

(f) $R_6 = R_3^*$.

(g) $R_7 = R_2 \cup R_3$.

(h) $R_8 = R_3 \cap R_4$.

3. What is the range and domain of each of the relations of problem 2?

4. Given a triangle with vertices $A(3,4)$, $B(\frac{3}{5},2)$, and $C(\frac{27}{5},0)$, find the point such that every line through the point divides the area of the triangle into two equal parts.

5. Given the points $A(1,5)$, $B(5,2)$, and $C(13,0)$:

(a) Show that the points lie on a straight line.

(b) Find the points $D(x,y)$ on the line such that the square of the distance from A to C is equal to the product of the numerical distances from A to B and from A to D.

6. Discuss and graph the following real relations:

(a) $R = \{0 \leq y \leq 3 - 2x$ and $x \geq 0\}$.

(b) $R = \{(x - 1)^2 = y(2 - y)\}$.

(c) $R = \{y^2 \leq x \leq 6 - y\}$.

(d) $R = \{x^2 + y^2 = 25$ or $2y = 5 - x\}$.

7. Find the equation of the locus of all points on the straight line determined by $A(0,b)$ and $B(1,m + b)$.

8. Find the distance from the point $P(6,2)$ to the line whose equation is $2y - x = 8$.

9. Establish a formula for the distance from a given point $P(x_0,y_0)$ to a given line determined by the two points $A(0,b)$ and $B(1,m + b)$.

10. Find the conditions for a locus of points such that the distance to the origin is always greater than 3 units and less than 5 units.

11. Find the equation of the locus of all points such that a rectangle, with a vertex at the origin and two sides on the positive x and y axes, will have a constant area if the fourth vertex is a point on the locus.

12. Discuss and graph the following relation called a witch.

$$R = \{x^2 y + 16y = 64\}.$$

13. Do as in 12 with:

$$R = \left\{y^2 = \frac{x^3}{4 - x}\right\} \quad \text{(called a cissoid).}$$

14. Do as in 12 with:

$$R = \left\{ y = \pm x \sqrt{\frac{2 - x}{2 + x}} \right\} \quad \text{(a strophoid).}$$

15. Do as in 12 with:

$$R = \{ y = \pm \sqrt{(x^2 - 16)(x + 2)^2(x - 6)} \}.$$

13
FUNCTIONS

13.1 FUNCTIONS

If we look at and compare the domains of relations, we note that some relations have exactly one range value for a given value in the domain. That is, in some relations, the range values are specified unambiguously for each domain value of the relation. For example, in section 12.3, Examples 1 and 2 are relations of this kind.

Such relations are called **functions**. The word "function" also occurs in our everyday vocabulary; for example, "His mood is a function of the weather." The notion of a rule which connects two variables unambiguously is to be found in every area of human activity. It is of fundamental importance in applications of mathematics.

13.1.0.1 Definition: If A and B are sets and R is a relation on $A \times B$, then **R is a function** if, for every element in the domain of R, there is exactly one element in the range of R such that the ordered pair belongs to R.

A function is a relation, a set of ordered pairs, such that no two ordered pairs have the same first element. Graphically, when we select a value on the horizontal axis which belongs to the domain, there is exactly one point above or below this domain value which belongs to the function.

Let us return for a moment to our initial consideration of the property of relations which leads us to define functions. We first consider a domain D. To each element of the domain set there is associated exactly one element from a second set. The collection of elements from the second set is the range set. Finally, the set of ordered pairs so formed is called a function. The condition or rule which associates to each element in the domain an element in the range is often denoted by the letters f or g. Since the set we have called a function is specified by the rule, we often designate the function itself by the letters f or g.

When a function f assigns an element b to an element a, we say that "the function f **maps** or **sends** a to b." We denote this condition by:

(a) $a \xrightarrow{f} b$ or by

(b) $f(a) = b$

The notation $a \xrightarrow{f} b$ emphasizes the mapping or sending property of a function. The notation $f(a) = b$ is read "f at a is equal to b." If $f(a) = b$, we say that "under the function f, b is the **image** of a and a is the **pre-image** of b." The rule aspect of the function is emphasized by $f(a) = b$. The notation $f(a)$ states that we are to apply the rule f to the element a. The right hand term in the equality then asserts that the element b results.

The notation can easily be formalized by defining the following sets:

$$f = \{(a,b) \in A \times B \mid \text{there is exactly one } b \in B \text{ such that } bFa\}.$$
$$f(a) = \{b \in B \mid bFa\}.$$

Since the set $f(a)$ consists of the single element b, we can write $f(a) = \{b\}$. By convention, we omit the braces and write $f(a) = b$. It follows that this is equivalent to writing bFa. The set or element $f(a)$ is often called the "f-correspondent of a" or "the correspondent of a under f."

Three ingredients are necessary to specify a function completely: (1) two sets A and B must be given; (2) a domain set $D \subset A$ must be specified; (3) a rule f must be given such that for each $a \in D$ there is a unique $f(a) = b \in B$ specified.

In describing a function, however, the ingredients may be represented in a variety of ways. For example:

(a) Venn diagram form.

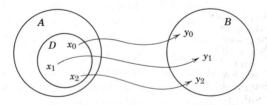

FIGURE 82.

(b) Listing of ordered pairs.

(i) $f = \{(x_0,y_0), (x_1,y_1), (x_2,y_2), \cdots\}$.

(ii)

x	x_0	x_1	x_2
$f(x)$	y_0	y_1	y_2

(iii)

x		$f(x)$
x_0	$\rightarrow$	y_0
x_1	$\rightarrow$	y_1
x_2	$\rightarrow$	y_2

(c) Graphically.

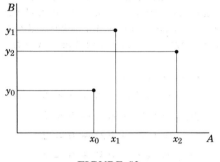

FIGURE 83.

(d) When A and B are number sets, algebraically (often called "functional" notation): $y = f(x)$.

13.1.1 In writing $y = f(x)$, x represents an unspecified element of the domain and y an element of the range. The symbol x which represents a domain element is often referred to as the **independent variable** and y is referred to as the **dependent variable**. The terminology is suggestive of the mapping or sending property of a function.

Perhaps a few examples will help to clarify the meaning and usefulness of functional notation.

(a) $f = \{(x,y) \in C \times C \mid y = 2x - 5\}$ where C is a set of real numbers. If the functional context in the set of real numbers is understood, we can write $f(x) = 2x - 5$.

Now we are free to choose an element from the domain set, that is, a value of the independent variable. If we choose $x = 1$, then $f(1) = 2(1) - 5 = -3$. Thus the value of the dependent variable is -3. Note that, under the function f, $1 \rightarrow -3$.

If $f(x) = 2x - 5$, then:

$$f(0) = 2(0) - 5 = -5$$

$$f(-1) = 2(-1) - 5 = -7$$

$$f\left(\frac{3}{2}\right) = 2\left(\frac{3}{2}\right) - 5 = -2$$

$$f\left(\frac{5}{2}\right) = 2\left(\frac{5}{2}\right) - 5 = 0$$

$$f(5) = 2(5) - 5 = 5$$

(b) $f(x) = x^2 + 4x + 6$.

In the context of real numbers, the statement $f(x) = x^2 - 4x + 6$ implies that the domain is the set of all real numbers, since $x^2 - 4x + 6$ has a real value for all real numbers. That is, for an arbitrary real number x, there is a real number y which is the image of x under f.

If $f(x) = x^2 - 4x + 6$, then:

$$f(-2) = (-2)^2 - 4(-2) + 6 = 18$$
$$f(0) = (0)^2 - 4(0) + 6 = 6$$
$$f(2) = (2)^2 - 4(2) + 6 = 2$$
$$f(4) = (4)^2 - 4(4) + 6 = 6$$

Note that the range value 6 occurs twice, for $x = 0$ and $x = 4$. This immediately tells us that the transpose of $f(x)$ is not a function. That is, by interchanging the elements in the ordered pairs, we have $x = y^2 - 4y + 6$ and thus for the transpose of $f(x)$, $g(x) = 2 \pm \sqrt{x - 2}$. Clearly, for $x > 2$ there are two values of $g(x)$.

Finally, the function $f(x) = x^2 - 4x + 6$ can be written in the form $f(x) = (x - 2)^2 + 2$. Since $(x - 2)^2$ is always positive or zero, the range of $f(x)$ must be the set of real numbers $y \geq 2$.

(c) $f(x) = \sqrt{9 - x^2}$.

In this example, the quantity $9 - x^2$ must be positive or zero to result in a real number. Thus $x^2 \leq 9$ or $-3 \leq x \leq 3$ are the only values of x leading to values of y. Since the determination of square roots is cumbersome, a natural operation to perform on $f(x) = y = \sqrt{9 - x^2}$ is to square both sides of the equation. We then have $y^2 = 9 - x^2$. But this latter equation does not specify a function! It is the relation which we have called a circle. Examination reveals that the relation includes the function as a subset. Recalling that the square root was to be understood to mean the positive square root, we have $0 \leq y \leq 3$. The function is the upper semicircle.

If $f(x) = \sqrt{9 - x^2}$, then:

$$f(0) = \sqrt{9 - (0)^2} = 3$$
$$f(1) = \sqrt{9 - (1)^2} = 2\sqrt{2}$$
$$f(-1) = \sqrt{9 - (-1)^2} = 2\sqrt{2}$$
$$f(3) = \sqrt{9 - (3)^2} = 0$$

13.1.2 Functions are relations and relations are sets. Thus the concept of equality of functions is a special case of the equality of sets. If f and g are functions on $A \times B$, $f = g$ means that f and g are identical subsets of

$A \times B$. That is, the functions are equal if their domains are identical and if for each element in the domain the images are the same.

When we consider the set of real functions, a natural question to ask is whether it is possible to establish binary operations on this set. As with the real numbers, the operations of addition, subtraction, multiplication, and division can be well defined. For convenience, we denote the domain and range of a function f by D_f and $f(D)$, respectively.

13.1.2.1 **Definition:** If f and g are real functions with domains D_f and D_g, then

(i) by the **sum** $f + g$ we mean the function h such that $h(x) = f(x) + g(x)$ and $D_h = D_f \cap D_g$.

(ii) by the **difference** $f - g$ we mean the function h such that $h(x) = f(x) - g(x)$ and $D_h = D_f \cap D_g$.

(iii) by the **product** fg we mean the function h such that $h(x) = f(x)g(x)$ and $D_h = D_f \cap D_g$.

(iv) by the **quotient** $\dfrac{f}{g}$ we mean the function h such that $h(x) = \dfrac{f(x)}{g(x)}$ for $g(x) \neq 0$ and $D_h = D_f \cap D_g$.

Note that the definition of the sum, difference, product, and quotient reduces the operations to operations with the real numbers. That is, if we select a value x in the given domain D_h, we obtain the image of x by evaluating $h(x)$ as defined for each operation. For example, let $f(x) = 2x - 1$ and $g(x) = x^2 - 2x$. The domains of both f and g are sets of real numbers. Now we can determine $h(x)$ for each of the four operations:

(i) The sum:

$$h(x) = f(x) + g(x) = (2x - 1) + (x^2 - 2x) = x^2 - 1$$
$$h(0) = f(0) + g(0) = (-1) + (0) = (0)^2 - 1 = -1$$
$$h(2) = f(2) + g(2) = (3) + (0) = (2)^2 - 1 = 3$$
$$h(-1) = f(-1) + g(-1) = (-3) + (3) = (-1)^2 - 1 = 0$$

(ii) The difference:

$$h(x) = f(x) - g(x) = (2x - 1) - (x^2 - 2x) = -x^2 + 4x - 1$$
$$h(1) = f(1) - g(1) = (1) - (-1) = -(1)^2 + 4(1) - 1 = 2$$

(iii) The product:

$$h(x) = f(x)g(x) = (2x - 1)(x^2 - 2x) = 2x^3 - 5x^2 + 2x$$
$$h(2) = f(2)g(2) = (3)(0) = 2(2)^3 - 5(2)^2 + 2(2) = 0$$

(iv) The quotient:

$$h(x) = \frac{f(x)}{g(x)} = \frac{2x - 1}{x^2 - 2x}$$

$$h(3) = \frac{f(3)}{g(3)} = \frac{5}{3}$$

Note that x cannot equal 0 or 2 since for these values $g(x) = 0$.

The definition of the operations is unambiguous for functions because of the fact that a unique image element is required by the definition of a function. There is one further operation with functions which enables us to obtain successive mappings of elements. That is, if $y = f(x)$ and $z = g(y)$, we would like to write $z = h(x)$. The function h is then called the **composite function** of g and f and is written $h = g(f)$.

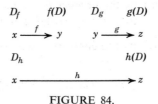

FIGURE 84.

13.1.2.2 **Definition:** If f and g are real functions with domains D_f and D_g, then by the **composite** $g(f)$ we mean the function h such that $h(x) = g[f(x)]$ and $D_h = \{x \in D_f \mid f(x) \in D_g\}$.

Note that h may be an empty set if the range of f and the domain of g have no elements in common. Also $g(f) \neq f(g)$ in general. Since the letters x, y, and z, used to indicate the variables, can be any convenient letters, that is, "place holders," we can consider the composition of $f(x) = x + 2$ and $g(x) = x^2$. That is, we can write $y = f(x) = x + 2$ and $z = g(y) = y^2$ or $z = f(y) = y + 2$ and $y = g(x) = x^2$.

As an illustration of the composite and the fact that the composite is not commutative, we compute $g(f)$ and $f(g)$ for $f(x) = x + 2$ and $g(x) = x^2$:

(i) $h = g(f)$: $h(x) = g(x + 2) = (x + 2)^2 = x^2 + 4x + 4$
(ii) $h = f(g)$: $h(x) = f(x^2) = x^2 + 2$

13.1.3 Certain special functions deserve mention. The **identity** relation E is clearly a function. The **empty** or absurd relation is also conventionally considered a function. The transpose of a function may or may not be a function. When the transpose of a function is a function, it is called the

inverse of the given function. The transpose of a function is a function if and only if, for each member of the range of the original function, there is exactly one element in the domain of the original function.

We have already noted that relations can often be separated or "decomposed" into the union of functions. If the domains of two or more functions are disjoint, then the union of the functions is a function. Finally, the intersection of two or more relations may be a function.

For illustrations:

Example 2 of 12.3 is the identity function.

Example 1 of 12.3 is its own inverse, that is, the transpose is a function.

Example 7 of 12.3 is not a function but its transpose is a function, that is, $f(x) = x^2 - 5x + 4$.

Example 5 of 12.3 is a relation such that R_1 and $R_1 \cap R_2$ are functions. But R_2 is not.

Exercises 13.1

1. Construct graphs for the functions $(a) f(x) = 2x - 5$ $(b) f(x) = x^2 - 4x + 6$ $(c) f(x) = \sqrt{9 - x^2}$ of section 13.1.1.

2. If $f(x) = 2 - x + 3x^2$, then find $f(1), f(-1), f(\frac{1}{2})$ and the domain and range of f. Graph f.

3. Given $f(x) = x + 1$ and $g(x) = \dfrac{x}{x + 1}$, then find

   $(a)\ f(x) + g(x)$ $(b)\ f(x) - g(x)$ $(c)\ f(x)g(x)$ $(d)\ f[g(x)]$.

4. Graph $f(x), g(x), f(x) + g(x), f(x) - g(x), f(x)g(x)$, and $f[g(x)]$ of exercise 3 and specify their domains.

5. If $R_1 = \{x^2 + y^2 = 9\}$ and $R_2 = \{y \geq 3 - x\}$, then $R_1 \cap R_2 = f$ is a function. Discuss and graph the function.

13.2   ELEMENTARY FUNCTIONS

Historically, the concept of "function" has evolved through stages. The word *function* seems to have been introduced by Descartes to refer to the powers of a variable. Leibniz used the term to denote quantities connected with the graphs of certain equations. By the eighteenth century, "function" had been extended to apply to various relations describing physical phenomena. The modern set concept of a function was arrived at by Lejeune Dirichlet (1805–1859).

Although the notion of a function seems very general, it is a unifying and central principle in the analysis of many problems. The concept is employed almost universally in the study of all the sciences. In mathematics, the function concept leads to an elaborate and extensive branch called *function theory*.

In elementary courses, the study of functions begins traditionally with the examination of examples which occur frequently in simple applications; for example, functions whose graphs are straight lines. In the following paragraphs, we will examine and comment on a few of the more elementary and common types of functions.

13.2.1 We often describe the positive size of things without respect to the direction or sign of the measurement; for example, the ideas of distance, area, and volume. This notion is carried out by the **absolute value** of a number.

13.2.1.1 Definition: By the **absolute value** of x we mean the number $|x| = x$ if $x \geq 0$ and $|x| = -x$ if $x < 0$.

13.2.1.2 Definition: The function $f(x) = |x|$ is called the **absolute value function.**

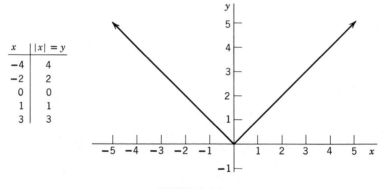

x	$|x| = y$
-4	4
-2	2
0	0
1	1
3	3

FIGURE 85.

A table of ordered pairs can easily be constructed and the absolute value function can be graphed. Note that the function is symmetric with respect to the y-axis. If we write $-x$ for x in $f(x)$, we have $f(-x) = f(x)$ and the function is not changed. In general, for any function, if $f(-x) = f(x)$, we say that the function is an **even function**, for example, $f(x) = x^2$ is an even function. If $f(-x) = -f(x)$, we say that the function is an **odd function**, for example, $f(x) = \dfrac{|x|}{x}$.

A variety of functions may be specified, using the absolute value notion. Figure 86 illustrates a few examples.

13.2.2 We often measure objects in terms of integral values. For example, we often specify the age or height of a person as the whole number of years or the whole number of inches. We can describe this idea as "the greatest integer that is less than or equal to a given number."

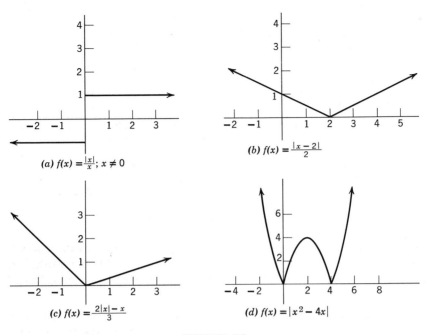

(a) $f(x) = \frac{|x|}{x}; x \neq 0$

(b) $f(x) = \frac{|x-2|}{2}$

(c) $f(x) = \frac{2|x|-x}{3}$

(d) $f(x) = |x^2 - 4x|$

FIGURE 86.

13.2.2.1 Definition: The number $[x]$ is equal to the **greatest integer** less than or equal to x.

13.2.2.2 Definition: The function $f(x) = [x]$ is called the **greatest integer function**.

The domain of the greatest integer function is the set of all real numbers

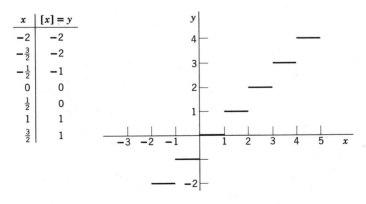

x	$[x] = y$
-2	-2
$-\frac{3}{2}$	-2
$-\frac{1}{2}$	-1
0	0
$\frac{1}{2}$	0
1	1
$\frac{3}{2}$	1

FIGURE 87.

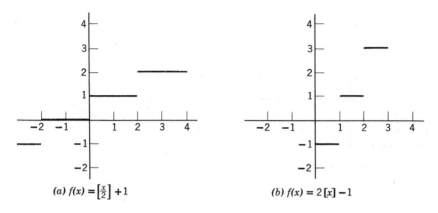

(a) $f(x) = \left[\frac{x}{2}\right] + 1$ (b) $f(x) = 2\,[x] - 1$

FIGURE 88.

while the range is the set of integers. Note that the domain can be separated into unit intervals which are closed on the left and open on the right in graphing this function. This type of function is often called a "step" function.

13.2.3 Among the simplest and most useful kinds of functions are those that describe straight lines. Such functions are called **linear functions**. We have already noted a few examples of linear functions in our consideration of relations. Vertical lines, however, do not represent functions; they are relations of the form $R = \{x = c\}$ where c is some fixed constant.

Rather than exhibit only one or two illustrations of linear functions, let us consider the general equation which describes the entire class of linear functions.

13.2.3.1 Definition: Any function of the form $f(x) = mx + b$, where m and b are constants, is called a **linear function**.

Let us examine the roles of the constants m and b in the description of a linear function. If $m = 0$, we note that the function takes the form $f(x) = b$. That is, the ordered pairs in f must be of the form (x,b). For every x, the y value is constant. A natural descriptive name is to say that for $f(x) = b$, we have a "**constant function**." These functions represent lines parallel to the x-axis (horizontal lines). A constant function has a range consisting of a single value.

Since the linear function consists of ordered pairs which satisfy the equation $f(x) = mx + b$, we can select convenient values of x and examine the y value which results for the range of the function. If we assign the value 0 to x, the value of $y = b$. That is, the ordered pair $(0,b)$ belongs to

the function. On a coordinate system, it is the point at which the graph
of the function crosses or intersects the y-axis. This value $y = b$ is called
the **y-intercept** of the line. Every linear function has a y-intercept equal
to the value b in $f(x) = mx + b$.

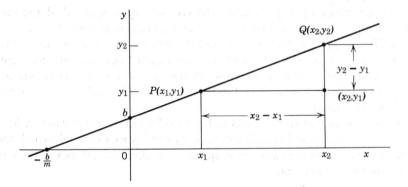

FIGURE 89.

A natural question to ask is whether we can determine a value of x such
that $y = 0$. Can we find the value of x such that $(x,0)$ belongs to f? Writing $f(x) = y = 0 = mx + b$, we have $x = -\dfrac{b}{m}$ for $m \neq 0$. That is, for
$m \neq 0$, we have $\left(-\dfrac{b}{m}, 0\right) \in f$. This is the point at which the graph of
the function intersects the x-axis. The value $x = -\dfrac{b}{m}$ is called the **x-
intercept** of the line.

In many problems, the x-intercepts of a function are of special interest
as solutions to the problems. The values of x which result in range values
0 are thus often given special names. They are called **"zeroes"** or **"roots"**
of the function.

Suppose that we can find two general points, that is, ordered pairs,
satisfying the function $f(x) = mx + b$. Let $P(x_1, y_1)$ and $Q(x_2, y_2)$ represent
these two points. We must then have:

$$y_2 = mx_2 + b \quad \text{and}$$

$$y_1 = mx_1 + b \quad \text{are true statements.}$$

If we compute the difference, we have:

$$y_2 - y_1 = mx_2 - mx_1 = m(x_2 - x_1) \quad \text{is true.}$$

Solving for m:

$$m = \frac{y_2 - y_1}{x_2 - x_1}$$

Now, sketching a figure of a representative situation, we can attempt to obtain a graphical interpretation of the quantity m and the differences $y_2 - y_1$ and $x_2 - x_1$.

The difference $y_2 - y_1$ is called the **rise** and $x_2 - x_1$ is called the **run**. If $y_2 - y_1 = 0$, we would have $m = 0$ and a horizontal line. For $x_2 - x_1 > 0$, if $y_2 - y_1 > 0$, then $m > 0$ and the line would "rise" to the right; if $y_2 - y_1 < 0$, then $m < 0$ and the line would "descend" to the right. The number m, which is the ratio of the rise to the run, is called the **slope of the line**. For $m > 0$, the line slopes "up"; and for $m < 0$, the line slopes "down."

Finally, note that the two constants m and b uniquely determine a line. That is, the constant b specifies the point on the y-axis through which the line must pass and the constant m specifies the direction (slope) of the line through this y-intercept.

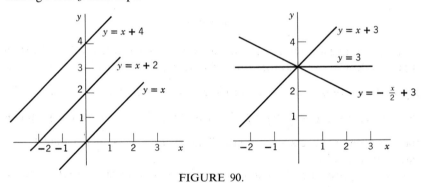

FIGURE 90.

13.2.4 Functions of the form $f(x) = ax^2 + bx + c$ arise in the study of projectile motions, the shapes of reflectors used in lights, telescopes, and radar antennas.

13.2.4.1 Definition: Any function of the form $f(x) = ax^2 + bx + c$, where a, b, and c are constants with $a \neq 0$, is called a **quadratic function**.

Two examples of quadratic functions are graphed in Figure 91:

(a) $f(x) = x^2 - 6x + 8$ (b) $f(x) = -x^2 + 2x + 3$

For $f(x) = x^2 - 6x + 8$, we have the graph "cupping" up. For $f(x) = -x^2 + 2x + 3$, the graph "cups" down. Comparing the graphs with their equations, we note that the squared terms are opposite in sign. The following theorem is suggested.

THEOREM. If $f(x) = ax^2 + bx + c$ and (a) if $a > 0$, then the range set is $y \geq m$ a constant; (b) if $a < 0$, then the range set is $y \leq M$ a constant.

We can write $f(x) = x^2 - 6x + 8 = (x - 3)^2 - 1$ and $f(x) = -x^2 + 2x + 3 = 4 - (x - 1)^2$. In our examples, then, $f(x) = x^2 - 6x + 8$ must have a range set $y \geq -1$ while $f(x) = -x^2 + 2x + 3$ has a range set $y \leq 4$.

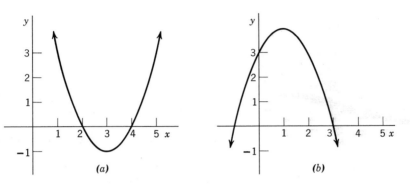

FIGURE 91.

Extreme values in the range for an interval in the domain are called **maximum** and **minimum** values. In general, if $f(x) = ax^2 + bx + c$, we have:

$$f(x) = a\left(x + \frac{b}{2a}\right)^2 + \left(\frac{4ac - b^2}{4a}\right), \text{ so that for } x = -\frac{b}{2a}$$

$$f(x) = \left(\frac{4ac - b^2}{4a}\right) \text{ is a maximum or minimum for } a < 0 \text{ or } a > 0,$$

respectively.

13.2.4.2 Definition: If $y = f(x)$ is a function and $\delta > 0$ is an arbitrary small number, then by a

    (i) **maximum** of $f(x)$ we mean an $f(x_0)$ such that $f(x_0) > f(x)$ for all $x \neq x_0$ in the interval $x_0 - \delta \leq x \leq x_0 + \delta$.

    (ii) **minimum** of $f(x)$ we mean an $f(x_0)$ such that $f(x_0) < f(x)$ for all $x \neq x_0$ in the interval $x_0 - \delta \leq x \leq x_0 + \delta$.

The values of x such that $(x,0)$ are in f are often of interest. For $f(x) = x^2 - 6x + 8$, we have $(2,0)$ and $(4,0)$ in f. For $f(x) = -x^2 + 2x + 3$, we have $(-1,0)$ and $(3,0)$ in f. In general, we can find the values of x which result in ordered pairs $(x,0)$ satisfying a function by factoring, using a formula, or by various methods of approximation. For quadratic functions we have a formula which can be obtained as follows:

$$f(x) = ax^2 + bx + c = 0 \quad \text{Given general function.}$$

$$a\left(x^2 + \frac{b}{a}x + \frac{b^2}{4a^2}\right) + \left(\frac{4ac - b^2}{4a}\right) = 0 \text{ by "completing the square."}$$

$$\left(x + \frac{b}{2a}\right)^2 = \frac{b^2 - 4ac}{4a^2}$$

$$x = \frac{-b \pm \sqrt{b^2 - 4ac}}{2a}$$

Thus, if $f(x) = ax^2 + bx + c$, the **roots** are $x = \dfrac{-b + \sqrt{b^2 - 4ac}}{2a}$ and $x = \dfrac{-b - \sqrt{b^2 - 4ac}}{2a}$, if these values exist. Note that these quantities are real numbers if and only if the quantity $b^2 - 4ac \geq 0$. The formula obtained above is called the **quadratic formula** and the expression $b^2 - 4ac$ is called the **discriminant** of the formula.

13.2.4.3 Definition: By the **roots** or **zeroes** of a function we mean the value(s) in the domain such that the range value of f is zero, that is, the values x_0 in $(x_0, 0) \in f$.

13.2.5 There are many more elementary functions of interest which we might study. For example, the functions $f(x) = \dfrac{1}{x}$ and $f(x) = \sqrt{r^2 - x^2}$ (see examples 6 of 12.3 and c of 13.1.1) are types of functions which occur quite commonly.

Elementary functions are grouped into general categories called **polynomials, rational functions, algebraic functions,** and **transcendental functions.** For example, linear and quadratic functions are polynomial functions. Functions such as $f(x) = \dfrac{1}{x}$ and $f(x) = \dfrac{x + 2}{x - 2}$ are called rational functions. The function $f(x) = \sqrt{r^2 - x^2}$ is said to be algebraic while functions such as $f(x) = 10^x$ are called transcendental.

13.2.5.1 Definition: Any function of the form
$$f(x) = a_0 x^n + a_1 x^{n-1} + \cdots + a_{n-1}x + a_n,$$
where $a_0, a_1, \cdots, a_{n-1}, a_n$ are constants with $a_0 \neq 0$ and n a positive integer, is called a **polynomial function.** The value of n is said to be the **degree** of the polynomial.

13.2.5.2 Definition: Any function which can be written as the quotient of polynomial functions is called a **rational function**.

13.2.5.3 Definition: Any function $f(x) = y$, where y is a solution of an equation of the form
$$P_0(x)y^n + P_1(x)y^{n-1} + \cdots + P_{n-1}(x)y + P_n(x) = 0$$
where $P_0(x)$, $P_1(x)$, $\cdots$, $P_{n-1}(x)$, $P_n(x)$ are polynomial functions, is called an **algebraic function**.

Note that the algebraic classification includes the rational, and the rational classification includes the polynomial functions. Close examination suggests a structuring analogous to the structure of the real numbers.

13.2.5.4 Definition: Any nonalgebraic function is called a **transcendental function**.

Exercises 13.2

1. Discuss and graph the following functions.

(a) $f(x) = \dfrac{x + |x|}{2}$

(b) $f(x) = |x - 3| - 4$

(c) $f(x) = 2x - [x]$

(d) $f(x) = [x - 2] + 2$

2. If $f(x) = mx + b$, then discuss the function $g(x) = \dfrac{f(x) - f(x_0)}{x - x_0}$ where $x \neq x_0$.

3. Discuss and graph the following functions.

(a) $f(x) = 2x^2 - 12x + 20$

(b) $f(x) = -x^2 + 8x - 16$

(c) $f(x) = x^3 - 5x^2 + 4x + 10$

(d) $f(x) = \dfrac{x^2 - 1}{x - 2}$

4. A type of function which has many applications is defined as follows:

13.2.5.5 Definition: Any function of the form $f(x) = kb^x$, where k and b are constants with $k \neq 0$ and $b > 0$, is called an **exponential function**.

(a) Discuss and graph the exponential function $f(x) = 10^x$. *Hint:* start with integral values of x to find ordered pairs.

(b) If $f(x)$ and $g(z)$ are exponential functions with the same base b, what can you say about the product and quotient functions $p(w) = f(x)g(z)$ and $q(w) = \dfrac{f(x)}{g(z)}$ where w is appropriately defined?

5. The transpose (or inverse) of an exponential function is a function.

13.2.5.6 Definition: If $b > 0$ and $b^y = x$, then we write $f(x) = \log_b x$ and call the function a **logarithmic function**.

(a) Discuss and graph the logarithmic function $f(x) = \log_{10} x$.

(b) If $f(x)$ and $g(z)$ are logarithmic functions with the same base b, what can you say about the sum and difference functions $s(w) = f(x) + g(z)$ and $d(w) = f(x) - g(z)$, where w is appropriately defined?

13.3   THE SLOPE FUNCTION

A powerful tool in the study of functions was developed by Isaac Newton during the years 1665 and 1666. The dynamic and "moving" concept which Newton called the "theory of fluxions" was followed by his development of the theory of universal gravitation, the beginnings of a potential theory, and the law for the composition of light.

Our modern point of view to these techniques, now called the calculus, is due, however, to Gottfried Wilhelm Leibniz. Leibniz' geometric approach first appeared in a short six-page article in a mathematical periodical published in 1684. Although both Newton's and Leibniz' developments of the calculus were somewhat vague, they led to an extremely fertile period in mathematics.

13.3.1 As a preliminary to a very brief introduction to a notion of the calculus, let us consider three paradoxes which were posed by an ancient Greek named Zeno of Elea (c. 450 B.C.).

The first paradox, referred to as the Dichotomy, asserts that motion is impossible. In order for an object to go from a point A to a point B, the paradox goes, the object must reach the midpoint of the distance between A and B, say M_1. Now in order to traverse the distance AM_1, the object

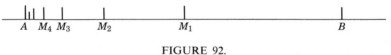

FIGURE 92.

must reach the midpoint, say M_2, of this distance. In order to reach M_2 the object must attain the midpoint of AM_2, say M_3. In order to attain any distinct point, the object must reach an "infinite" number of midpoints. Since an unending number of steps would then be required to reach any distinct point, the object must remain motionless.

The second paradox is called Achilles and the tortoise, and asserts that

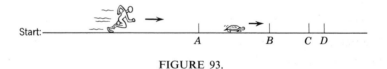

FIGURE 93.

if a tortoise were to start first in a race with Achilles, Achilles, even though he moved faster, could never overtake the tortoise. If the tortoise were at point A when Achilles started, the tortoise would be at a point B

further on by the time Achilles reached point A. When Achilles reaches point B the tortoise would be at a point C further on, and so on.

The third paradox, called the Arrow, concludes that an arrow must always be at rest in flight. Because an arrow on the fly is in some fixed position at any instant, it must be at rest in that instant. Consequently, because the arrow is at rest in every instant, the arrow must always be at rest, that is, motionless!

It was not until the fifteenth century that the effect of Zeno's paradoxes was overcome. The paradoxes illustrate the fundamental concepts around which the calculus is developed. The initial ideas can be described as the concept of an "infinite sequence" and the "limit of a sequence."

For example, consider the following succession of numbers:

$$1, \frac{1}{2}, \frac{1}{4}, \frac{1}{8}, \frac{1}{16}, \frac{1}{32}, \frac{1}{64}, \frac{1}{128}, \frac{1}{256}, \frac{1}{512}, \ldots$$

If each succeeding number is one-half the preceding number, then we could continue to write the succession of numbers indefinitely. It also seems reasonable to note that if we were to continue beyond some nth number, we could make the numbers succeeding this nth number smaller than any number, say $k > 0$. That is, we could, by continuing the succession "far" enough, obtain numbers which would be as close to zero (small) as we wished.

For example, consider:

$$\frac{7}{2}, \frac{10}{3}, \frac{13}{4}, \ldots, \frac{7+3n}{2+n}, \ldots$$

where n is a positive integer indicating the nth number as well as the method whereby the numbers are formed. Since the expression $\dfrac{7+3n}{2+n}$ describes how to obtain any number in the succession, it is evident that the succession can be continued indefinitely. Although it is not as evident as in the previous example, if we write

$$\frac{7+3n}{2+n} = \frac{\dfrac{7}{n}+3}{\dfrac{2}{n}+1}$$

we note that we can make the numbers "approach" the value 3 as closely as we please by choosing a sufficiently large n.

The above ideas are formalized in the following definitions.

13.3.1.1 Definition: By an **infinite sequence** we mean the ordered range set of a function whose domain is the set of all positive integers. If $f(n) = s_n$, we write $\{s_n\}$ for the sequence.

A sequence is thus a succession of quantities:

$$s_1, s_2, s_3, \cdots, s_n, \cdots$$

where the subscript denotes the domain value of the function defining the sequence. We call the s_i **terms** of the sequence and s_n the nth term of the sequence. The examples above would be indicated by $\left(\dfrac{1}{2^n}\right)$ and $\left(\dfrac{7 + 3n}{2 + n}\right)$.

13.3.1.2 Definition: By the **limit of a sequence** $\{s_n\}$ we mean a quantity L (if it exists) such that for any given small number $\epsilon > 0$, there is an integer N such that for all domain values $n \geq N$ of the sequence $\{s_n\}$ we have $|s_n - L| < \epsilon$. We write $\underset{n \to \infty}{\text{limit}}\ s_n = L$ and read "the limit of the sequence as n becomes as large as you please is L."

For our examples, we have

$$\underset{n \to \infty}{\text{limit}} \frac{1}{2^n} = 0 \text{ and}$$

$$\underset{n \to \infty}{\text{limit}} \frac{7 + 3n}{2 + n} = 3.$$

The significance of the concepts of infinite sequences and limits is that they enable us to bridge the "gap" from the static collection concept of sets of elements to the dynamic connected or continuous concept of "moving" points. The notions of sequences and limits can be generalized to a much broader area of application.

If we consider a sequence $\{x_n\}$ of domain values of some given function $y = f(x)$ such that $\underset{n \to \infty}{\text{limit}}\ x_n = x_0$, we will have associated with this sequence a second sequence $\{f(x_n)\}$ such that a $\underset{n \to \infty}{\text{limit}}\ f(x_n) = L$ may exist. The two sequences may be combined for convenience with the notation: $\underset{x \to x_0}{\text{limit}}\ f(x) = L$.

13.3.2 With the above preparation, let us return to the consideration of functions. Let $y = f(x)$ be a function with $P(x_0, y_0)$ and $Q_1(x_1, y_1)$ two distinct points on f. Geometrically, the two points determine a line called a secant. The secant has a slope:

$$m_1 = \frac{y_1 - y_0}{x_1 - x_0}$$

Now suppose $Q_2(x_2,y_2)$ is another point on f between the points P and Q_1. P and Q_2 determine another secant with a slope:

$$m_2 = \frac{y_2 - y_0}{x_2 - x_0}$$

Now consider a sequence $\{Q_n\}$ such that each succeeding Q_n is closer to P on f than its predecessors, that is, $\lim_{n\to\infty} Q_n = P$. The sequence $\{Q_n\}$ defines a sequence $\{m_n\}$ where $m_n = \dfrac{y_n - y_0}{x_n - x_0}$. Does the limit $\lim_{n\to\infty} m_n = m$ exist? Intuitively, it seems clear that if such a number m exists, it must be

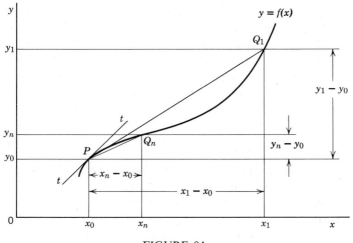

FIGURE 94.

the slope of the line which just "touches" f at the point P. This line is called the **tangent** line to f at P (marked t-t on Figure 94).

So that we can work directly with the functional notation, we examine the situation with respect to the domain and range values of f. The sequence $\{Q_n\}$ defines sequences $\{x_n\}$ and $\{y_n\}$ in the domain and range sets of the function. Each of the latter sequences form a sequence of differences, $\{x_n - x_0\}$ and $\{y_n - y_0\}$. For convenience, we denote a representative term of each sequence by $\Delta x = x_n - x_0$ and $\Delta y = y_n - y_0$. That is, Δx and Δy are variables representing elements in the sequences of differences. Since we have $\lim_{n\to\infty} Q_n = P$, we have for the sequence $\{\Delta x\}$, $\lim_{n\to\infty} \Delta x = 0$. This **does not** mean that $\Delta x = 0$ for any n. This **does** imply that Δx can be made arbitrarily small.

Now let us reverse the process. Let x_0 be a domain value of f and define a sequence $\{\Delta x\}$ such that $\underset{n \to \infty}{\text{limit}}\ \Delta x = 0$. With this beginning we ask whether we can find an expression for $\dfrac{\Delta y}{\Delta x}$ such that we can calculate the value of $\underset{\Delta x \to 0}{\text{limit}}\ \dfrac{\Delta y}{\Delta x}$.

We have $\Delta y = y_n - y_0 = f(x_n) - f(x_0)$ and $\Delta x = x_n - x_0$ so that we can write $\Delta y = f(x_0 + \Delta x) - f(x_0)$. Thus we have

$$\underset{n \to \infty}{\text{limit}}\ m_n = \underset{\Delta x \to 0}{\text{limit}}\ \frac{\Delta y}{\Delta x} = \underset{\Delta x \to 0}{\text{limit}}\ \frac{f(x_0 + \Delta x) - f(x_0)}{\Delta x}$$

for the **slope** of the tangent line to f at $P(x_0, y_0)$ *if it exists*.

Since the domain value x_0 is an arbitrary value, we can safely drop the subscript with the understanding that x stands for some domain value which is "fixed" in the process of calculating the limit. The expression for the slope of f at x defines a function conventionally denoted by f'. The range values of f' are values of the slope of f at values x in the domain of f. A variety of notational devices are used to indicate the slope function.

13.3.2.1 Definition: By the **slope function** or **derivative** of a function $y = f(x)$, we mean the limit:

$$y' = f'(x) = \frac{dy}{dx} = Df(x) = \underset{\Delta x \to 0}{\text{limit}} \frac{f(x + \Delta x) - f(x)}{\Delta x}$$
if it exists.

13.3.3 Although we have not developed tools to cope with the evaluation of limits in general, many limits can be evaluated intuitively. For example, if $f(x) = 2x^2$ we can form $\Delta y = f(x + \Delta x) - f(x)$ so that $\Delta y = 2(x + \Delta x)^2 - 2x^2 = 4x\Delta x + 2\Delta x^2$. Now, dividing by Δx, we have

$$\underset{\Delta x \to 0}{\text{limit}}\ (4x + 2\Delta x) = 4x = f'(x)$$

The evaluation of the limit appears intuitively clear since "x" is some x_0 and Δx can be made arbitrarily small. The usefulness of the function $f'(x) = y'$ in graphing $f(x) = y$ is evident, for by choosing a value of x we not only obtain an ordered pair $(x, f(x))$ but also the slope of the tangent line to $f(x) = y$ at this point.

As a second example, consider the function defined by $f(x) = x^3 - 3x + 6$.

Let us calculate $f'(x) = y'$:

$\Delta y = [(x + \Delta x)^3 - 3(x + \Delta x) + 6] - (x^3 - 3x + 6) = 3x^2\Delta x + 3x\Delta x^2 + \Delta x^3 - 3\Delta x$

$\dfrac{\Delta y}{\Delta x} = 3x^2 + 3x\Delta x + \Delta x^2 - 3$ so that

$\underset{\Delta x \to 0}{\text{limit}}\ (3x^2 - 3 + 3x\Delta x + \Delta x^2) = 3x^2 - 3 = 3(x^2 - 1) = f'(x)$

Forming a table, we can graph $f(x) = y$. Note that, for $x = 1$ and $x = -1$, we have $f'(x) = 0$ and so a horizontal tangent line at the points $(1,4)$ and $(-1,8)$.

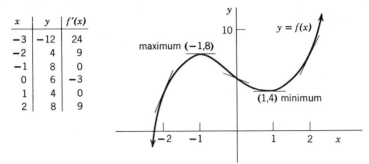

x	y	$f'(x)$
-3	-12	24
-2	4	9
-1	8	0
0	6	-3
1	4	0
2	8	9

FIGURE 95. *Note:* the scales are unequal to obtain a balanced appearance.

The maximum and minimum values of a function can be obtained by setting $f'(x) = 0$. In addition to this, the usefulness of the derivative function can be illustrated in the approximation of the roots of a function. The idea, called Newton's method for approximating the roots, is illustrated in Figure 96.

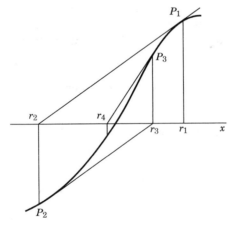

FIGURE 96.

If we can find an initial "guess" for a root, say r_1, then we can form the triangle r_1, P_1, r_2. Our second "guess" will be r_2 for a better approximation of the root. For this triangle, we have

$$f'(r_1) = \frac{f(r_1)}{r_1 - r_2} \qquad \text{or} \qquad r_2 = r_1 - \frac{f(r_1)}{f'(r_1)}$$

We can repeat the process to obtain further approximations. In general, if our initial "guess" is reasonable, the process will result in closer and closer approximations to the root. Each approximation can be checked by evaluating $f(r_n)$ for r_n our nth "guess." The process can be described by the formula

$$r_{k+1} = r_k - \frac{f(r_k)}{f'(r_k)}$$

For our example, we have $f(-3) = -12$ and $f(-2) = 4$ so that we can use $r_1 = -2$ as a first "guess." Then

$$r_2 = -2 - \frac{4}{9} = -\frac{22}{9}$$

$$r_3 = -\frac{22}{9} - \frac{f\left(-\frac{22}{9}\right)}{f'\left(-\frac{22}{9}\right)} = -\frac{22}{9} + \frac{(928)(27)}{(729)(403)}$$

so that $r_3 = -2.359$ which results in $f(-2.359) = 0.054$.

In conclusion, a natural direction for further study would be to develop rules for the manipulation of limits and the consideration of the structure of the operation we have called "obtaining the derivative" of a function. An interesting and important question which arises is whether, given a function, we can find another function such that the given function is its derivative. This latter process is called the **integration** of a function.

Exercises 13.3

1. Find the limits as $n \to \infty$ of the sequences defined by the following functions.

(a) $f(n) = \dfrac{2n - 3}{n^2}$ (b) $f(n) = \dfrac{n - 3}{1 - n}$ (c) $f(n) = \dfrac{3n}{2n - 1}$

2. Find the limits of the sequences defined by the following functions.

(a) $f(x) = 3x + 2$ as $x \to 2$ (b) $f(x) = \dfrac{x + 3}{x - 2}$ as $x \to 1$

3. Form the expressions $\dfrac{f(x + \Delta x) - f(x)}{\Delta x}$ for the following functions and simplify.

(a) $f(x) = 2x^2 - 4x + 7$ (b) $f(x) = \dfrac{1}{x}$ (c) $f(x) = \dfrac{x}{x - 1}$

(d) $f(x) = x(x^2 - 1)$ (e) $f(x) = \dfrac{2}{x^2}$ (f) $f(x) = \dfrac{x^2 - 1}{2x + 3}$

4. Find the limit as $\Delta x \to 0$ for each of the simplified expressions in exercise 3. Write the results as the derivatives of the respective functions.

5. Given $f(x) = 2x^3 - 6x^2 + 3$:
(a) find the derivative $f'(x) = y'$.
(b) graph $f(x) = y$.

(c) find the maximums and minimums of $f(x) = y$.

(d) approximate the three roots of $f(x) = y$.

Exercises 13

1. Construct graphs for the following functions.

(a) $f(x) = \dfrac{x+3}{x}$ (b) $f(x) = \sqrt{x}$ (c) $f(x) = |2x - 1|$

(d) $f(x) = 2x\,|x - 1|$ (e) $f(x) = \left[\dfrac{x+4}{2}\right]$ (f) $f(x) = |x| - \dfrac{1}{[x]}$

2. If $f(x) = \dfrac{x^2 - 3}{x + 1}$, then find: $f(0), f(-2), f(1), f(3)$, and

$$g(x) = \frac{f(x + 2) - f(x)}{2}.$$

3. If $f(x) = x^2 - 1$ and $g(x) = \dfrac{x - 1}{x + 1}$, then find:

(a) $f(x) - g(x)$ (b) $f(x)g(x)$ (c) $\dfrac{f(x)}{g(x)}$ (d) $f[g(x)]$ (e) $g[f(x)]$

4. Find the explicit functions $f(x) = mx + b$ which satisfy the following conditions:

(a) the points $(0,4)$ and $(2,8)$ satisfy $f(x)$.

(b) the point $(1,1)$ satisfies $f(x)$ and the slope is equal to 3.

(c) the y-intercept is 5 and the point $(-2,7)$ satisfies $f(x)$.

(d) the points $(-2,-1)$ and $(2,1)$ satisfy $f(x)$.

5. Graph the functions of exercise 4.

6. If $f(x) = x^2 - 3x + 2$, then find the function $g(x) = f(x + 1) - f(x)$. Graph the functions f and g on a single set of coordinate axis and discuss their relationship to each other.

7. Functions, called **trigonometric functions**, are of considerable importance in the study of circular and periodic phenomena. Geometrically, the domains of these functions consist of lengths along the arcs of circles, and the ranges consist of distances to the horizontal and vertical lines through the center of the circles, as in Figure 97 on page 228.

For convenience, consider a circle with radius $r = 1$ unit placed with its center at the origin of a coordinate system. Any point P on the circle will have coordinates (x,y) with respect to the coordinate system. Now, if we establish an initial point for the measurement of an arc length along the circle, we can associate a third number, say θ, which describes the position of P with respect to the initial point on the circle. By convention, the values of θ can be considered positive when measured in a counterclockwise direction and negative when measured in a clockwise direction. Since the circumference of the circle equals 2π units, θ values can be conveniently indicated in terms of multiples of "π" units.

Note that each θ value determines a unique point P on the circle and that P, in turn, determines a unique pair of numbers x and y.

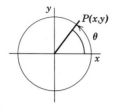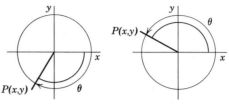

FIGURE 97.

13.2.5.7 Definition: The function $S = \{(\theta,y) \mid y = P(\theta)\}$ where θ is the arc length along a circle of unit radius and y is the associated vertical distance from the horizontal axis is called the **sine function** written $y = \sin \theta$.

13.2.5.8 Definition: The function $C = \{(\theta,x) \mid x = P(\theta)\}$ where θ is the arc length along a circle of unit radius and x is the associated horizontal distance from the vertical axis is called the **cosine function** written $x = \cos \theta$.

Using known properties of the circle, we can find ordered pairs belonging to the sine and cosine functions. Figure 98 suggests how we might graph the sine function on a separate set of coordinate axes.

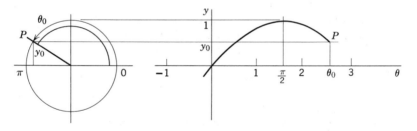

FIGURE 98. $y = \sin \theta$.

By experimenting and reading in other sources,

(a) find the values of $y = \sin \theta$ and $x = \cos \theta$ for θ equal to $0, \dfrac{\pi}{6}, \dfrac{\pi}{4}, \dfrac{\pi}{3}, \dfrac{\pi}{2}, \pi, \dfrac{3\pi}{2}$, and 2π.

(b) construct the graphs of $y = \sin \theta$ and $x = \cos \theta$ for the interval $-2\pi \leq \theta \leq 2\pi$.

(c) Write a discussion concerning your observations of these functions. What is the range set for each function? Is the pythagorean theorem useful? Are the sine and cosine functions related? Are the functions even? Odd? Are the transposes functions?

8. Find the limits as $n \to \infty$ of the sequences defined by:

(a) $f(n) = \dfrac{3n + 2}{2n^2}$ (b) $f(n) = \dfrac{n^2 + 2n - 1}{3n^2}$ (c) $f(n) = \dfrac{(n - 2)^2}{n^2 - 1}$

9. Find the limits of the sequences defined by:

(a) $f(x) = \dfrac{x^2 + 2x + 1}{x + 1}$ as $x \to -1$ (b) $f(x) = \dfrac{2x^2 - 5x - 3}{x^2 - 9}$ as $x \to 3$

10. Given $y = f(x)$ and $y' = f'(x)$ exists, show that as $x \to x_0$ we have $f(x) \to f(x_0) + f'(x)(x - x_0)$.

11. Square corners are to be cut from a rectangular piece of sheet metal measuring 10 inches by 12 inches to form an open-topped box. How large should the cuts be in order to obtain a box with a maximum volume?

12. Functions whose transposes are functions define unambiguous pairings between elements in the domain and range sets of the function.

(a) If $A = \{1, 2, 3, 4\}$ and $B = \{1, 2, 3, 4\}$, find three functions which define unambiguous pairings between A and B.

(b) If A and B are the sets in part (a), find three functions which do not define unambiguous pairings between A and B.

(c) If f and g are two of the functions found in part (a), then show that the composite function $h = f(g)$ defines an unambiguous pairing of elements in A with A.

13. Given the line $x - 2y + 2 = 0$, find the coordinates of the points P and Q on the curve $\dfrac{x}{y - 1} = \dfrac{8}{5x - 36}$ such that the tangent lines to the curve at these points will be respectively perpendicular and parallel to the given line.

14. Given $f(x) = x^2 - 9$, find the area of the triangle formed in the fourth quadrant by the coordinate axes and the tangent line to the graph at the point $(2, -5)$. For what value of x will this triangle have a maximum area?

15. The position of a toy projectile is given by $y = \dfrac{2}{3}x - \left(\dfrac{x}{10}\right)^2$ where y is the height and x the horizontal distance traveled in feet.

(a) How high does the projectile rise?

(b) How far does the projectile travel horizontally?

14
COUNTING

14.1 SEQUENTIAL COUNTING

In many practical problems we are faced with the necessity of counting, of weighing the chances of probable outcomes, rather than determining the specific results of definite actions.

The natural numbers are used in counting by applying a process called "**matching**." For example, in counting the number of chairs in a room, we begin by selecting a first chair and saying "1," then a second chair and saying "2," thence a third chair and saying "3," etc. Continuing in this way, we can match a chair to each successive counting number until we have reached the last chair and thus a last number indicating the cardinal name for the set of chairs.

The order in which the chairs are selected, in our example, is immaterial in determining the number of chairs. Furthermore, every correct "counting" of the chairs must result in the same cardinal name for the set of chairs. Since a finite set is a set for which the process of counting terminates, given any finite set and the set of natural numbers, we can determine uniquely the number of elements in the finite set by a matching process.

The notion of matching is commonly described by the words *association*, *pairing*, and *correspondence*. The process defines an unambiguous pairing of elements between two sets.

14.1.0.1 Definition: If A and B are sets and f is a function on $A \times B$ such that A is the domain of f and B is the range of f, and if the transpose f^* of f is a function, then f is said to be a **one-to-one correspondence** between A and B.

14.1.0.2 Definition: A **matching** of two sets A and B is a one-to-one correspondence between A and B.

14.1.1 The counting of sets with an indefinite number of elements poses a real problem—the problem of explicitly describing a matching process that guarantees the inclusion of every element in a given set. In such situations, **mathematical induction**, using the inductive property of the natural numbers, enables us to describe in a few statements an indefinite number of steps.

THE METHOD OF MATHEMATICAL INDUCTION

(1) Let N be a set of natural (counting) numbers and S a set of statements. Define a function f on $N \times S$ such that $f(n) = s_n$, that is, $f = \{(n, s_n) \in N \times S \mid f(n) = s_n\}$.
(2) Prove that $(1, s_1) \in f$.
(3) Prove the conditional statement that if $(n, s_n) \in f$, then $(n + 1, s_{n+1}) \in f$.
(4) Then, by mathematical induction, we can assert that the set S includes all s_n such that $f(n) = s_n$. That is, f is a matching between N and S.

The number of elements in a set is determined by a process of matching with a representative member of a cardinal class. The cardinal name of the class is called the number of elements in the set. For any set A, let us denote by $n(A)$ the number of elements in the set A. For convenience, we include $n(\emptyset) = 0$. The method of mathematical induction now enables us to prove in a few steps two fundamental theorems of counting.

THEOREM 1. If A and B are disjoint finite sets, then $n(A \cup B) = n(A) + n(B)$.

Proof:
   (i) Let A be a fixed set so that $n(A) = a$ and consider if $B = \emptyset$, then $n(B) = 0$ so that $n(A) + n(B) = a + 0 = a$. But $n(A \cup B) = a$ since $A \cup B = A$ for $B = \emptyset$. Thus $n(A \cup B) = n(A) + n(B)$ for $B = \emptyset$.
  (ii) If $n(B) = 1$, then, since A and B are disjoint, we have $n(A \cup B) = a + 1$. But $n(A) + n(B) = a + 1$, so that $n(A \cup B) = n(A) + n(B)$ for $n(B) = 1$.
 (iii) For $n(B) = b$, if $n(A \cup B) = n(A) + n(B)$, we have for B' such that $n(B') = n(B) + 1 = b + 1$; $n(A \cup B') = n(A \cup B) + 1 = [n(A) + n(B)] + 1 = n(A) + n(B')$.
  (iv) Thus, if A is a fixed set, $n(A \cup B) = n(A) + n(B)$ for all finite sets B.
   (v) For each finite set B, we have similarly $n(A \cup B) = n(A) + n(B)$ for all finite sets A.
  (vi) Thus, if A and B are disjoint finite sets, we have $n(A \cup B) = n(A) + n(B)$.

THEOREM 2. If A and B are finite sets, then $n(A \times B) = n(A)n(B)$ where $A \times B$ is the cartesian product set of ordered pairs.

Theorem 2 is proved in a manner similar to theorem 1. Note that theorem 1 requires that the sets be disjoint. Theorem 2, however, does not require that the sets be disjoint nor even distinct. We can form $A \times A$ for any finite set A and obtain $n(A \times A) = [n(A)]^2$.

If two finite sets have elements in common, then each element in the intersection of the two sets would be counted twice in the sum $n(A) + n(B)$. This restriction on the sets can be eliminated by subtracting the number of elements in the intersection of the two sets. This leads us to a third and more general theorem.

THEOREM 3. If A and B are finite sets, then $n(A \cup B) = n(A) + n(B) - n(A \cap B)$.

To illustrate these three theorems, let us consider the following sets: $A = \{a, b, c, d, e\}$, $B = \{k, l, m, n\}$, $C = \{b, c, k, m\}$.

$n(A \cup B) = n(A) + n(B) = 5 + 4 = 9$.
$n(A \cup C) = n(A) + n(C) - n(A \cap C) = 5 + 4 - 2 = 7$.
$n(B \cup C) = n(B) + n(C) - n(B \cap C) = 4 + 4 - 2 = 6$.
$n(A \times A) = [n(A)]^2 = (5)^2 = 25$.
$n(A \times B) = n(A)n(B) = 5 \times 4 = 20$.
$n(A \times C) = n(A)n(C) = 5 \times 4 = 20$.

14.1.2 In many situations, the results of counting depend on successive choices. For example, when three persons "match" coins, we might wish

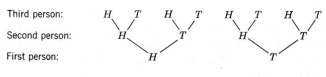

Third person:

Second person:

First person:

FIGURE 99.

to know how many total alternative arrangements of the three coins are possible. That is, the first person tosses a coin, then the second person tosses a coin, and finally the third person tosses a coin. If each coin has two faces, heads and tails, how many arrangements of the three coins are possible?

A convenient diagram which helps us to count the arrangements is called a **tree diagram**. A tree diagram displays a tabular listing of all of the possible successive alternatives in a given situation.

The tree diagram shows clearly that for each of the two alternatives in "tossing" the first coin, there are two alternatives for the second. For each of the alternatives from the first and second, there are two possibilities for the third. Thus there are $(2)(2)(2) = 8$ possible ways of arranging the coins among the three persons "matching" coins.

As a second example, suppose we wish to form serial numbers preceded by a single letter. If the set of letters consists of $L = \{a, b, c\}$ and the numbers consist of $A = \{1, 2, 3, 4\}$, how many serial numbers can we form if each serial number is to consist of a letter from L and three numbers from A such that no two numbers in a given serial number are alike?

Letter	First number	Second number	Third number
3	4	3	2

FIGURE 100.

A serial number will then consist of four items, a letter and three numbers. Let us sketch a set of "boxes" which are to be filled with the letter and three numbers. There are three possible letters which can be used to fill the first box. Once the first box has been filled, there are four possible numbers to occupy the second box. Now, since we have used one of the numbers, there are only three possible numbers for the next box. Finally, we have two alternative numbers for the fourth and last box.

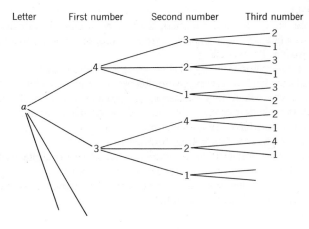

FIGURE 101. Partial tree diagram.

Some reflection on the situation indicates that there must be $(3)(4)(3)(2) = 72$ possible serial numbers which can be formed with the given sets as required. The serial numbers can be displayed by constructing a tree diagram.

The above examples suggest a method of counting when a succession of alternatives occur. Using "boxes" is suggestive, but it does not indicate the process whereby one obtains the total number of possibilities. It is clear that the construction of tree diagrams becomes unmanageable very rapidly with larger numbers of alternatives. A principle for counting the number of total alternatives when given successive steps with a given number of alternative choices for each step is suggested by the examples.

THEOREM 4. The **Principle of Sequential Counting**.
If there are n_1 first choices, n_2 second choices, n_3 third choices, up to n_r choices on the rth choice, then there are $n_1 n_2 n_3 \cdots n_r = n$ total ways of making the r successive choices.

In many situations, a given choice may determine the number of possible choices on the succeeding choice so that succeeding choices may not be determined until a given choice is made.

A common type of problem of choice is illustrated by the question: How many arrangements are possible with a set of n distinct elements? For definiteness, let us consider $S = \{a, b, c\}$. Applying the theorem, we have immediately, $(3)(2)(1) = 6$ possible arrangements. We leave it for the reader to construct a tree diagram to verify and determine the specific arrangements possible.

Exercises 14.1

1. If N is the set of natural numbers, then $N \times N$ can be matched with N, contrary to what we might expect. Discover and describe a procedure which will accomplish this matching.
2. List the 24 possible matchings of $C = \{1, 2, 3, 4\}$ with itself.
3. Using mathematical induction, prove theorems 2 and 3 of section 14.1.1.
4. If M is a set of students in a mathematics class and E a set of students in an English class such that $n(M) = 38$ and $n(E) = 42$, then find $n(M \cup E)$ if
   (a) the two classes have no students in common.
   (b) there are eight students taking both classes.
5. If an auto license consists of three letters followed by three digits with possible repetitions, how many license numbers can be formed?
6. How many numbers less than 321 can be formed by using digits chosen from the set $\{1, 2, 3, 4\}$? Sketch a tree diagram.

14.2   PERMUTATIONS

Rearrangements or reorderings of the elements of a finite set are of immediate interest in many applications. The first historical evidence of the study of arrangements are to be found in the mystic trigrams of the Chinese and Japanese. Arrangements of straight and broken lines, taken three at a time, are to be seen on amulets and charms of the people of India.

In the sixteenth century, Nicolo Tartaglia (c. 1556), an Italian tutor of mathematics, suggested arrangement problems connected with the throwing of dice. Buteo, a French writer of the sixteenth century, discussed the possible numbers of combinations a lock could be given with a given number of movable cylinders when each cylinder could have six possible positions.

Rearrangements or reorderings of finite sets are usually called **permutations**. Although the study of permutations began with problems occurring in games of chance and in the consideration of setting insurance rates, the applications have been extended and broadened into almost every area in which mathematics can be used.

14.2.0.1 Definition: A **permutation** of a finite set S is a matching of S with itself.

For example, if $S = \{a, b, c\}$, then we can consider ordered triples of elements of S: (a,b,c) is an arrangement of elements of S and (b,a,c) is a permutation of S.

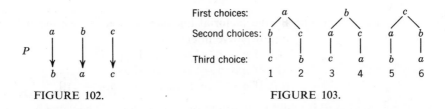

FIGURE 102.   FIGURE 103.

A permutation is an ordering of a set S. In our example, the ordering is easily accomplished; however, in many sets the elements may not be so easily distinguished and ordered. This can be overcome by first constructing a matching with the natural numbers and then identifying the elements of the set with the respective numbers associated in the matching. That is, a labeling of elements will usually enable us to distinguish and order the elements in a given set.

If $S = \{a, b, c\}$, then we note that there are six possible permutations of S. That is, since a permutation is a matching, we can select any of the elements for the first, either of the two remaining elements for the second, and the third element must be the remaining element: $(3)(2)(1) = 6$. A tree diagram displays the permutations clearly.

Properties of the various permutations can be noted by arranging the permutations in a table with the given elements shown in the top row and the elements as ordered by the permutations in succeeding rows. The permutations are described to the left of each row.

TABLE 47

The given set:	S	a	b	c
Identity:	P_1	a	b	c
Cyclic:	P_2	b	c	a
Cyclic:	P_3	c	a	b
'a' stationary:	P_4	a	c	b
'b' stationary:	P_5	c	b	a
'c' stationary:	P_6	b	a	c

14.2.1 Question: Given a finite set S, how many permutations of S are there? The principle of sequential counting enables us to answer the question easily.

THEOREM 5. Given a set S such that $n(S) = k$, then there are $k(k - 1)$ $(k - 2) \cdots (3)(2)(1) = p$ permutations of the set S.

For example, the number of ways in which six persons can be arranged in a row of six chairs is $(6)(5)(4)(3)(2)(1) = 720$. The product form used in finding the number of permutations of a set plays an important role in counting.

14.2.1.1 Definition: By the **factorial function**, written $n!$, we mean for non-negative integers n:
    (i) If $n = 0$, $n! = 0! = 1$.
    (ii) If $n = 1$, $n! = 1! = 1$.
    (iii) If $n \neq 0$ or 1, then $n! = n[(n - 1)!]$

The function $n!$ is read "n factorial" or "factorial n." The value $0! = 1$ is a convenient convention which enables us to express many formulas in a simple, concise way. We can now state theorem 5 concisely as: If $n(S) = k$, then $P_k = k!$ where P_k stands for the number of permutations of a set with k elements.

Solutions to a variety of problems are possible by using permutations and factorial notation. For example, if there are five girls and five boys: (*a*) in how many ways can we arrange them in a row? (*b*) if boys and girls alternate, how many arrangements are there? (*c*) how many distinct couples can we form?

Solutions.

(*a*) The number of arrangements (distinct) is $P_{10} = 10!$; $10! = 3,628,800$

(*b*) In this situation, we have an initial choice of a girl or a boy, then this choice determines two sets of five boys and five girls each. In each set we can arrange the boys (or girls) in $5! = 120$ ways. Thus we have $(2)(5!)(5!) = (2)(120)(120) = 28,800$ ways in which the boys and girls can be arranged alternately in a row.

(c) Since to form a couple we can choose any one of the five boys, then any one of the five girls, we have $(5)(5) = 25$. Note that choosing a girl first and then a boy will not result in a distinct couple. If $B = \{b_1, b_2, b_3, b_4, b_5\}$ and $G = \{g_1, g_2, g_3, g_4, g_5\}$, then we can form a display of all the possible couples as $B \times G$:

$$
\begin{array}{ccccc}
(b_1,g_1) & (b_1,g_2) & (b_1,g_3) & (b_1,g_4) & (b_1,g_5) \\
(b_2,g_1) & (b_2,g_2) & (b_2,g_3) & (b_2,g_4) & (b_2,g_5) \\
(b_3,g_1) & (b_3,g_2) & (b_3,g_3) & (b_3,g_4) & (b_3,g_5) \\
(b_4,g_1) & (b_4,g_2) & (b_4,g_3) & (b_4,g_4) & (b_4,g_5) \\
(b_5,g_1) & (b_5,g_2) & (b_5,g_3) & (b_5,g_4) & (b_5,g_5)
\end{array}
$$

In considering the above problem, we might ask how many arrangements there would be if we were to seat the five girls and five boys around a circular table. Arrangements of this kind are called **cyclic** arrangements. In order to determine the distinct number of arrangements, we select an arbitrary person and count with respect to that person. If we count counterclockwise, there are 9 possible choices (for our previous problem) for the next seat, then 8, etc. Thus we will have $(1)(9!) = 362,880$ possible cyclic arrangements of ten boys and girls around a circular table. Note that rotating the people around the table does not disturb the arrangements.

If boys and girls alternate around the table, we choose a boy or a girl for our initial reference. In either case, our next choice will be from a set with only five choices, then we must choose from the opposite set with four choices, then we next have four choices again, etc. The requirement that boys and girls alternate reduces the number of choices drastically. The number of arrangements with the restriction will then be: $(1)(5!)(4!) = 2,880$.

14.2.2 Even further restrictions may be required in problems. Given a set S with $n(S) = m$, we might wish to know how many permutations are possible with the set of all subsets T such that $n(T) = k$, $k < m$.

For example, consider the set of five boys and five girls. If there are only four chairs available in a row, how many arrangements are possible with the boys and girls? That is, how many ordered subsets T are possible with $n(T) = 4$? We have 10 choices for the first chair, 9 for the second, etc. Thus there are $(10)(9)(8)(7) = 5,040$ possible arrangements of the ten boys and girls in the four chairs.

14.2.2.1 Definition: Given a finite set S with $n(S) = m$, by a **permutation of a subset** T with $n(T) = k$, or by a **permutation of m things taken k at a time**, we mean a matching of subsets T with $n(T) = k$.

The total number of possible permutations of m things taken k at a time is denoted by $_mP_k$. The value of $_mP_k$ can be determined by noting how we can form distinct ordered subsets T with $n(T) = k$. To form a set T, we have m choices for the initial element, $(m - 1)$ choices for the second element, etc. On the kth selection, we have $(m - k + 1)$ choices. Thus:

THEOREM 6. The total number of permutations of m things taken k at a time is $_mP_k = (m)(m - 1) \cdots (m - k + 1)$. We can write this more concisely as

$$_mP_k = \frac{m!}{(m - k)!}$$

In our example with the boys and girls, as a further restriction we might ask how many arrangements would be possible if boys and girls were to alternate in the four available chairs. By sequential counting, we have $(10)(5)(4)(4) = 800$ possible arrangements.

Thus far we have only considered situations in which the elements of a set were distinct. Situations occur where the same element may be repeated or where two or more elements cannot be distinguished. For example, in the spelling of words, letters are often repeated.

The word *beginning* has nine letters with the letter *n* occurring three times and the letters *i* and *g* each occurring twice. We might ask, how many arrangements are possible with the nine given letters in the word *beginning*?

In order to determine how to answer this question, let us consider a simpler problem. Suppose we have five letters: *a, a, b, b, b*. For the moment let us distinguish between the separate letters by writing subscripts on each letter (by matching with the set of natural numbers, cardinal 5): a_1, a_2, b_3, b_4, b_5. The number of permutations of the five distinct elements is now clearly $5! = 120$. Among these permutations, we will have arrangements which will differ only in the subscripts of the letters, for example, a_1, b_3, a_2, b_5, b_4 and a_2, b_4, a_1, b_3, b_5. Now the two letters a_1 and a_2 can be arranged in 2! ways while the letters b_3, b_4, b_5 can be arranged in 3! ways. Thus we conclude that there are $(2!)(3!) = 12$ arrangements of a given permutation which will look alike when the subscripts are omitted. That is, the permutations can be grouped in sets of twelve which appear alike when the subscripts are removed.

Now $P_5 = 120$ is the number of permutations of the five distinct letters so that if P is the number of permutations which can be distinguished when the subscripts are removed, we have $(2!)(3!)(P) = P_5 = 5!$ or solving for $P = \dfrac{5!}{2!\,3!} = \dfrac{120}{12} = 10$ possible permutations of the five letters when we have two elements of one kind and three elements of another kind.

The number of distinct permutations of the letters in the word *beginning* can now be determined in a similar manner to be $P = \dfrac{9!}{3!\,2!\,2!} = 15{,}120$.

THEOREM 7. If a set S consists of $n = n_1 + n_2 + n_3 + \cdots + n_k$ elements, of which n_1 are alike of one kind, n_2 are alike of another kind, and so on to n_k alike of a kth kind, then the number of distinct permutations P of the n elements of the set S is equal to

$$P = \frac{n!}{n_1!\,n_2!\cdots n_k!}$$

Exercises 14.2

1. Consider the word *persevere*,
   (a) How many distinct permutations are there of the subset of different letters used in the word?
   (b) How many permutations (distinct) are there of the letters in the word?
   (c) Using factorial notation, express the total number of distinct permutations of the letters or a subset of the letters used in the word.
2. Using the definition of the factorial function and the properties of the natural numbers, show that:
   (a) $(n + 1)! - n! = n(n!)$
   (b) $(m)(m - 1)\cdots(m - k + 1) = \dfrac{m!}{(m - k)!},\ k < m$
   (c) $\dfrac{(m + n)!}{(m!)(n!)} = \dfrac{(m + n - 1)!}{(m!)(n - 1)!} + \dfrac{(m + n - 1)!}{(n!)(m - 1)!}$
3. A certain make of auto comes in four types of body designs, six choices of color, and four choices of upholstery.
   (a) Make a tree diagram describing the possible choices of autos.
   (b) How many distinct autos are possible?
4. A traveling salesman visits three towns regularly. There are four roads from town A to town B, two roads from town A to town C, and three roads from B to C.
   (a) In how many ways can the salesman drive from A to C by way of B?
   (b) In how many ways can he drive from B to A by way of C?
   (c) How many ways can he make a round trip from C, visiting both A and B?

14.3 COMBINATIONS

In the permutation of a set, the order in which the elements are arranged is important. In many practical situations, the order in which the elements occur is not important; rather, the division of a given set into parts is the problem of interest. For example, apples may be grouped into "good" and "bad" apples; eggs into large or small.

The simplest and most common division of a set is into two subsets. When a set is divided in this way, we say that we have constructed a **dichotomy** of the set.

14.3.0.1 Definition: A **dichotomy** of a set S is a function whose range is a two-element set.

For example, if $S = \{a, b, c, d\}$ and $R = \{0, 1\}$, then we can construct the following dichotomies where one element of S has the image 0.

TABLE 48

Image:	0	1
Domain:	a	b, c, d
	b	a, c, d
	c	a, b, d
	d	a, b, c

Of course we could also construct dichotomies of the set where no elements have the image 0, where two elements have the image 0, where three elements have the image 0, and where all four elements have the image 0. A dichotomy can thus be thought of as the selection of a subset with a given cardinal name from the given set. Another point of view is to note that we can consider a dichotomy as a permutation with two kinds of image elements repeated. A dichotomy is also called a **combination**.

If a set S has $n(S) = m$ elements, we can construct dichotomies with a fixed number, say $r \leq m$, elements having the image 0. As with permutations, we ask how many such dichotomies can be constructed with the set S? We refer to this number as "the number of combinations of an m element set into r and $m - r$ subsets" or "**the combinations of m things taken r at a time**." The combinations of m things taken r at a time is denoted by $\binom{m}{r}$.

For example, if $S = \{a, b, c, d, e\}$, we can indicate a dichotomy with $r = 2$ by placing the subscript 0 on two elements of S and the subscript 1 on the remaining three elements of S: a_0, b_0, c_1, d_1, e_1. In how many ways can we arrange these subscripts? By theorem 7 of 14.2.2 we have $P = \dfrac{5!}{(2!)(3!)} = 10$ possible arrangements so that $\binom{5}{2} = 10$.

If $n(S) = m$ and $r \leq m$, we can divide S into two disjoint subsets with r and $m - r$ elements. If $\binom{m}{r}$ is the number of possible dichotomies with r elements having the image 0, then we note that we obtain exactly the same number of dichotomies with $m - r$ elements having the image 0 by interchanging the images throughout. That is, we can immediately write $\binom{m}{r} = \binom{m}{m - r}$. For $r = 0$, we also have $\binom{m}{0} = \binom{m}{m} = 1$. That is, there is only one dichotomy which assigns all elements (or no elements) to one of the two image elements. We can evaluate $\binom{m}{r}$ by applying theorem 7 to obtain:

THEOREM 8. The number of dichotomies of an n element set into r and $n - r$ subsets is equal to

$$\binom{n}{r} = \frac{n!}{r! \, (n - r)!}$$

THEOREM 9. The total number of dichotomies possible for an n element set is equal to 2^n.

As an example, consider a group of six men and three women. In how many ways can we form a committee of six from this group? In how many ways can we form committees with four men and two women?

For the first question, we have $\binom{9}{6} = \frac{9!}{6! \, 3!} = 84$ possible committees of six. In the second case, we must consider two separate dichotomies. For the men we have $\binom{6}{4} = \frac{6!}{4! \, 2!} = 15$ and for the women $\binom{3}{2} = \frac{3!}{2! \, 1!} = 3$. To obtain the desired committee, we pair a group of four men with a group of two women. Thus we have $(15)(3) = 45$ possible committees with four men and two women.

In many applications, dichotomies are called samples. Given a group of twenty-five light bulbs, how many different samples of ten bulbs can be selected? Solution: $\binom{25}{10} = \frac{25!}{10! \, 15!} = 3,268,760$.

14.3.1 Two men, Blaise Pascal (1623–1662) and Pierre Fermat (1601–1665), stand out for their contributions to the mathematical theory of counting. Stimulated by questions posed by the gambler Chevalier De Mere, Pascal began a correspondence with Fermat which led to an early treatise on the subject of probability by Christian Huygens (1629–1695), an eminent physicist and astronomer of the period.

Of special interest to us is the important inductive rule known as **Pascal's rule** and the resulting set of numbers forming **Pascal's triangle**.

THEOREM 10. (Pascal's Rule) $\binom{n + 1}{r} = \binom{n}{r - 1} + \binom{n}{r}$.

Proof:

1. $\dbinom{n+1}{r} = \dfrac{(n+1)!}{r!\,(n+1-r)!}$

2. $(n+1)! = (n+1)n!$ and

   $r! = r(r-1)!$ and

   $(n+1-r)! = (n+1-r)(n-r)!$

3. $\dbinom{n+1}{r} = \dfrac{(n+1)n!}{r(r-1)!\,(n+1-r)(n-r)!}$

4. $\dbinom{n+1}{r} = \dfrac{n!}{(r-1)!\,(n-r)!}\,\dfrac{(n+1)}{r(n+1-r)}$

5. $\dfrac{(n+1)}{r(n+1-r)} = \dfrac{1}{n+1-r} + \dfrac{1}{r}$

6. $\dbinom{n+1}{r} = \dfrac{n!}{(r-1)!\,(n-r)!}\left(\dfrac{1}{n+1-r} + \dfrac{1}{r}\right)$

7. $\dbinom{n+1}{r} = \dfrac{n!}{(r-1)!\,[n-(r-1)]!} + \dfrac{n!}{r!\,(n-r)!}$

8. $\dbinom{n+1}{r} = \dbinom{n}{r-1} + \dbinom{n}{r}$

The justifications for the steps are left for the reader. Note that Pascal's rule is an iterative formula which tells us how to construct successive combinations. We can form a table of successive combinations by assuming various values of r and n with $r \leq n$. When these numbers are arranged as shown in Table 49, the set of numbers is called Pascal's triangle.

TABLE 49

Pascal's Triangle

Values of n	Values of r:								Sum of rows
	0	1	2	3	4	5	6	7	
0	1								1
1	1	1		Entry is $\dbinom{n}{r}$					2
2	1	2	1						4
3	1	3	3	1					8
4	1	4	6	4	1				16
5	1	5	10	10	5	1			32
6	1	6	15	20	15	6	1		64
7	1	7	21	35	35	21	7	1	128

Observe that Pascal's rule tells us that any entry in the triangle is the sum of the entry immediately above the desired entry and the entry above and to the left of the desired entry. The triangle is of use for small values of n for it enables us quickly to determine the value of $\binom{n}{r}$. The sums indicated in the right margin also indicate the total number of possible dichotomies of a given set of n elements (theorem 9).

A useful application of combinations and Pascal's triangle is illustrated in the **binomial formula**. When we deal with number sets, we encounter binomial expressions and powers of binomials. For example, $(x + y)^2$ is a power of a binomial. When simplified, the expression is called an expansion of the binomial, for example, $x^2 + 2xy + y^2$. Let us examine the expansion of $(x + y)^3$.

$$(x + y)^3 = (x + y)(x + y)(x + y) = x(x + y)(x + y) + y(x + y)(x + y)$$
$$= xx(x + y) + xy(x + y) + yx(x + y) + yy(x + y)$$
$$= xxx + xxy + xyx + xyy + yxx + yxy + yyx + yyy$$
$$= x^3 + 3x^2y + 3xy^2 + y^3$$

Observe that eight terms are formed in the process of expansion. Each of these eight terms consists of the factors x and y. If we interpret the x and y as image elements, we can consider each of the eight terms as an ordered dichotomy of a three-element set. When the eight terms are grouped in terms of the number of elements with images x, we can count the dichotomies of each kind to obtain:

$$(x + y)^3 = \binom{3}{3}x^3 + \binom{3}{2}x^2y + \binom{3}{1}xy^2 + \binom{3}{0}y^3$$
$$= x^3 + 3x^2y + 3xy^2 + y^3$$

The above illustrate special cases of powers of a binomial. In the general case, we have a similar situation.

THEOREM 11. (**The binomial formula**) For any natural number n and numbers x and y, we have

$$(x + y)^n = \binom{n}{n}x^n + \binom{n}{n-1}x^{n-1}y + \binom{n}{n-2}x^{n-2}y^2 + \cdots$$
$$+ \binom{n}{2}x^2y^{n-2} + \binom{n}{1}xy^{n-1} + \binom{n}{0}y^n$$

The numerical coefficients are the numbers of dichotomies possible for each kind of term. These numerical coefficients can be obtained for small n from Pascal's triangle.

For example, for $n = 5$ we have

$$(x + y)^5 = x^5 + 5x^4y + 10x^3y^2 + 10x^2y^3 + 5xy^4 + y^5$$

Due to the relationship of the number of dichotomies or combinations with the expansion of a power of a binomial, the numbers are often called **"binomial coefficients."**

14.3.2 The notion of a dichotomy is readily extended to the notion of constructing successive dichotomies. That is, rather than considering the division of a set into just two subsets, we can divide a set into k disjoint subsets.

14.3.2.1 Definition: A **multinomial classification** of a set S is a function whose range is a k-element set. The classification is often called a **k-part classification**.

THEOREM 12. The number of k-part classifications of a set of n elements with r_1 elements having a "first" image, r_2 elements having a "second" image, and so on to r_k elements having a "kth" image is equal to

$$\frac{n!}{r_1!\, r_2! \cdots r_k!}$$

where $r_1 + r_2 + r_3 + \cdots + r_k = n$.

Dichotomies and k-part classifications are often the first step in the study of many sciences such as the life sciences, medical sciences, chemistry, etc. That is, the study of many sciences begins with the classification of elements, say of animals and plants, into species and phyla, and so on. This process is called taxonomy.

Exercises 14.3

1. Prove that: (a) $\dbinom{m}{r} = \dbinom{m}{m-r}$ (b) $\dbinom{m}{1} = m$

2. How many hands of thirteen cards from an ordinary deck of fifty-two cards contain exactly six clubs? Exactly six of any suit? Six each of any two suits?

3. Fill out Pascal's triangle to $n = 10$ and expand $(x + y)^{10}$; $(x - y)^5$; $(x + 2y)^4$.

4. In how many ways can a set of twelve objects be divided into two equal sets? Into three equal sets? Into four equal sets?

5. Consider all possible dichotomies obtained by tossing ten coins.
   (a) How many dichotomies are possible?
   (b) Classify the dichotomies according to $r = 0$ to 10. How many dichotomies are in each class?

Exercises 14

1. Prove the following by mathematical induction.
   (a) The product of two successive natural numbers is an even number.
   (b) The product of two odd natural numbers is an odd number.
   (c) The product of two even natural numbers is an even number.
2. Prove by induction that, for any natural number n, the derivative of $f(x) = x^n$ is $f'(x) = nx^{n-1}$.
3. If A is the set of positive even numbers less than 150, and B is the set of multiples of six less than 150, and C is the set of multiples of five less than 150, then find
   (a) $n(A \cup B \cup C)$ (b) $n(A \cap B \cap C)$ (c) $n(A - B)$ (d) $n(A \times B)$
4. If A and B are any two finite sets, then show that

$$n[(A - B) \cup (B - A)] = n(A) + n(B) - 2n(A \cap B).$$

5. There are twenty-four letters in the Greek alphabet. How many three-letter societies can be formed by using Greek letters without repetition? With repetition?
6. The telephone numbers on a single exchange consist of four digits.
   (a) How many distinct telephone numbers are possible?
   (b) How many distinct pairs of callers and receivers are possible on this exchange?
7. How many three-digit numbers can be formed, using digits from the set $\{0, 1, 2, 3, 4, 5\}$, without repetition? With repetition?
8. In how many ways can a basketball coach form a team, if he has four forwards, four guards, and two centers, and two of the forwards can play center but the other players only play their positions?
9. Show that

$$\binom{n}{0} + \binom{n}{2} + \binom{n}{4} + \cdots + \binom{n}{n} = \binom{n}{1} + \binom{n}{3} + \cdots + \binom{n}{n-1}$$

   if n is even. Write the equation for the case when n is odd. (*Hint:* consider the binomial formula with $x = 1$ and $y = -1$.)
10. A carton of 100 light bulbs contains ten defective bulbs. Find the percentage of all samples of ten bulbs containing no defective bulbs; containing exactly one defective bulb; containing exactly two defective bulbs.
11. In how many ways can a ten-question multiple-choice examination be answered if there are four choices, a, b, c, and d to each question? If no two consecutive questions are answered the same, how many ways are there?
12. A committee consisting of eight persons is to be selected from six lawyers, ten businessmen, and four teachers.
    (a) If the committee is to consist of three lawyers, four businessmen, and a teacher, how many committees can be formed?
    (b) If the committee is to consist of no more than three persons from any of the groups, how many committees can be formed?
13. There are five steps in the manufacture of a particular article: forming, fitting, assembly, finishing, and testing. If there are two persons forming,

three fitting, eight assembling, two finishing, and three testing, how many different groups of five can manufacture the particular article?

14. Expand $(x + y + z)^2$, $(x + y + z)^3$, and $(x + y + z)^4$.

    (a) Find a general expression for the coefficient C of a term of the form $C x^n y^m z^k$ in the expansion of $(x + y + z)^r$.

    (b) How many terms are there in the expansion of $(x + y + z)^r$?

    (c) Show that the sum of the coefficients C in part (a) is equal to 3^r.

15. Exercise 14 suggests the multinomial theorem, analogous to the binomial formula. State the multinomial theorem for the expansion of

$$(x_1 + x_2 + \cdots + x_s)^r.$$

15
PROBABILITY

15.1 A PROBABILITY MEASURE

References to the subject of probability do not occur in the literature of mathematics until the end of the fifteenth century when Pacioli (c. 1445–1509) asks how the stakes in a game of chance should be divided, if two men must quit before either has won or lost the game. A work on probability by Jacques Bernoulli (1654–1705), titled the *Ars conjectandi*, was published in 1713. In his work Bernoulli suggested that the ideas might be applied to civil, moral, and economic affairs. Another mathematician who contributed to the study of probability was Abraham de Moivre (1667–1754). His work, *The Doctrine of Chances* (1718), was dedicated to Sir Isaac Newton who was, at the time, president of the Royal Society of England.

A Frenchman, Pierre-Simon Laplace (1749–1827), who rose from humble origins to serve as minister of the interior under Napoleon, made a notable contribution on probability in his *Theorie analytique des probabilites* which was published in Paris in 1812. A common complaint, however, was the familiar one of students that the statement "thus it plainly appears" meant many painful hours of study to fill the gaps to find out how it "plainly appeared."

As we have already noted Fermat and Pascal created the foundations for the new mathematical theory of probability. In the ensuing years, the applications of probability have been developed into an important tool in the study of the social, economic, and political sciences. The closely allied subject of statistics has grown to become one of the most active fields of mathematics. Statistics is primarily the study of probability problems associated with the collection and analysis of sets of data. It is concerned with the problems of making decisions and drawing inferences on the basis of partial sets of data.

247

15.1.1 The words *chance*, *likely*, and *probably* occur quite commonly in our everyday vocabulary. For example, the weatherman comments that "The chance of rain is 50%." A student may remark, "I'll probably receive a C in this course." A man waiting for a train says "The train is likely to be late again." What is the explicit meaning of these statements?

Different interpretations can lead to a variety of meanings for probability. For our purposes, we will consider the interpretation of probability

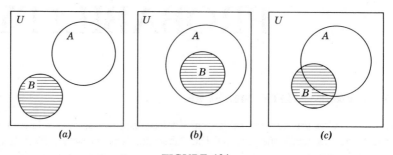

(a)   *(b)*   *(c)*

FIGURE 104.

(a) $A \cap B = \emptyset$.   (b) $B \subset A$.   (c) $A \cap B \neq \emptyset$ and $B \not\subset A$.

as a numerical measure of the relative frequency of occurrence of a particular kind of an element in a given universal set of elements.

For example, consider a universal set U and two sets A and B in U. Figure 104 suggests the possibilities for relationships between A and B in U. Suppose we are interested in an element $x \in B$. Then for the situation where A and B are disjoint, we can say that $x \notin A$. Also, if $B \subset A$, then we can say that $x \in A$. However, in the event that $A \cap B$ is not empty and $B \not\subset A$, knowing that $x \in B$ does not assure us that $x \in A$ nor $x \notin A$.

In the latter case, if $x \in B$ and $A \cap B \neq \emptyset$ and $B \not\subset A$, the Venn diagram seems to tell us intuitively that if "other things are equal," then an element $x \in B$ is just about as likely to be in A as not in A. In order to describe this notion, we proceed to develop a numerical measure of "the likelihood of an element belonging to a given set."

As a more concrete example, consider a shaker with ten small balls in it. Suppose six of the balls are black, three are red, and one white and otherwise they are alike. Now if we mix the shaker of balls and draw one of the balls without looking, we might ask a number of questions concerning the ball which was drawn. Is the ball red? Is it black? White? What are the chances that the ball is one of these colors?

Intuitively, one method of answering these questions is to use simple counting. The ball we have drawn is one of these colors, but we cannot say for sure which color it is. If the chance for drawing one ball is just as

much as for any other ball, we might say that the chance that the ball drawn
is black is $\dfrac{6}{10}$; that it is red is $\dfrac{3}{10}$; and that it is white is $\dfrac{1}{10}$.

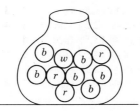

FIGURE 105.

The basic ideas of the frequency interpretation of probability can be
abstracted from the foregoing illustrations. The following points should
be noted.

1. By a probability we mean a number—a relative frequency.
2. A probability statement does *not* refer to any individual element.
   Rather, it implies some property of a subset of elements relative to
   a given set.
3. A probability statement does *not* mean that a particular outcome
   is to be expected a certain number of times. It does imply an "expect-
   ancy" or prognosis "in the long run."

15.1.1.1 Definition: If R is a nonempty set, which we call the **fundamental reference set**, and A is a subset of R defined
by some property, then by the **relative frequency
of A in R** we mean the number

$$f_n(A,R) = \frac{n(A \text{ in } R)}{n(R)}$$

where $n(A \text{ in } R)$ is the number of elements of A
in R and $n(R)$ is the number of elements in R.

15.1.1.2 Definition: By the **fundamental probability of A in R** we mean
the number $p(A) = f_n(A,R)$ if $n(R)$ is finite and
$p(A) = \lim_{n(R)\to\infty} f_n(A,R)$ if $n(R)$ is infinite.

Now let us consider a slightly more complicated situation. Suppose
we throw two dice in the usual manner. We might ask: What are the
possible outcomes? What is the probability of a seven? What is the
probability of two sixes?

If we let the number of spots appearing "up" on one die be the first
element of an ordered pair and the spots appearing on the other die be

the second element, we can display the outcomes in an "array." If we are only interested in the sum of the spots, we can simplify the tabulation into sums.

(1,1)	(1,2)	(1,3)	(1,4)	(1,5)	(1,6)		2	3	4	5	6	7
(2,1)	(2,2)	(2,3)	(2,4)	(2,5)	(2,6)		3	4	5	6	7	8
(3,1)	(3,2)	(3,3)	(3,4)	(3,5)	(3,6)		4	5	6	7	8	9
(4,1)	(4,2)	(4,3)	(4,4)	(4,5)	(4,6)		5	6	7	8	9	10
(5,1)	(5,2)	(5,3)	(5,4)	(5,5)	(5,6)		6	7	8	9	10	11
(6,1)	(6,2)	(6,3)	(6,4)	(6,5)	(6,6)		7	8	9	10	11	12

(a)   (b)

FIGURE 106.

A tree diagram can also be constructed to indicate the number of possible spots that might appear up in throwing two dice successively.

If we consider the fundamental reference set R to be the array in Figure 106(a) or (b), our definitions enable us immediately to compute the probability of a seven: $p(7) = \dfrac{1}{6}$. Also $p(6,6) = \dfrac{1}{36}$. However, let us not be deceived by the apparent simplicity of the situation. In actuality,

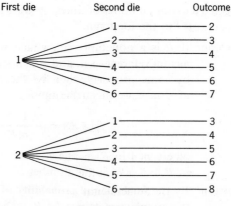

FIGURE 107.

the pair of dice may be thrown an indefinite number of times. If we **assume** that Figure 106(a) or (b) represents the actual reference set, then the probability statement $p(7) = \dfrac{1}{6}$ will reflect our definition of probability.

Note that the statement $p(7) = \dfrac{1}{6}$ does **not** refer to any individual throw of the dice. The statement **does** refer to the expected relative frequency of occurrence of a seven in throwing a pair of dice an indefinite number of times. Even with this interpretation, in the face of empirical evidence, we may be forced to conclude with respect to a particular pair of dice that the probability may be different.

Thus we must conclude that the numerical evaluation of the probability of an outcome rests on the assumption of a fundamental reference set and the existence of a well defined limit for the relative frequency interpretation.

15.1.2 In order to discuss probability in the language of mathematics, it is convenient to develop a special vocabulary for describing and translating probabilistic situations.

Probability situations are often called **experiments**. For every experiment there is a definite set of **possible outcomes** which we will call a **sample space** U. A particular outcome is called an **occurrence** or a **sample point** of U. An **event** is a subset A of the sample space U. For a given experiment there may be different sample spaces. The choice of a sample space in a given experiment is usually quite "natural." The sample space should, however, include all outcomes which may occur in the experiment. An outcome can be considered a particularly simple or basic event. However, many events are not outcomes.

By an experiment we mean a projected activity such as throwing dice, drawing cards from a deck, tossing coins, recording the results of tests, checking the quality of manufactured items, etc. For definiteness, let us consider an experiment consisting of tossing three coins. The possible outcomes might be listed as:

$$U_1 = \{\text{no heads, one head, two heads, three heads}\}$$

In this interpretation, the sample space U consists of the four elements called "no heads," "one head," "two heads," and "three heads." On the other hand, if we identify the coins, we might consider:

$$U_2 = \{T_1T_2T_3,\ T_1T_2H_3,\ T_1H_2T_3,\ H_1T_2T_3,\ T_1H_2H_3,\ H_1T_2H_3,$$
$$H_1H_2T_3,\ H_1H_2H_3\}$$

The sample space would then consist of the eight elements listed in U_2. Still other sample spaces might be possible, such as might occur if we were to consider a coin falling "on edge" or being lost. In any given problem, the choice of a sample space will depend upon the relevance of the outcomes, the way in which we assign a measure of probability, and the simplicity with which we can express the events of interest in the sample space.

When the three coins are tossed, a sample point of U occurs. That is, if we take U_1 for our sample space, tossing of the coins results in an element in U_1 appearing. If we are interested in one of these occurrences, then our event will or will not occur. We may be interested in two or more of the occurrences, in which case the event must be described as not occurring in any outcome but as possibly occurring in a sequence of outcomes. For example, if we are interested in the event "no heads followed by three heads," the total event cannot occur except in a sequence of outcomes.

15.1.2.1 Definition: By a **sample space** we mean a set U of possible outcomes of an experiment.

15.1.2.2 Definition: An **event** is a subset of a sample space.

Now let us consider how a numerical measure can be associated to the events in a sample space. Some reflection on the examples of 15.1.1 should suggest that events which cannot occur—that is, the null set of a sample space—should "naturally" have the value 0 assigned to them. Furthermore, if an event is certain—that is, the event is the whole of the sample space—the value 1 seems appropriate to assign to the event. Of course, this presumes that we can separate the outcomes and count them. If not, a limit process might be applied to obtain adequate results.

If an event is a proper subset of the sample space, we note that the numerical measure "ought to" lie in the interval 0 to 1. Also if A is an event and $\bar{A}$ is the complement of A in U, we would expect that the numerical measure to be associated to the union $A \cup \bar{A}$ should be 1. These considerations lead us to the following definition of a "**probability measure**" of an event in a sample space U.

15.1.2.3 Definition: A **probability measure** in a sample space U is a real valued function p defined over all subsets of U such that:
   (i) $0 \leq p(A) \leq 1$ for every subset A of U.
   (ii) $p(U) = 1$ and $p(\emptyset) = 0$.
   (iii) If A and B are subsets of U such that $A \cap B = \emptyset$, then $p(A \cup B) = p(A) + p(B)$.

In most experiments, the set U is considered finite and a definite value $p(u)$ is assigned to each single element subset $\{u\}$ of U. Perhaps the most important thing to notice is that a probability measure must satisfy the fundamental theorems of counting.

In order to determine the probability measure of an event in a given experiment we must first establish a sample space. Next, we must determine the relevant events. That is, we must specify the pertinent subsets of the given sample space U. Third, we must assign a probability measure to the sample space. Finally, we can often compute the probability of any particular event of interest by applying the fundamental theorems of counting.

Before continuing to the examination of some illustrations, the following additional terminology will be useful.

15.1.2.4 Definition: Two events A and B are said to be **mutually exclusive** if and only if $A \cap B = \emptyset$.

15.1.2.5 Definition: Two events A and B are said to be **independent** if and only if $p(A \cap B) = p(A)p(B)$.

Exercises 15.1

In the following, find the intuitive or "naive" probability for the given event.

1. If we throw two dice, what is the probability of throwing a "five"? An "eight"?
2. In tossing three coins, what is the probability of two heads and a tail on two successive tosses? What is a sample space for this question?
3. Consider exercise 6 of Exercises 14. What is the probability of a telephone number with four digits all alike?
4. Consider exercise 8 of Exercises 14. What is the probability of a particular guard being on the team formed by the coach, if the coach picks a team at "random"?
5. Consider exercise 10 of Exercises 14. What is the probability of obtaining a sample of ten bulbs with one defective bulb? If the carton of 100 bulbs contains twenty defective bulbs, what is the probability of obtaining a sample of ten bulbs with one defective bulb?

15.2 EXAMPLES

Now let us return to our experiment with the ten balls in a shaker. Two sample spaces suggest themselves:

$$U_1 = \{b_1, b_2, b_3, b_4, b_5, b_6, r_7, r_8, r_9, w_{10}\}$$
$$U_2 = \{b, r, w\}$$

Suppose we interest ourselves in the events:

$$A = \{a \text{ red ball}\} \text{ and } B = \{a \text{ black or white ball}\}$$

We can assign the probability measure or "weight" $\frac{1}{10}$ to each of the single element subsets of U_1. Notice that this assignment satisfies the requirements of the definition of a probability measure for the sample space U_1. For the sample space U_2, however, this assignment of values falls short of the definition. In this situation, there is no formal way of assigning a probability measure. A natural assignment is obtained by considering the counting process and the physical situation. We assign $p(b) = \frac{3}{5}$, $p(r) = \frac{3}{10}$, $p(w) = \frac{1}{10}$. This assignment not only satisfies the requirements of the definition we have given for a probability measure but also our intuitive understanding of what we mean by "probability."

The probability of the event A is now readily computed as $p(A) = \dfrac{3}{10}$.

Note that for U_1 we have $p(A) = p(r_7) + p(r_8) + p(r_9) = \dfrac{1}{10} + \dfrac{1}{10} + \dfrac{1}{10} = \dfrac{3}{10}$. We also have $p(B) = p(b) + p(w) = \dfrac{6}{10} + \dfrac{1}{10} = \dfrac{7}{10}$. The events A and B are **mutually exclusive** since $A \cap B = \emptyset$. The events A and B are **not independent** since $p(A \cap B) = 0$ and $p(A)p(B) = \left(\dfrac{3}{10}\right)\left(\dfrac{7}{10}\right) \neq 0$.

Many experiments consist of repetitions of a single "simpler" experiment. For example, we might consider an experiment consisting of drawing a ball from the shaker twice or more. In an experiment of this kind, there are two possibilities. After drawing the first ball we can either replace the drawn ball and begin over again or continue by drawing a second ball without replacing the first ball.

An experiment consisting of the repetition of a "simpler" experiment or **trial** is called a repeated trials experiment. If the repeated trials are **independent** in the sense that the original experiment is repeated, then the trials are said to be **"with replacement."** If successive trials depend upon previous trials, the trials are said to be **"dependent"** or **"without replacement."**

Consider drawing two balls from the shaker with ten balls. First, let us consider the case with replacement. We can form a sample space by considering the set of all ordered pairs of first and second draws from the shaker. That is, for U_1 we can form $U_1 \times U_1$ (see Figure 108).

$$(b_1,b_1)(b_2,b_1) \cdots\cdots (w_{10},b_1)$$
$$(b_1,b_2)(b_2,b_2) \cdots\cdots (w_{10},b_2)$$
$$\cdots\cdots\cdots\cdots\cdots\cdots$$
$$(b_1,w_{10})(b_2,w_{10}) \cdots\cdots (w_{10},w_{10})$$

FIGURE 108.

Note that the sample space $U_1 \times U_1$ consists of the 100 possible outcomes in drawing two balls with replacement. It seems quite natural to assign the measure $\dfrac{1}{100}$ to each sample point (x_i,y_j) in the sample space. If we consider each single draw as an independent event, we have $p(x_i,y_j) = p(x_i)p(y_j) = \left(\dfrac{1}{10}\right)\left(\dfrac{1}{10}\right) = \dfrac{1}{100}$. For the sample space $U_2 = \{b, r, w\}$, we have $U_2 \times U_2$ (see Figure 109).

$$(b,w)\ (r,w)\ (w,w) \qquad\qquad \tfrac{3}{50}\ \tfrac{3}{100}\ \tfrac{1}{100}$$
$$(a)\ (b,r)\ (r,r)\ (w,r) \qquad (b)\ \tfrac{9}{50}\ \tfrac{9}{100}\ \tfrac{3}{100}$$
$$(b,b)\ (r,b)\ (w,b) \qquad\qquad \tfrac{9}{25}\ \tfrac{9}{50}\ \tfrac{3}{50}$$

FIGURE 109.

In order to obtain the probability measures of the outcomes, we consider the elements of U_2 which form ordered pairs in $U_2 \times U_2$. As independent events we have $p(b) = \dfrac{3}{5}$, $p(r) = \dfrac{3}{10}$, and $p(w) = \dfrac{1}{10}$. For $p(b,w)$ we then have $p(b,w) = p(b)p(w) = \left(\dfrac{3}{5}\right)\left(\dfrac{1}{10}\right) = \dfrac{3}{50}$. In a similar manner we can assign probability measures to the other ordered pairs in $U_2 \times U_2$. Checking, note that this assignment of probability measures satisfies the definition.

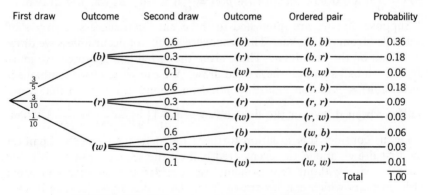

FIGURE 110. Tree for two draws from a shaker of balls.

With either sample space and their associated probability measures, we can find the probabilities of drawing various pairs of balls from the shaker with replacement. For example, the probability of drawing two red balls is $p(r,r) = \dfrac{9}{100}$. The probability of the event "exactly one white and one black ball" is $p(b,w) + p(w,b) = \dfrac{3}{50} + \dfrac{3}{50} = \dfrac{6}{50}$.

The notion of repeated independent trials can be generalized to n-independent trials. The sample space can be obtained by forming the cartesian product space of n-tuples of the original sample space with itself. The probability measure of a sample point is then assigned by using the rule for independent events.

15.2.1 Now let us consider the case of drawing two balls from the shaker in succession without replacement. Clearly, in this case, the results we might expect in drawing a second ball depend on what has been drawn for the first ball. For our first draw we have the sample space $U_1 = \{b_1, b_2, b_3, b_4, b_5, b_6, r_7, r_8, r_9, w_{10}\}$. If we ask, what is the probability of drawing a red ball?, we should readily answer $p(r) = \dfrac{3}{10}$.

Now, if we ask what is the probability of drawing a red ball again on the second draw, we note that the sample space for our second draw has changed. We have drawn either a red ball or some other colored ball on the first draw. If we have drawn a red ball, then our new sample space might be described as $R_1 = \{$nine balls, two of them red$\}$. If we have not drawn a red ball, then our new sample space would be $R_2 = \{$nine balls, three of them red$\}$. We can now assign a probability for drawing a red ball on the second draw, depending on the outcome of the first draw: $p(r) = \dfrac{2}{9}$ if a red ball was drawn, $p(r) = \dfrac{3}{9}$ if a red ball was not drawn.

Suppose that we are interested in the event "two successive draws of red balls" from the shaker. The event surely will not occur unless we draw a red ball on the first draw. Then, given that a red ball is drawn, we must draw a red ball again on the second draw. We can write p(two red balls in succession) $= p$(red on first draw)p(red on second draw, given that a red ball has been drawn in the first draw) $= \left(\dfrac{3}{10}\right)\left(\dfrac{2}{9}\right) = \dfrac{6}{90} = \dfrac{1}{15} = 0.066$.

Let us consider this situation further. Let A be the event "red ball on the first draw" and B the event "red ball on the second draw." For our sample space without replacement, we consider the set of all possible ordered pairs which can be drawn from the shaker by successive draws. The total number of pairs is 90. The number of pairs belonging to the event set A is 27. The number in B is also 27. The event $A \cap B$ consists of all those pairs in which both balls are red, $n(A \cap B) = 6$. Thus we can compute the probability that both balls drawn will be red as $p(A \cap B) = \dfrac{6}{90}$. Note that we can write $p(A)p$(red on second draw, given that a red ball was drawn on the first draw) $= p(A \cap B)$.

We denote the probability p(red on the second draw, given that a red ball has been drawn on the first draw) by $p(B \mid A)$. We can then write, $p(B \mid A) = \dfrac{p(A \cap B)}{p(A)} = \dfrac{2}{9}$. As before, note that the probability $p(B \mid A)$ is not the same as $p(B)$.

Given a sample space U, the notion of "the probability of an event B, given that an event A has occurred" is called a **conditional probability**.

15.2.1.1 Definition: If A and B are events in the same sample space U and $p(A) \neq 0$, then by the **conditional probability of B, given A**, denoted by $p(B \mid A)$, we mean

$$p(B \mid A) = \frac{p(A \cap B)}{p(A)}.$$

Returning to the situation where we draw balls **with replacement**, we note that $p(B \mid A) = \dfrac{p(A \cap B)}{p(A)} = p(B)$. That is, when the events A and B are independent events, we have $p(B \mid A) = p(B)$. This is exactly as our intuition would have it, that independent events are events such that the occurrence of one of the events does not affect the probability of the other event, providing $p(A) \neq 0$.

15.2.2 A **tree diagram** is often useful in describing experiments. A particular outcome of successive experiments or trials is represented by a **path** through the tree. Each experiment or trial is represented by a set of **branches**, each outcome by a **joint**. Successive trials are called **levels** of the tree.

For example, the following tree (Figure 111) illustrates the experiment consisting of drawing balls from the shaker. There are ten balls—six black, three red, and one white—in the shaker. The possible outcome of a given draw without replacement can be designated by (b) for black, (r) for red, and (w) for white.

A probability measure called a **weight** can then be assigned to each branch of the tree. The weight to be assigned to a given branch is the probability of the outcome at the terminal end of the branch, given the outcome at the initial end. That is, the weight is the conditional probability of the outcome at the terminal end, given the outcome at the initial end of the branch. Finally, we assign a weight to each path of the tree. This weight is set equal to the product of the weights of the branches along the path. This method yields a probability measure for the paths which satisfies the requirements of the definition for a probability measure. The tree diagram then enables us to find the probability of events in the sample space defined by the ends of the paths of the tree.

For example, if $A = \{$one black, one red, and one white ball in three draws$\}$, then $A = \{(b,r,w),\ (b,w,r),\ (r,b,w),\ (r,w,b),\ (w,b,r),\ (w,r,b)\}$ and $p(A) = \dfrac{1}{40} + \dfrac{1}{40} + \dfrac{1}{40} + \dfrac{1}{40} + \dfrac{1}{40} + \dfrac{1}{40} = \dfrac{3}{20}$. If $B = \{$two or three red balls in three draws$\}$, then $p(B) = \dfrac{1}{20} + \dfrac{1}{20} + \dfrac{1}{20} + \dfrac{1}{120} + \dfrac{1}{120} + \dfrac{1}{120} + \dfrac{1}{120} = \dfrac{11}{60}$.

An interesting example of a tree diagram is in the study of a duel or "gunfight." Suppose a marshal (M) is going to have a gunfight with a "badman" (B). The marshal can draw and fire his first shot in 0.3 second

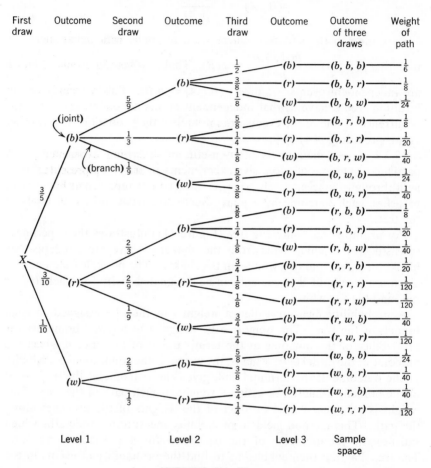

First draw	Outcome	Second draw	Outcome	Third draw	Outcome	Outcome of three draws	Weight of path

FIGURE 111. Tree.

with a probability of 0.6 of hitting his man. He can fire each succeeding shot in 0.2 second with a probability of 0.8 of hitting his target. The badman can outdraw the marshal by 0.1 second but he hits his target with a probability of only 0.35 on his first shot. He fires each succeeding shot in 0.2 second with a probability of 0.5 of hitting his target.

If the marshal and badman meet and each man fires two shots, determine what the probabilities are for each of them surviving.

To construct a tree diagram, we first determine the order of the possible events. For convenience, consider the following time scale:

$$0 \quad 1 \quad 2 \quad 3 \quad 4 \quad 5 \quad 6 \quad \text{in tenths of a second}$$
$$B \quad M \quad B \quad M$$
$$1 \quad 1 \quad 2 \quad 2$$

The letters and numbers below the time scale indicate the men firing and their first and second shots. The outcome of each action or shot is a "hit" or "miss" or, what is equivalent, the survival of one or both of the men. There are four levels or trials.

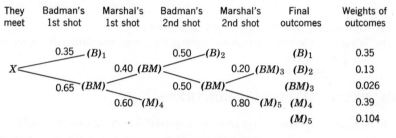

They meet	Badman's 1st shot	Marshal's 1st shot	Badman's 2nd shot	Marshal's 2nd shot	Final outcomes	Weights of outcomes
	0.35 $(B)_1$		0.50 $(B)_2$		$(B)_1$	0.35
X		0.40 (BM)		0.20 $(BM)_3$	$(B)_2$	0.13
	0.65 (BM)		0.50 (BM)		$(BM)_3$	0.026
		0.60 $(M)_4$		0.80 $(M)_5$	$(M)_4$	0.39
					$(M)_5$	0.104

FIGURE 112. "Gunfight."

The probabilities of survival can be read off from the tree. The probability of the badman surviving is $p(B) = 0.48$. The probability of the marshal surviving is $p(M) = 0.494$. The probability that they both survive is $p(BM) = 0.026$.

Exercises 15.2

1. Describe explicitly the sample spaces and compute the probabilities for:
   (a) The tossing of five coins and the probability of the event "no more than two heads."
   (b) Two successive throws of a pair of dice and the probability of the event "two pair." A pair being 2 ones, 2 twos, etc.
2. A container has sixty colored tags: ten blue, twenty white, and thirty red.
   (a) Construct tree diagrams for the experiments with three successive draws with replacement and without replacement.
   (b) Find the probability of the event "two blue and one white" with replacement and without replacement.
3. A "shell game" is played as follows: A small pea is hidden under one of three "shells" at random and the player attempts to guess under which "shell" the pea lies.
   (a) Construct a tree diagram for five plays of the game, if the probability of guessing correctly is one-third.
   (b) If winning pays double what losing costs, is the game a "fair" game?

4. A deer hunter with bow and arrows shoots three arrows at a deer. He kills (K), hits (H), or misses (M) the deer with the probabilities listed in the following table:

First Arrow		Second Arrow		Third Arrow	
Prob.	Outcome	Prob.	Outcome	Prob.	Outcome
0.3	K	0.5	HK	0.2	HMK
		0.5	HM	0.8	HMM
0.3	H	0.1	MK	0.6	MHK
		0.1	MH	0.4	MHM
0.4	M	0.8	MM	0.1	MMK
				0.1	MMH
				0.8	MMM

(a) Construct a tree diagram of the deer hunt.
(b) What are the probabilities of killing the deer, wounding the deer, and missing the deer?

15.3 PROBABILITY DISTRIBUTIONS

In constructing tree diagrams of repeated experiments, we note that the sample space of outcomes generated is associated with an "induced" probability measure. We are often interested in another outcome space of events and ask whether we can develop a probability measure for the space of interest. That is, if $U = \{d_1, d_2, \cdots, d_n\}$ is the sample space of outcomes "naturally" generated and $R = \{r_1, r_2, \cdots, r_k\}$ is an outcome space of special interest, we wish to define a function with domain U and range R such that a probability measure will be "induced" on R.

Suppose that we can find a function $f(d_i) = r_j$ with domain U and range R. If we assign to each element of R the sum of the weights of the pre-images of the element of R in U, then it can be shown that this assignment of weights to the elements of R will constitute a probability measure in R. Such a probability measure is said to be a "**measure induced by the function f on R.**"

For example, consider our experiment of drawing three colored balls from a shaker without replacement. Suppose that we are specially interested in the number of black balls drawn. We can call the outcome space of interest $R = \{0, 1, 2, 3\}$. The function f is defined by noting the number of black balls in each of the outcomes of U. Table 50 exhibits the domain set U with their associated measures and the range set R defining the function f.

The measure induced on R by f is found by determining the sum of the weights for a given element in R. For convenience we can table the range set and the measure induced by the function f (Table 51). A graph of the

TABLE 50

Outcomes and Weights for Determining a Measure
Induced by the Functions f, g, and h (given).

Weight of Outcomes in U	Sample Space U Domain of Functions	Sample Space R, Range f	Sample Space T, Range g	Sample Space H, Range h
$\frac{1}{6}$	(b,b,b)	3	0	0
$\frac{1}{8}$	(b,b,r)	2	0	1
$\frac{1}{24}$	(b,b,w)	2	3	0
$\frac{1}{8}$	(b,r,b)	2	0	1
$\frac{1}{20}$	(b,r,r)	1	0	2
$\frac{1}{40}$	(b,r,w)	1	3	1
$\frac{1}{24}$	(b,w,b)	2	2	0
$\frac{1}{40}$	(b,w,r)	1	2	1
$\frac{1}{8}$	(r,b,b)	2	0	1
$\frac{1}{20}$	(r,b,r)	1	0	2
$\frac{1}{40}$	(r,b,w)	1	3	1
$\frac{1}{20}$	(r,r,b)	1	0	2
$\frac{1}{120}$	(r,r,r)	0	0	3
$\frac{1}{120}$	(r,r,w)	0	3	2
$\frac{1}{40}$	(r,w,b)	1	2	1
$\frac{1}{120}$	(r,w,r)	0	2	2
$\frac{1}{24}$	(w,b,b)	2	1	0
$\frac{1}{40}$	(w,b,r)	1	1	1
$\frac{1}{40}$	(w,r,b)	1	1	1
$\frac{1}{120}$	(w,r,r)	0	1	2

induced measure with the range set is often useful in studying the properties of the induced measure.

TABLE 51

Range values in R	0	1	2	3
Induced measure	$\frac{1}{30}$	$\frac{3}{10}$	$\frac{1}{2}$	$\frac{1}{6}$

As a second example, consider the function g defined as "the draw on which a white ball is obtained with 0 indicating that no white ball is drawn." We denote the range set by $T = \{0, 1, 2, 3\}$. As before, we can table the range set and the measure induced by g. A graph of the induced

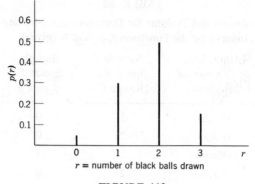

FIGURE 113.

measure with the range set can also be constructed. Note that the most probable value of g is 0 while for f it was the value 2.

TABLE 52

Range values in T	0	1	2	3
Induced measure	$\frac{7}{10}$	$\frac{1}{10}$	$\frac{1}{10}$	$\frac{1}{10}$

As a third example, consider the function h defined as "the number of red balls drawn." We denote the range set by $H = \{0, 1, 2, 3\}$. Table 53

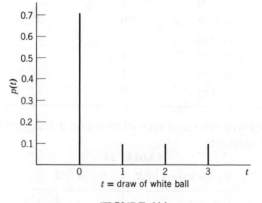

FIGURE 114.

and Figure 115 describe the probability measure induced by h over the range set H.

In the three examples, we observe that the probability measure induced by a function over a range set defines in turn a real valued function whose

TABLE 53

Range values in H	0	1	2	3
Induced measure	$\frac{7}{24}$	$\frac{21}{40}$	$\frac{7}{40}$	$\frac{1}{120}$

domain set is the set of outcomes of interest and whose range set is a probability measure in the domain set. Functions of this kind are called **probability distributions**.

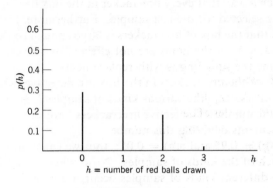

h = number of red balls drawn

FIGURE 115.

15.3.0.1 Definition: By a **probability distribution** we mean a real valued function whose range set constitutes a probability measure in the domain set of the function.

The notion of a probability distribution is essential to the theory of statistics. When the probability distribution of an outcome space is known, it enables us to make decisions and predictions with a known probability of success.

15.3.1 A simple yet very useful and important probability distribution, called the **binomial probability distribution**, illustrates a broad application to a large class of problems.

We have noted that the simplest and most common division of a set is into two subsets. For example, many items, such as cigarettes, light bulbs, ball-point pens, and firecrackers, can be classified as "good" or "defective."

For definiteness, let us consider a large box of firecrackers. We wish to determine how "good" the firecrackers are. Let us say that a firecracker is "good" if it goes off with a "bang" approximately four seconds after the fuse is lit. It is clear that we should not test every firecracker in the box. Thus let us consider a small sample, say four firecrackers selected for testing from the box. Letting g denote a "good" firecracker and b a defective firecracker, we list the possible kinds of samples to expect.

TABLE 54

(g,g,g,g)

$(g,g,g,b)(g,g,b,g)(g,b,g,g)(b,g,g,g)$

$(g,g,b,b)(g,b,g,b)(b,g,g,b)(b,g,b,g)(g,b,b,g)(b,b,g,g)$

$(b,b,b,g)(b,b,g,b)(b,g,b,b)(g,b,b,b)$

(b,b,b,b)

Let us suppose that the sample of four firecrackers will be selected from the box in such a way that every firecracker in the box has an equal probability of being selected for the test sample. Furthermore, for convenience, let us assume that the box of firecrackers is large enough so that the probabilities associated with the items are not effected by successive selections. That is, assume the sampling is with replacement.

Now, if 5% of the firecrackers in the box are defective, what will be the probabilities of selecting the various kinds of samples? Since the events of interest are "the number of defective firecrackers," we let $B = \{0, 1, 2, 3, 4\}$ be a set of elements denoting this number.

We have $p(g) = 0.95$ and $p(b) = 0.05$; thus we can compute the probabilities for each of the kinds of samples. Now, when we ask in how many ways can the different kinds of samples occur, we note that there are five terms which are arranged in dichotomies. A bit of reflection suggests that a binomial expansion will describe this situation (recall 14.3).

$$(g + b)^4 = g^4 + 4g^3b + 6g^2b^2 + 4gb^3 + b^4$$
$$= (g,g,g,g) + 4(g,g,g,b) + 6(g,g,b,b) + 4(g,b,b,b) + (b,b,b,b)$$

Since $p(g,g,g,g) = 0.81451$, $p(g,g,g,b) = 0.04287$, $p(g,g,b,b) = 0.00225$, $p(g,b,b,b) = 0.00012$, and $p(b,b,b,b) = 0.00001$, the binomial expansion defines an induced measure over the set B which is a probability distribution. Table 55 and Figure 116 illustrate the induced measure and distribution of the sample of four firecrackers from the 5% defective box.

TABLE 55

Range values in B	0	1	2	3	4
Induced measure	0.8145	0.1715	0.0135	0.0005	0.00001

15.3.1.1 Definition: By a **binomial probability distribution** we mean a probability distribution obtained as the result of expanding a power of a binomial.

15.3.1.2 Definition: The probability measure induced by a binomial expansion is called a **binomial measure**.

If an experiment has two possible outcomes, say "good" and "bad" with probabilities p and q, respectively, and if the experiment is repeated

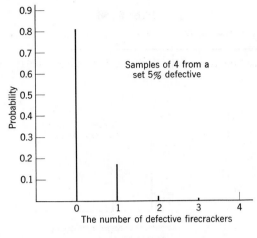

FIGURE 116.

independently *n* times, then a binomial measure and probability distribution is defined over the range set of the numbers of "good" (or "bad") outcomes.

As a further illustration, suppose the firecrackers are 20% defective. The selection of a sample of four items from the box can be displayed by a tree diagram showing the induced measure.

The tree diagram and the binomial expansion of $(g + b)^4$ enable us to table the induced measure and distribution.

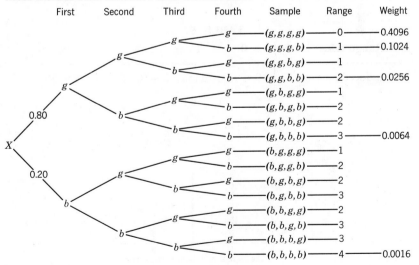

FIGURE 117.

TABLE 56

Range values in B	0	1	2	3	4
Induced measure	0.409	0.409	0.154	0.026	0.002

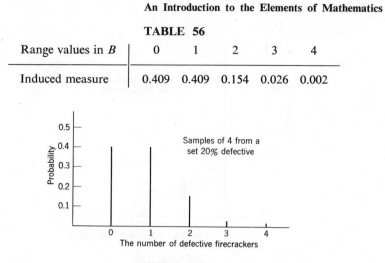

FIGURE 118.

Note that the range values of the binomial distribution depend on three variables: the value in the event set we have called B, the number of independent trials or sample size n, and the fundamental probability of an outcome p. If one or more of these variables changes in value, the associated probability will also be changed.

For example, if a box of firecrackers is 40% defective, the induced measure and distribution will be as shown in Table 57 and Figure 119.

TABLE 57

Range values in B	0	1	2	3	4
Induced measure	0.1296	0.3456	0.3456	0.1536	0.0256

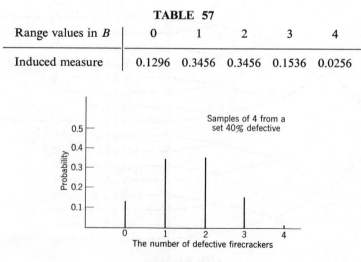

FIGURE 119.

As a final illustration, consider the distribution obtained if a sample of eight is selected from a box of 40% defective firecrackers. We have:

$$p(g) = 0.6 \text{ and } p(b) = 0.4$$

$$(g + b)^8 = g^8 + 8g^7b + 28g^6b^2 + 56g^5b^3 + 70g^4b^4$$
$$+ 56g^3b^5 + 28g^2b^6 + 8gb^7 + b^8$$

$$p(g^8) = 0.0168, \ p(g^7b) = 0.0112, \ p(g^6b^2) = 0.0075$$

$$p(g^5b^3) = 0.0049, \ p(g^4b^4) = 0.0033, \ p(g^3b^5) = 0.0022$$

$$p(g^2b^6) = 0.0015, \ p(gb^7) = 0.0010, \ p(b^8) = 0.0006$$

Using this information, we can table the induced measure for the range set $B = \{0, 1, 2, 3, 4, 5, 6, 7, 8\}$ (see Table 58) and graph the resulting binomial probability distribution.

TABLE 58

B	0	1	2	3	4	5	6	7	8
P	0.017	0.090	0.210	0.275	0.231	0.123	0.042	0.008	0.001

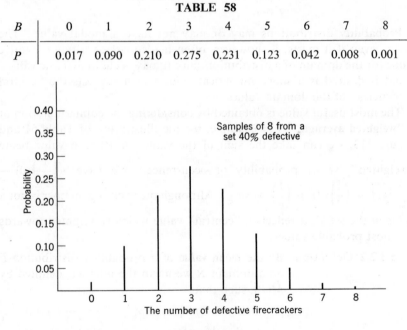

FIGURE 120.

In conclusion, if we require that the box of firecrackers should be in general no more than 5% defective, we can select a sample of four as described and if, on testing these four, none are defective, we can assume with some confidence that the box of firecrackers is as good as desired. On the other hand, if we find one defective firecracker in our sample of four, we note that if the box is only 5% defective the chance for this occurrence is slim and that the likelihood is that the box contains a larger percentage of defective firecrackers than we should allow.

15.3.2 In describing probability distributions, it is convenient to have some descriptive numerical measures of the distributions. In the examples we have considered, notice that there appears to be a most probable value in the domain of the distribution in most cases.

For example, in Figure 113, the event "two black balls" denoted by 2 is the most likely occurrence. In Figure 114, the value 0 is the most likely in the set T. In Figure 115, the value 1 is most likely. However, in Figure 118, both 0 and 1 are equally likely.

15.3.2.1 Definition: By the **mode** of a probability distribution we mean the value r_i in the domain of the distribution such that $p(r_i) > p(r_j)$ for all r_j in the domain such that $j \neq i$.

Probability distributions may or may not have a modal value. The mode, even if it exists, is, however, often inadequate as a representative value for the domain of a distribution since it may occur at extreme values. What is desired is a single numerical value which suggests the "central tendencies" of the domain values.

The most useful value is obtained by considering the common notion of a "**weighted average**." For example, for the illustration of Table 51 and Figure 113, we can take the sum of the values in R, each value being "weighted" by its probability of occurrence. We have: $\left(\frac{1}{30}\right)(0) + \left(\frac{3}{10}\right)(1) + \left(\frac{1}{2}\right)(2) + \left(\frac{1}{6}\right)(3) = \frac{9}{5}$. Although the resulting number is not a value in the set R, it reflects a "central" value which is weighted towards the most probable values.

15.3.2.2 Definition: By the **mean value** of a probability distribution P on a domain R we mean the number, denoted by $M(P)$, such that:

$$M(P) = r_1 p(r_1) + r_2 p(r_2) + \cdots + r_k p(r_k)$$

where $R = \{r_1, r_2, \cdots, r_k\}$ and $p(r_i)$ is the probability associated with the outcome r_i.

For example, the mean value of the distribution illustrated by Figure 114 is:

$$\left(\frac{7}{10}\right)(0) + \left(\frac{1}{10}\right)(1) + \left(\frac{1}{10}\right)(2) + \left(\frac{1}{10}\right)(3) = \frac{3}{5}.$$

For Figure 115, we have:

$$\left(\frac{7}{24}\right)(0) + \left(\frac{21}{40}\right)(1) + \left(\frac{7}{40}\right)(2) + \left(\frac{1}{120}\right)(3) = \frac{9}{10}.$$

For Figure 118, we have:

$$(0.409)(0) + (0.409)(1) + (0.154)(2) + (0.026)(3) + (0.002)(4) = 0.803$$

Although the mean value of a probability distribution can be effectively used to describe the distribution, it does not suggest the "spread" or "variation" of values in the domain of the distribution. It is entirely possible that two distributions can have the same mean value yet be quite different due to the "spreading" of their domain sets.

For example, suppose we toss a coin until a head appears or until we have tossed the coin three times. We can define the following two functions on the outcome space of the experiment.

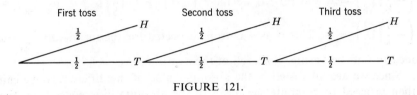

FIGURE 121.

Let f be the "number of heads" and g be the "number of tails." The sample spaces and weights are listed in Tables 59 and 60.

TABLE 59

Weight	Outcome	Range of f	Range of g
$\frac{1}{2}$	H	1	0
$\frac{1}{4}$	TH	1	1
$\frac{1}{8}$	TTH	1	2
$\frac{1}{8}$	TTT	0	3

TABLE 60

(a)		
Range of f	0	1
Measure	$\frac{1}{8}$	$\frac{7}{8}$

(b)				
Range of g	0	1	2	3
Measure	$\frac{1}{2}$	$\frac{1}{4}$	$\frac{1}{8}$	$\frac{1}{8}$

Both of the probability distributions defined by the induced measures on the ranges of f and g have the mean value $\frac{7}{8}$. The distributions are, however, plainly different. To describe this difference in the "variation" of the domains of probability distributions, we consider the differences of the domain values from the mean value.

For example, for the distributions defined by Table 60, we have:

(a) for domain f: $\left(1 - \dfrac{7}{8}\right) = \dfrac{1}{8}$ and $\left(0 - \dfrac{7}{8}\right) = -\dfrac{7}{8}$.

(b) for domain g: $\left(3 - \dfrac{7}{8}\right) = \dfrac{17}{8}, \left(2 - \dfrac{7}{8}\right) = \dfrac{9}{8}, \left(1 - \dfrac{7}{8}\right) = \dfrac{1}{8},$

$\left(0 - \dfrac{7}{8}\right) = -\dfrac{7}{8}.$

If we consider the mean value for these sets of differences, however, we note that the means are always equal to 0. That is, for (a) we have $\left(\dfrac{1}{8}\right)\left(\dfrac{7}{8}\right) +$ $\left(-\dfrac{7}{8}\right)\left(\dfrac{1}{8}\right) = 0$ and for (b) we have $\left(\dfrac{17}{8}\right)\left(\dfrac{1}{8}\right) + \left(\dfrac{9}{8}\right)\left(\dfrac{1}{8}\right) + \left(\dfrac{1}{8}\right)\left(\dfrac{1}{8}\right) +$ $\left(-\dfrac{7}{8}\right)\left(\dfrac{1}{2}\right) = 0$. This is as was to be expected for the mean value $\dfrac{7}{8}$ is a measure of the "center" of each of the distributions.

Since we are interested in the absolute value of the differences, we can then proceed to compute the mean of the absolute differences from the mean value of the distribution. For our examples, we then obtain:

(a) $\left(\dfrac{1}{8}\right)\left(\dfrac{7}{8}\right) + \left(\dfrac{7}{8}\right)\left(\dfrac{1}{8}\right) = \dfrac{7}{32}.$

(b) $\left(\dfrac{17}{8}\right)\left(\dfrac{1}{8}\right) + \left(\dfrac{9}{8}\right)\left(\dfrac{1}{8}\right) + \left(\dfrac{1}{8}\right)\left(\dfrac{1}{4}\right) + \left(\dfrac{7}{8}\right)\left(\dfrac{1}{2}\right) = \dfrac{7}{8}.$

15.3.2.3 Definition: By the **mean deviation** of a probability distribution P on a domain $R = \{r_1, r_2, \cdots, r_k\}$ we mean the mean value of the absolute differences $|r_i - M(P)|$, denoted by $D(P)$: $D(P) = |r_1 - M(P)|\, p(r_1) + |r_2 - M(P)|\, p(r_2) + \cdots + |r_k - M(P)|\, p(r_k)$.

The mean deviation supplies us with a numerical measure which describes the "spread" or "variation" of values in the domain of a probability distribution. However, for theoretical reasons, a much more useful and commonly used measure for describing the "variation" is the **variance** and the **standard deviation**.

To obtain the variance (rather than using the absolute values), the differences are squared. The mean value of the differences squared is then called the variance. The standard deviation is then obtained by taking the positive square root of the variance.

15.3.2.4 Definition: By the **variance** of a probability distribution P on a domain $R = \{r_1, r_2, \cdots, r_k\}$ we mean the number denoted by $V(P)$ such that:

$$V(P) = [r_1 - M(P)]^2 p(r_1) + [r_2 - M(P)]^2 p(r_2)$$
$$+ \cdots + [r_k - M(P)]^2 p(r_k)$$

where $p(r_i)$ is the probability associated with r_i, and $M(P)$ is the mean value of the probability distribution.

15.3.2.5 Definition: By the **standard deviation** of a probability distribution P on a domain R we mean the number denoted by $S(P)$ such that $S(P) = \sqrt{V(P)}$.

For example, the variances and standard deviations for the distributions defined in Table 60 are:

(a) $V(P) = \left(0 - \frac{7}{8}\right)^2\left(\frac{1}{8}\right) + \left(1 - \frac{7}{8}\right)^2\left(\frac{7}{8}\right) = \left(\frac{49}{64}\right)\left(\frac{1}{8}\right) + \left(\frac{1}{64}\right)\left(\frac{7}{8}\right) = \frac{7}{64}$

$S(P) = \sqrt{\frac{7}{64}} = 0.331$

(b) $V(P) = \left(\frac{49}{64}\right)\left(\frac{1}{2}\right) + \left(\frac{1}{64}\right)\left(\frac{1}{4}\right) + \left(\frac{81}{64}\right)\left(\frac{1}{8}\right) + \left(\frac{289}{64}\right)\left(\frac{1}{8}\right) = \frac{71}{64}$

$S(P) = \sqrt{\frac{71}{64}} = 1.053$

Exercises 15.3

1. Consider exercise 10 of Exercises 14 and exercise 5 of Exercises 15.1. Construct a probability distribution for samples of ten bulbs from the carton of 100 light bulbs containing ten defective light bulbs. Find the mean value and standard deviation of the distribution.
2. Toss five coins 500 times, tabulating the number of heads occurring on each toss. Construct a probability distribution based on your empirical results, and compute the mean value and standard deviation for this distribution.
3. Consider tossing five "ideal" coins. Then
   (a) develop a fundamental reference set.
   (b) define a function whose domain is the fundamental reference set and whose range is the "number of heads."
   (c) show that the probability distribution induced by the function is a binomial probability distribution.
   (d) construct a graph of the distribution and compute its mean value and standard deviation.
   (e) compare the results of this exercise with the results of exercise 2.
4. Consider the example of the firecrackers given in 15.3.1. Using the sample

size of four, construct a table of the probabilities for obtaining a sample with one defective firecracker, if the box of firecrackers is 5% defective, 10% defective, 15% defective, etc. Construct the graph of the function whose domain is the per cent of defective firecrackers in the box and whose range is the probability of obtaining one defective in a sample of four. Interpret and discuss the possible meaning to be attached to this function.

5. Consider exercise 2 of Exercises 15.2, concerning a container with 60 colored tags.
   (a) If f is defined as the function described by "the number of blue tags drawn in three successive draws from the container without replacement," table the range values and induced measure for f and construct a graph for the probability distribution so defined.
   (b) Compute the mean value and standard deviation of the distribution for part (a).
   (c) If g is described by "the number of red tags following a blue tag in three successive draws from the container without replacement," then do as in parts (a) and (b) with respect to g.

Exercises 15

1. If five cards are drawn at random without replacement from a standard deck of cards, then
   (a) what is the probability that they form a flush?
   (b) a straight?
   (c) a straight flush?

2. Suppose that the probability is 0.55 for the birth of a male child. If a woman is to have five children, then find
   (a) the probability that she will have three boys and two girls, before she has any children.
   (b) the probability that she will have children of both sexes.
   (c) the probability that she will have son, daughter, son, daughter, son in that order.
   (d) the probability that she will have two daughters, given that she already has two sons.
   (e) the probability that she will have three sons and two daughters, given that she already has a son and a daughter.

3. A certain room has two doors. The probability that both doors are locked is $\frac{3}{4}$. The probability that a key to one of the doors is among twelve keys in the drawer of a desk is $\frac{1}{2}$. If a person selects two keys at "random" from among the twelve keys in the drawer, what is the probability of his being able to enter the room?

4. Two letters are selected from the word **PROBABILITY** at "random." What is the probability that the letters selected are the same? Are vowels?

5. There are two similar containers. One container has six black balls, three red balls, and one blue ball. The other container has five blue balls, four black balls, and one red ball. One of the containers is selected at "random"

and one ball is drawn from it. If the ball is black, a second ball is drawn from the other container.

(*a*) What is the probability that a blue ball is drawn?

(*b*) What is the probability that two black balls are drawn?

(*c*) What is the probability that a blue ball is drawn in the second draw?

6. A professional baseball player has estimated the probability of his getting on base and progressing around the bases. If *O*, *F*, *S*, *T*, and *R* indicate being out or stranded, on first, second, third, and scoring a run, respectively, then the probabilities are as indicated in Table 61.

TABLE 61

Probability when	$p(O)$	$p(F)$	$p(S)$	$p(T)$	$p(R)$
at bat	0.575	0.20	0.10	0.05	0.075
on first	0.60	· · ·	0.20	0.10	0.10
on second	0.50	· · ·	· · ·	0.20	0.30
on third	0.50	· · ·	· · ·	· · ·	0.50

(*a*) What are the probabilities of his scoring? Of being out or stranded?

(*b*) What is the mean number of bases that he can expect to attain? (*Hint:* Construct a function whose range is the number of bases attained before being put out or stranded.)

7. A television set has six power tubes, ten regular tubes, and eight peanut tubes. Table 62 gives the probable life of a random tube of each kind.

TABLE 62

Type	The probability of the tube becoming inoperative in the given period in 1,000's of hours				
	0–1	1–2.5	2.5–5	5–10	10–20
power	0.05	0.03	0.10	0.20	0.80
regular	0.02	0.01	0.05	0.10	0.60
peanut	0.04	0.03	0.08	0.15	0.80

(*a*) What is the probability that *no* tubes become inoperative during the first 1,000 hours of use?

(*b*) What is the probability that at least one tube will become inoperative in 5,000 hours of use?

(*c*) If one power tube and two peanut tubes are replaced at the end of 2,500 hours of operation, what is the probability that at least one tube will become inoperative in the next 2,500 hours of use?

8. Consider the "shell game" of exercise 3 in Exercises 15.2. If *f* is the function described as "the number of times the player is ahead in five games" and *g* is "the amount the player is ahead in five games," then table the range values and induced measures for *f* and *g* and graph the probability distributions so defined. Compute the mean values and standard deviations for the two distributions.

9. What is the probability that a permutation of 5 numbers leaves no numbers fixed?

10. A mouse is placed at the start of a maze arranged as shown in Figure 122. If the mouse does not turn around and leave any junction by the same route as it enters, but chooses the other corridors with equal probability, then

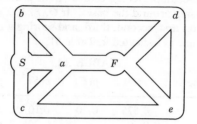

FIGURE 122.

(a) construct five levels of a tree diagram for the maze.

(b) define the function "level at which the mouse finishes" and form a table of the range values and induced measures of the function.

(c) Construct a graph of the probability distribution of the five range values tabled in (b).

(d) Estimate the mean value and variance for the probability distribution.

11. On occasion it happens that a sample space U can be divided into two events A and B such that $p(A)$ and $p(B)$ are known. Furthermore, the probabilities $p(C)$, $p(C \mid A)$, and $p(C \mid B)$ may be known for a third event C. Now if we observe that the event C has occurred, we may wish to know how likely it is that A has occurred or that B has occurred. That is, we would like to know the value of $p(A \mid C)$ and $p(B \mid C)$.

If $A \cup B = U$, then find $p(A \mid C)$ and $p(B \mid C)$ in terms of $p(A)$, $p(B)$, $p(C)$, $p(C \mid A)$, and $p(C \mid B)$. (This is a special case of a formula called Bayes formula.)

12. A manufacturing plant has two coil-winding machines. Machine A winds 100 coils per day and machine B winds 200 coils per day. Machine A produces 5% defective coils while B produces 8% defectives.

If, at the end of a day's production, a single coil is inspected and it turns out to be defective, then what is the probability that it was wound by machine A?

13. Seven ranked tennis players A_1, B_2, C_3, D_4, E_5, F_6, and G_7, are to play in a tennis match consisting of three rounds of play. Six players are selected at random to play in the first round, the seventh drawing a bye. The winners of the first round, along with the seventh player, are paired at random to play in the second round. The winners of the second round then play for the match.

If the probability of a player losing against another player is equal to his ranking divided by the sum of the two players' rankings (for example,

$P(B_2 \text{ loses to } E_5) = \frac{2}{7})$, what is the probability that A_1 wins the tennis match? That G_7 wins the match?

14. A manufacturer of ball point pens uses simple sampling to control the quality of shipments made to distributors. The sampling consists of selecting ten random samples from each shipment and testing the sample pens to see that they are operative. If the manufacturer wants a probability of 0.90 that shipments in the long run are no more than 10% defective, then how many defective pens should be allowed in a given sample of ten pens?

15. (Exercise 14 continued): If, when more than the allowed number of defective pens are found in a sample, the entire shipment of pens is inspected so that there are essentially no defectives in that shipment when it is shipped out, what will be the actual quality of pens in the long run received by the distributors, if the pens when manufactured were in fact 10% defective? 20% defective?

APPENDICES

APPENDICES

appendix A
SELECTIONS
FOR FURTHER
READING

The following selections have been divided into two lists: for the average reader, and for those teachers and others interested in source and background material.

List I

1. Black, M.	*Critical Thinking*	
	Prentice-Hall (1952)	
2. Breuer, J.	*Introduction to the Theory of Sets*	
	Prentice-Hall (1958)	
3. Copi, I. M.	*Symbolic Logic* (or *Introduction to Logic*)	
	The Macmillan Co. (1954)	
4. Court, N. A.	*Mathematics in Fun and in Earnest*	
	The Dial Press (1958)	
5. Dadourian, H. M.	*How to Study, How to Solve*	
	Addison-Wesley Publishing Co. (1951)	
6. Dubisch, R.	*The Nature of Number*	
	The Ronald Press (1952)	
7. Kline, M.	*Mathematics and the Physical World*	
	Thomas Y. Crowell Co. (1959)	
8. Levi, H.	*Elements of Algebra*	
	Chelsea Publishing Co. (1954)	
9. Morris, M.	*Signs, Language, and Behavior*	
	Prentice-Hall (1946)	
10. Polya, G.	*How to Solve It*	
	Princeton University Press (1948)	
11. Sloan, R. W.	*An Introduction to Modern Mathematics*	
	Prentice-Hall (1960)	
12. Struik, D. J.	*A Concise History of Mathematics*	
	Dover Publications, Inc. (1948)	

13. Thurston, H. A.   *The Number System*
                           Interscience Publishers, Inc. (1956)
14. Walpole, H. R.   *Semantics*
                           W. W. Norton Co. (1941)
15. Whitehead, A. N.   *An Introduction to Mathematics*
                           Oxford University Press (1958)
16. Newman, J. R.   *The World of Mathematics* (4 vol.)
                           Simon and Schuster (1956)

List II

1. Allendoerfer & Oakley   *Principles of Mathematics*
                           McGraw-Hill (1955)
2. Black, M.   *The Nature of Mathematics*
                           The Humanities Press (1950)
3. College Entrance   Report of the Commission on Mathematics: 2 vol.
   Examination Board   and pamphlets.
                           Educational Testing Service (1959)
4. Committee on the   *Elementary Mathematics of Sets*
   Undergraduate   *Universal Mathematics*
   Program   *Modern Mathematical Methods* (2 vol.)
                           Mathematical Association of America (1954–58)
5. Eves, H. and   *An Introduction to the Foundations and Fundamental*
   Newsom, C. V.   *Concepts of Mathematics*
                           Rinehart & Co. (1958)
6. Exner, R. M. and   *Logic in Elementary Mathematics*
   Rosskopf, M. F.   McGraw-Hill (1959)
7. Kemeny, Snell,   *Introduction to Finite Mathematics*
   Thompson   Prentice-Hall (1957)
8. Kershner, R. B. and   *The Anatomy of Mathematics*
   Wilcox, L. R.   The Ronald Press (1950)
9. Nagel, E.   "Principles of the Theory of Probability"
                           International Encyclopedia of Unified Science, Vol. I
                           No. 6
                           University of Chicago Press (1939)
10. National Council   Twenty First Yearbook, *The Learning of Mathematics*,
    of Teachers of   *Its Theory and Practice* (1953)
    Mathematics
11. School Mathematics   *Studies in Mathematics* Vol. I, "Some Basic Mathe-
    Study Group   matical Concepts" (1959)
    Luce, R. D.   Complete series is of interest.
                           Write: Yale University.
12. Stabler, E. R.   *Introduction to Mathematical Thought*
                           Addison-Wesley Publishing Co. (1953)
13. Suppes, P.   *Introduction to Logic*
                           D. Van Nostrand Co. (1957)
14. Waismann, F.   *Introduction to Mathematical Thinking*
                           Frederic Ungar Publishing Co. (1951)
15. Wilder, R. L.   *Foundations of Mathematics*
                           John Wiley and Sons (1952)

appendix B
GLOSSARY
OF SYMBOLS

∧   "and" called a conjunction
∨   "or" called a disjunction
∼   "not" or "no" called a denial
→   "if ···, then ···" called an implication
↔   "if and only if" called an equivalence
∴   "therefore"
( )   parentheses, used to indicate grouping
[ ]   brackets, used to indicate grouping
{ }   braces, used to indicate a set or grouping
/   "such that" or, when used over another connective, is read "not"
∈   "member of" or "belongs to"
∉   "not a member of"
⊂   "subset of"
⊄   "not a subset of"
∪   "union"
∩   "intersection"
$\bar{A}$ "complement of A"
Px "x has the property P" or "x is P"
Fx "F is a condition on x"
$(\exists x)$ "there is an x": $(\exists x)Px$ is read "there is an x such that x is P"
(x) "for all x": $(x)Px$ is read "for all x, x is P"
$n(A)$ the number of elements in the set A
$S(n)$ the number of elements in the set S
=   "equals"
≠   "not equal to"

$+$	"plus," addition symbol
$\times$	"times," multiplication
e	additive identity, also used to denote the irrational number "e"
i	multiplicative identity (in context)
$-x$	additive inverse of x
x^{-1}	multiplicative inverse of x
$>$	"greater than"; also $\geq$, "greater than or equal to"
$<$	"less than"; also $\leq$, "less than or equal to"
$\sqrt{x}$	"square root of x"
(a, b)	the ordered pair consisting of a comma b
$A \times B$	the cartesian product set of A and B

$$\left.\begin{array}{l} a \circ b = c \\ a * b = c \\ x \, R \, y = z \end{array}\right\}$$ binary operations o, $*$, R

$(A \mid B)$	Dedekind cut
$a \xrightarrow{f} b$	"f maps or sends a to b"
$f(a) = b$	"f at a is b"
$\lim\limits_{n \to \infty} S_n = L$	"the limit of S_n, as n becomes as large as you please, is L"
$\lvert x \rvert$	absolute value of x
$[x]$	greatest integer x
b^x	"b to the x," an exponential function
$\log_b x$	"the logarithm of x to the base b"
$n!$	"n factorial"
$P_k = k!$	the number of permutations of a set with k elements
$_mP_k$	the number of permutations of m things taken k at a time $(k \leq m)$
$\dbinom{m}{r}$	the number of combinations of m things taken r at a time
Δx	"delta x"; also Δy, "delta y"
π	"pi," the ratio of the circumference of a circle to its diameter
ϕ	"phi," denoting the "golden ratio"
ϵ	"epsilon," denoting a small positive number
δ	"delta," denoting a small positive number
$\emptyset$	denoting the empty or null set
$\aleph_0$	"aleph null" denoting the cardinal name of the set of natural numbers

appendix C
INDEX OF DEFINITIONS

appendix **D**

ANSWERS TO MANY ODD-NUMBERED EXERCISES

1.2: 3. Suggestion:

ᛧ God, good, sun, fire, hot (positive)

ᛉ Bad, dark, cold (negative)

♀ Man, person, he, she (human)

↑ House, home, village, shelter

⟶ Go, move, future, far (motion or time)

↑ Up, high, rise

↓ Down, stop, sit, stay

∿ River, stream, water

ᴧ Mountain, hill, peaks

⊸ Food, animals, birds, fish

1.3: 1. precise   adj.   strictly defined or accurately stated.

     concise   adj.   brief and to the point.

     condition   n.   anything called for as a requirement before the performance, completion, or effectiveness of something else.

5. Def. By coordinate we mean one of a set of numbers which locates a point in space.

Def. By a mixture we mean a substance containing two or more elements which have not lost their individual characteristics.

Def. By pitch we mean to determine or set the key of a tune, instrument, or voice.

Def. By pitch we mean the distance between two corresponding points on adjacent gear teeth or on adjacent threads of a screw, measured along the axis.

Def. By pitch we mean the slope of the sides of a roof expressed as the ratio of its height to its span.

287

1:    1. (a) gravity, pound, weight, heavy.
         (b) conceal, disguise, cloak, cover.
      7. (a) The difference between the word "chicken" and the object chicken which
             one can cook and eat.
         (b) The difference between the statement "I am good" and the fact of being
             good.
      9. Def. By erg we mean the unit of work done by a force of one dyne operating
              over a distance of one centimeter.
         Def. By stock we mean a colony of connected zooids, forming a compound
              organism.
         Def. By composite we mean that property of a large group of plants having
              flower heads that consist of a large number of small flowers in clusters
              surrounded by small leaves.
         Def. By flare we mean a foggy spot on film, caused by a reflection of light
              from the lens.

2.1: 1. (a) Words are the counters of wise men, and the money

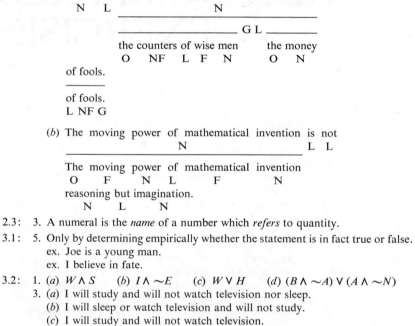

```
        N    L  _____    N
                _____ G L _____
              the counters of wise men      the money
                 O    NF   L  F   N            O    N
        of fools.
        _____
        of fools.
        L NF G
```

        (b) The moving power of mathematical invention is not
```
        _____  L  L
                              N
        The moving power of mathematical invention
            O      F     N    L      F         N
        reasoning but imagination.
            N       L      N
```

2.3: 3. A numeral is the *name* of a number which *refers* to quantity.

3.1: 5. Only by determining empirically whether the statement is in fact true or false.
         ex. Joe is a young man.
         ex. I believe in fate.

3.2: 1. (a) $W \wedge S$ (b) $I \wedge \sim E$ (c) $W \vee H$ (d) $(B \wedge \sim A) \vee (A \wedge \sim N)$
      3. (a) I will study and will not watch television nor sleep.
         (b) I will sleep or watch television and will not study.
         (c) I will study and will not watch television.
         (d) It is false that I will not study nor sleep.

3.3: 1. (a) T   (b) T   (c) F   (d) T   (e) T
      3. (a) F T T T   (b) F T T T
         (c) F F F T   (d) F F F T
      5. (a) $P \wedge Q$ (b) $P \wedge \sim Q$
         (c) $\sim P \wedge Q$ (d) $\sim P \wedge \sim Q$
         (e) $(P \wedge Q) \vee (P \wedge \sim Q)$ (f) $(P \vee Q) \wedge (\sim P \vee \sim Q)$
         (g) $(P \wedge \sim Q) \vee (\sim P \wedge \sim Q)$ (h) $P \vee \sim P$
         (i) $P \wedge \sim P$

3.4:   1. *(a)* T   *(b)* T   *(c)* T

       3. *(a)* T T F T T T T T   *(b)* F F F F F T T T

            (c) T F T T F F F T   *(d)* T T F T T T T T

       5. *(a)* T T T T   *(b)* T T F T

            (c) T T T T T T T T

3.5:   1. *(a)* C *(b)* S *(c)* C

            (d) C *(e)* C *(f)* N

            (g) C *(h)* C *(i)* C

            (j) C

       3. *(a)* $G \wedge B$ *(b)* B *(c)* $(B \wedge T) \rightarrow K$

            (d) $B \vee M$ *(e)* $\sim B$ *(f)* —

            (g) $A \rightarrow B$ *(h)* $A \leftrightarrow B$ *(i)* $(M \vee E) \wedge \sim H$

3:     1. *(a)* $B \wedge \sim S$ *(b)* $T \rightarrow R$ *(c)* $H \vee (C \wedge W)$

            (d) $(N \wedge E) \rightarrow (L \wedge Y)$ *(e)* $D \vee (\sim D \rightarrow I)$

       3. *(a)* If man is mortal and Joe is a man, then Joe is a mortal.

            (b) If Joe is not a man, then Joe is not a mortal.

            (c) Joe is or is not a man.

            (d) Joe is a man if and only if Joe is a mortal.

       5. *(a)* T   *(b)* T

            (c) T   *(d)* F

       7. *(a)* $\sim(P \wedge \sim Q)$ *(b)* $\sim P \vee \sim Q$

            (c) $\sim(P \vee Q)$ *(d)* $(P \wedge Q) \rightarrow R$

       9. *(a)* $(G \rightarrow S) \wedge (\sim G \rightarrow \sim S)$ *(b)* $S \leftrightarrow T$

            (c) $(J \vee K) \rightarrow (L \wedge C)$ *(d)* $\sim(T \rightarrow P)$

     11. *(a)* T T F F   *(b)* T F T T

           (c) T F T T T T T T   *(d)* F T T F

     13. *(a)* $P \vee Q \vee R$ *(b)* $(P \wedge Q) \vee R$

          (c) $\sim P$ *(d)* P

4.1:   1. $(B \vee D)$, $B \rightarrow F$, $\sim F$, $\therefore$ D valid.

       3. *(a)* invalid.   *(b)* valid.

4.2:   1. *(a)* (3) 1, equiv. j   *(b)* (4) 1, equiv. g

                 (4) 3, simpl.   (5) 3, 4, mod. pon.

                 (5) 2, 4, disj. syll.   (6) 2, 5, mod. pon.

       3. (4) 2, equiv. i   (9) 7, 8, mod. pon.

            (5) 1, equiv. n   (10) 4, simpl.

            (6) 4, simpl.   (11) 3, simpl.

            (7) 5, 6, mod. pon.   (12) 10, 11, disj. syll.

            (8) 3, simpl.   (13) 9, 12, conj.

                                        (14) 2, 13, cond. concl.

       5. (5) 4, add.   (9) 8, simpl.

            (6) 5, equiv. d   (10) 2, 3, mod. toll.

            (7) 6, equiv. k   (11) 9, add.

            (8) 1, 7, disj. syll.   (12) 10, 11, disj. syll.

4.3:   1. *Pf.* 1. $B \rightarrow L$ 3. $Y \wedge B$ 5. B

                2. $L \rightarrow M$ 4. $B \rightarrow M$ 6. $\therefore$ M

       3. *Pf.* 1. $(M \vee F) \rightarrow S$ 4. F 7. $\sim F$

                2. $\sim S \rightarrow F$ 5. $\sim(M \vee F)$ 8. $\sim F \vee S$

                3. $\sim S$ 6. $\sim M \wedge \sim F$ 9. $\therefore$ S

       5. *Pf.* 1. $(E \wedge S) \rightarrow I$ 8. I

                2. $I \leftrightarrow (F \vee C)$ 9. $[I \rightarrow (F \vee C)] \wedge [(F \vee C) \rightarrow I]$

3. $S \wedge \sim F$ 10. $I \to (F \vee C)$
4. E 11. $F \vee C$
5. $E \to (S \to I)$ 12. $\sim F$
6. $(S \to I)$ 13. C
7. S 14. $\therefore \ E \to C$

4:      1. (a) invalid.   (b) valid.
        3. (a) (4) 2, simpl.   (b) (4) 2, simpl.
                (5) 4, equiv. k   (5) 2, simpl.
                (6) 1, 5, disj. syll.   (6) 5, equiv. l
                (7) 3, equiv. h   (7) 6, simpl.
                (8) 6, 7, mod. pon.   (8) 4, 7, conj.
                (9) 2, simpl.   (9) 8, equiv. a, g
                (10) 8, 9, mod. pon.   (10) 1, 9, disj. syll.
                (11) 4, 10, disj. syll.   (11) 3, 10, mod. toll.

        5. *Pf.* 1. $R \to A$ 3. $\sim B$ 5. $\therefore \ A$
                 2. $\sim R \to B$ 4. R
        7. *Pf.* 1. $(W \vee \sim W) \wedge \sim P$ 3. $T \to P$ 5. $\sim P$
                 2. $W \to T$ 4. $W \to P$ 6. $\therefore \ \sim W$
        9. *Pf.* 1. $P \vee (Q \wedge R)$ 4. $\sim S \vee \sim T$ 7. $(P \vee Q) \wedge (P \vee R)$
                 2. $Q \to (S \wedge T)$ 5. $\sim (S \wedge T)$ 8. $P \vee Q$
                 3. $\sim S$ 6. $\sim Q$ 9. $\therefore \ P$

6.1:   7. (a) No   (b) Yes   (c) No
           (d) No   (e) Yes, B and C   (f) Yes, B of A

6.3.   1. (b) i. $N \cup V = \{a, e, i, o, u, j, h, n, d\}$
                ii. $N \cap C = \{j, h, n, d\}$
                iii. $V \cup C = U$ iv. $N \cap \bar{V} = N \cap C$
                v. $C \cap \bar{N} = \{b, c, f, g, k, l, m, p, q, r, s, t, v, w, x, y, z\}$
                vi. $\bar{C} = V$
        3. (a) $D - (B \cup C)$ (b) $(B \cap C) - A$
           (c) $(A \cap B) - (C \cup D)$ (d) $A \cap [B \cap (C \cap D)]$

6.4:   1. *Pf.* Th. 2.   *Pf.* Th. 3.
           1. $\emptyset = A \cap \bar{A}$ 1. $A = A \cup \emptyset$
           2. $= A \cap (\bar{A} \cup \emptyset)$ 2. $= A \cup (B \cap \emptyset)$
           3. $= (A \cap \bar{A}) \cup (A \cap \emptyset)$ 3. $= (A \cup B) \cap (A \cup \emptyset)$
           4. $= \emptyset \cup (A \cap \emptyset)$ 4. $= (A \cup B) \cap A$
           5. $= (A \cap \emptyset) \cup \emptyset$ 5. $\therefore \ A = A \cap (A \cup B)$
           6. $\therefore \ \emptyset = A \cap \emptyset$

6:      1. (a) $E = \{2, 4, 6, 8\}$ (b) $F = \{1, 3, 5, 7, 9\}$ (c) $P = \{1, 2, 3, 5, 7\}$
        3. (a) True   (b) False   (c) False   (d) True   (e) True
           (f) True   (g) True   (h) False   (i) True
        7.

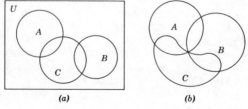

(a)   (b)

7.1: 3. (a) $\overline{P} \cup Q$ (b) $P \cap \overline{Q} = P - Q$
         (c) $\overline{(P \cup Q)} \cup (P \cap Q)$ (d) $\overline{Q - P} = P \cup Q$

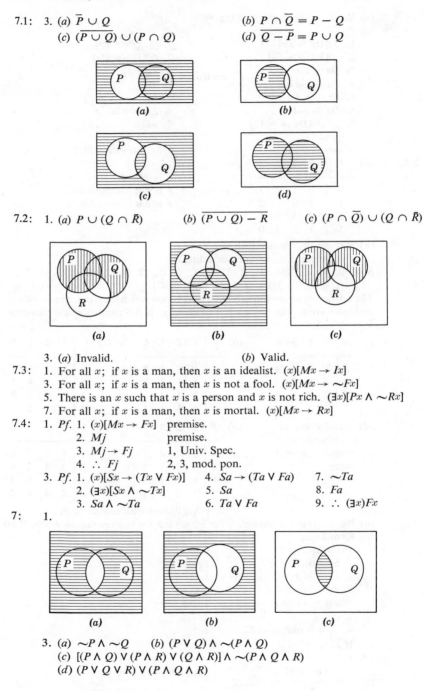

(a)   (b)

(c)   (d)

7.2: 1. (a) $P \cup (Q \cap \overline{R})$ (b) $\overline{(P \cup Q) - R}$ (c) $(P \cap \overline{Q}) \cup (Q \cap \overline{R})$

(a)   (b)   (c)

    3. (a) Invalid.   (b) Valid.

7.3: 1. For all x; if x is a man, then x is an idealist. $(x)[Mx \to Ix]$
      3. For all x; if x is a man, then x is not a fool. $(x)[Mx \to \sim Fx]$
      5. There is an x such that x is a person and x is not rich. $(\exists x)[Px \wedge \sim Rx]$
      7. For all x; if x is a man, then x is mortal. $(x)[Mx \to Rx]$

7.4: 1. *Pf.* 1. $(x)[Mx \to Fx]$ premise.
            2. Mj premise.
            3. $Mj \to Fj$ 1, Univ. Spec.
            4. $\therefore$ Fj 2, 3, mod. pon.
      3. *Pf.* 1. $(x)[Sx \to (Tx \vee Fx)]$ 4. $Sa \to (Ta \vee Fa)$ 7. $\sim Ta$
              2. $(\exists x)[Sx \wedge \sim Tx]$ 5. Sa 8. Fa
              3. $Sa \wedge \sim Ta$ 6. $Ta \vee Fa$ 9. $\therefore$ $(\exists x)Fx$

7: 1.

(a)   (b)   (c)

    3. (a) $\sim P \wedge \sim Q$ (b) $(P \vee Q) \wedge \sim (P \wedge Q)$
        (c) $[(P \wedge Q) \vee (P \wedge R) \vee (Q \wedge R)] \wedge \sim (P \wedge Q \wedge R)$
        (d) $(P \vee Q \vee R) \vee (P \wedge Q \wedge R)$

5. (a) Valid   (b) Invalid   (c) Valid.

9. (a) Pf.

    1. $(x)[Dx \rightarrow Fx]$

    2. $(x)[Vx \rightarrow \sim Fx]$

    3. $Da \rightarrow Fa$

    4. $Va \rightarrow \sim Fa$

    5. $Fa \rightarrow \sim Va$

    6. $Da \rightarrow \sim Va$

    7. $\therefore (x)[Dx \rightarrow \sim Vx]$

(b) Pf.

    1. $(\exists x)[Px \wedge Lx]$

    2. $(x)[Lx \rightarrow Mx]$

    3. $Pa \wedge La$

    4. Pa

    5. La

    6. $La \rightarrow Ma$

    7. Ma

    8. $Pa \wedge Ma$

    9. $\therefore (\exists x)[Px \wedge Mx]$

8.2: 1. (a)

F	0	1	2	3
0	0	1	2	3
1	3	0	1	2
2	2	3	0	1
3	1	2	3	0

(b) 16

(c) F is closed.

F is not commutative.

F is not associative.

(d) R is not distributive with respect to F.

F is not distributive with respect to R.

3. $S = \{\emptyset, \{1\}, \{2\}, \{3\}, \{4\}, \{1, 2\}, \{1, 3\}, \{1, 4\}, \{2, 3\}, \{2, 4\}, \{3, 4\}, \{1, 2, 3\},$
$\{1, 2, 4\}, \{1, 3, 4\}, \{2, 3, 4\}, \{1, 2, 3, 4\}\}.$

The relation of union forms a binary operation which is closed, commutative, and associative. The element $\emptyset$ is an identity. $S \times S$ consists of 256 elements.

5. $S = \{1, 2, 3, 4\}$

(a)

A	1	2	3	4
1	1	2	3	4
2	4	1	2	3
3	3	4	1	2
4	2	3	4	1

(b)

B	1	2	3	4
1	1	3	2	4
2	3	1	4	2
3	2	4	3	1
4	4	2	1	3

(c)

C	1	2	3	4
1	1	2	3	4
2	2	3	4	1
3	3	4	1	2
4	4	1	2	3

(d) A and C are not distributive with respect to each other.

(e)

P	1	2	3	4
1	2	3	4	1
2	3	4	1	2
3	4	1	2	3
4	1	2	3	4

T	1	2	3	4
1	1	2	3	4
2	2	4	2	4
3	3	2	1	4
4	4	4	4	4

T is distributive with respect to P.

8.3: 1. (a) No   (b) R forms an abelian group but the two operations F and R do not form a ring.

3. T_4: e is unique in G.

Pf. 1. Suppose $e \neq e'$ Prem. ind. pf.

    2. $x \circ e = x$ and $x \circ e' = x$ 1, A_3

    3. $x \circ e = x \circ e'$ 2, subst.

    4. $e \circ x = e' \circ x$ 3, T_3

    5. $e = e'$ 4, T_2

    6. $\therefore$ e is unique in G.   1, 5.

T_5: If $x \in G$, then $x \circ x^{-1} = x^{-1} \circ x$.

Pf. 1. $x \circ x^{-1} = e$ A_4

    2. $x^{-1} \circ x \in G$ A_4, A_1

3. $(x^{-1} \text{ o } x) \text{ o } e = x^{-1} \text{ o } (x \text{ o } e)$ 2, A_1, A_2
4. $e \text{ o } e = x^{-1} \text{ o } x$ 3, A_4, A_3
5. $e = x^{-1} \text{ o } x$ 4, A_3
6. $\therefore$ $x \text{ o } x^{-1} = x^{-1} \text{ o } x$ 1, 5, subst.

T_6: For each $x \in G$, x^{-1} is unique in G.
Pf. 1. Suppose $x^{-1} \ne x'^{-1}$ 4. $x^{-1} \text{ o } x = x'^{-1} \text{ o } x$
     2. $x \text{ o } x^{-1} = e$ and $x \text{ o } x'^{-1} = e$ 5. $x^{-1} = x'^{-1}$
     3. $x \text{ o } x^{-1} = x \text{ o } x'^{-1}$ 6. $\therefore$ x^{-1} is unique.

T_7: If $x \in G$, $(x^{-1})^{-1} = x$
Pf. 1. $x^{-1} \in G$ 5. $(x^{-1})^{-1} \text{ o } (x^{-1} \text{ o } x) = x$
     2. $(x^{-1}) \text{ o } (x^{-1})^{-1} = e$ 6. $(x^{-1})^{-1} \text{ o } e = x$
     3. $[x^{-1} \text{ o } (x^{-1})^{-1}] \text{ o } x = e \text{ o } x$ 7. $\therefore$ $(x^{-1})^{-1} = x$
     4. $[(x^{-1})^{-1} \text{ o } x^{-1}] \text{ o } x = x$

T_8: If $a,b \in G$, then there is a unique $x \in G$ such that $a \text{ o } x = b$.
Pf. 1. $a \text{ o } (a^{-1} \text{ o } b) = (a \text{ o } a^{-1}) \text{ o } b$ 7. $a^{-1} \text{ o } (a \text{ o } x) = a^{-1} \text{ o } (a \text{ o } y)$
     2. $= e \text{ o } b = b$ 8. $(a^{-1} \text{ o } a) \text{ o } x = (a^{-1} \text{ o } a) \text{ o } y$
     3. Let $x = a^{-1} \text{ o } b$ 9. $e \text{ o } x = e \text{ o } y$
     4. $a \text{ o } x = b$ 10. $x = y$
     5. Suppose $y \in G$ such that   11. $\therefore$ there is a unique $x \in G$ such
         $a \text{ o } y = b$.   that $a \text{ o } x = b$.
     6. $a \text{ o } x = a \text{ o } y$

8:   1. (b)

R	0 1 2
0	0 1 2
1	1 2 0
2	2 0 1

F	0 1 2
0	0 1 2
1	2 0 1
2	1 2 0

     (c) R forms an abelian group.
         F does not not form a group.
     (d) No, no.
   3. S, with $+$ and $\times$, forms a field.
   5. T_{12}: For all $x, y \in F$, $x * (-y) = -(x * y)$.
     Pf. 1. $y \text{ o } (-y) = e$ prem., A_7
         2. $x * [y \text{ o } (-y)] = e$ 1, T_{11}
         3. $(x * y) \text{ o } (x * -y) = e$ 2, A_6
         4. $\therefore$ $x * (-y) = -(x * y)$ 3, T_5, A_7.

     T_{13}: For all $x, y \in F$, $(-x) * (-y) = x * y$
     Pf. 1. $[(-x) \text{ o } x] * (-y) = e$ prem., A_7, T_{11}
         2. $[(-x) * (-y)] \text{ o } [x * (-y)] = e$ 1, A_6
         3. $[(-x) * (-y)] \text{ o } [-(x * y)] = e$ 2, T_{12}
         4. $\therefore$ $(-x) * (-y) = x * y$ 3, A_7

9.1:   1. (a) 26   (b) 9   (c) —   (d) 366
   3. (a) 22, 32, 33, 41 and 10, 12, 13, 17
   7. (a) Mult. of 3: 6, 9, 15, 24, 30, 42
         Mult. of 5: 15, 30, 35
         Mult. of 6: 6, 24, 30, 42
     (b) Div. by 2: 6, 24, 30, 42
         Div. by 3: 6, 9, 15, 24, 30, 42
         Div. by 7: 35, 42

        (c) 4 is factor of: 24

            6 is factor of: 6, 24, 30, 42

            7 is factor of: 35, 42

        (d) $35 = 5 \times 7$; $42 = 2 \times 3 \times 7$

9.2:   5. (a) $(1,8) = -7$, $(1,3) = -2$, $(1,1) = 0$, $(6,1) = 5$, $(14,1) = 13$.

        (b) Addition: $(a,b) + (c,d) = (a + c, b + d)$.

           Multiplication: $(a,b)(c,d) = (ac + bd, bc + ad)$.

9.3:   1. (a) Equality: $(a,b) = (c,d)$ if and only if $ad = bc$.

           Sum: $(a,b) + (c,d) = (ad + bc, bd)$.

           Product: $(a,b)(c,d) = (ac,bd)$.

        (b) Definition: $(2,5) = \frac{2}{5}$. Equality: $(2,3) = (6,9)$.

           Sum: $(2,3) + (5,6) = (27,18) = (3,2)$.

           Product: $(2,3)(5,6) = (10,18) = (5,9)$.

9.4:   3. $-2 = (A \mid B)$ for $A = \{x \leq -2\}$, $B = \{x > -2\}$.

      $\frac{2}{3} = (A \mid B)$ for $A = \{x \leq \frac{2}{3}\}$, $B = \{x > \frac{2}{3}\}$.

      $\sqrt{5} = (A \mid B)$ for $A = \{x < a \text{ for } a^2 = 5, a > 0\}$ and

                     $B = \{x > a \text{ for } a^2 = 5, a > 0\}$.

      $-\sqrt{3} = (A \mid B)$ for $A = \{x < a \text{ for } a^2 = 3, a < 0\}$ and

                     $B = \{x > a \text{ for } a^2 = 3, a < 0\}$.

     5. $203.826 = 2(100) + 0(10) + 3(1) + 8(\frac{1}{10}) + 2(\frac{1}{100}) + 6(\frac{1}{1000})$

9:   3. (a) For $n = 1$, $(ab)^n = ab = a^n b^n$.

        If for some n, $(ab)^n = a^n b^n$, then we have for $n + 1$:

        $(ab)^{n+1} = (ab)^n(ab) = a^n b^n ab = a^n ab^n b = a^{n+1} b^{n+1}$.

        Thus: $(ab)^n = a^n b^n$ for all natural numbers n.

       (b) For $n = 1$, $a^m a^n = a^m a = a^{m+1} = a^{m+n}$ for any fixed m.

        If for some n, $a^m a^n = a^{m+n}$, then we have for $n + 1$:

        $a^m a^{n+1} = a^m a^n a = a^{m+n} a = a^{m+n+1}$.

        Thus: $a^m a^n = a^{m+n}$ for all n and any fixed m.

        Similarly, $a^m a^n = a^{m+n}$ for all m and any fixed n.

        Finally, $a^m a^n = a^{m+n}$ for all m and n (natural numbers).

     5. *Pf:* 1. Definition, 2. Commutative, 3. Associative, 4. Inverse, 5. Zero,

        6. Commutative and definition.

     7. (a) (i) 9   (ii) 9   (iii) 14

        (b) (i) $65 = 9(7) + 2$ (ii) $113 = 9(12) + 5$ (iii) $239 = 14(17) + 1$

     9. (a) $\frac{11}{6}$ (b) $\frac{51}{60}$ (c) $\frac{23}{12}$ (d) $\frac{17}{30}$ (e) $-\frac{17}{12}$ (f) $\frac{19}{60}$ (g) $-\frac{29}{60}$

        (h) $\frac{131}{60}$ (i) $\frac{3}{20}$ (j) $\frac{5}{3}$ (k) $\frac{5}{9}$ (l) $\frac{35}{6}$ (m) $\frac{3}{2}$

   13. (a) 3   (b) 8   (c) 14

   15. Suppose an integer n is not divisible by 3. Then $n = 3m + r$ where $r = 1$ or

       $r = 2$. If $r = 1$, then $n + 2 = 3(m + 1)$ and $n + 2$ is divisible by 3. If

       $r = 2$, then $n + 1 = 3(m + 1)$ and $n + 1$ is divisible by 3. Hence one of n,

       $n + 1$, or $n + 2$ is divisible by 3.

10.1:   1. (i) 36   (ii) $\frac{2}{3}$ (iii) -2 (iv) 50

        (v) 15   (vi) 4   (vii) $\frac{37}{12}$

     3. (i) $(x + 4)(x + 3)$ (ii) $(m - 8)(m + 3)$ (iii) $x(2x + 3)(2x - 3)$

        (iv) $3(x - 1)(x - 1)$ (v) $(1 - 8a)(1 - 8a)$ (vi) $(5y - 2x)(5y + 2x)$

10.2:   1. (a) 5   (b) 7   (c) 12   (d) -1 (e) 3   (f) 3, -3

10:   1. (a) U   (b) $\emptyset$

     3. (a) $\frac{11}{3}$ (b) $\frac{19}{2}$ (c) -3 (d) 6   (e) $\frac{21}{4}$ (f) $-\frac{97}{2}$

     5. (a) $(a + b)(c + d)$ (b) $3(2x + a)(2x - a)$ (c) $(x + \frac{1}{2})(x + \frac{1}{2})$

        (d) $3(1 + 2x)(1 - x)$ (e) $(a - 3)(a - 3)$ (f) $(2x - 3)(2x - 3)$

7. (a) $x < \frac{3}{2}$ (b) $-1 < x < 0$ (c) $-\frac{1}{2} < x < 2$ (d) $x \geq 6$
   (e) $x < -2$ or $2 < x$ (f) $x \leq -\frac{5}{2}$ or $0 < x < 3$.

9. (a) Sketch: $\dfrac{r}{m} = \dfrac{m}{x} = \dfrac{n}{h}$ and $\dfrac{r}{n} = \dfrac{m}{h} = \dfrac{n}{r-x}$
   $rx = m^2$ and $r(r-x) = n^2$ so that $r^2 = m^2 + n^2$.

   (b) Sketch: Note similar triangles and $\dfrac{x}{h} = \dfrac{h}{r-x}$.

11. (a) $b = \dfrac{p - 2a}{2}$ (b) $C = \frac{5}{9}(F - 32)$ (c) $p = \dfrac{A}{1 + rt}$

   (d) $r = \dfrac{A - p}{pt}$ (e) $n = \dfrac{2S}{a + 1}$ (f) $a = \dfrac{2S}{n} - 1 = \dfrac{2S - n}{n}$

13. (a) $5(5x^2 + 2xy + 20y^2)$ (b) $(2a + b)(b - c)$
   (c) $(2x - 1)(2x + 3)$ (d) $(2x + 2a + 1)(2x + 2a - 1)$

15. $x = 3$, $y = 5$.

11.1:   1. (a) The *yard* is the standard of length in the British system and is the distance between two fine lines engraved in a bronze bar kept in the Standards Office in London. The *meter* is the standard in the metric system and is the distance between two lines on a platinum-iridium bar kept in a vault of the International Bureau of Weights and Measures at Sévres, France.

British Units	Metric Units
1 mile = 1760 yards	1 kilometer = 1000 meters
1 yard = 3 feet	1 meter = 100 centimeters
1 foot = 12 inches	1 centimeter = 10 millimeters
1 inch = 1000 mils	1 millimeter = 1000 microns

   (b) The United States fixed the relationship between the British and Metric Units by an Act in 1866 to be: 1 yard $= \dfrac{3600}{3937}$ meter.

Conversion Table

1 mile = 1.6093 kilometers	1 meter = 3.281 feet
1 kilometer = 0.6214 miles	1 meter = 39.37 inches
1 foot = 30.48 centimeters	1 inch = 2.540 centimeters

11.2:   1. 99 square inches.
    3. $R = 80.66$ ohms.
    5. Federal tax = $2282.05; State tax = $994.87.

11:   1. Let b_1 and b_2 be the parallel sides and s_1 and s_2 the nonparallel sides, with h the distance between b_1 and b_2 (the altitude). The area $A = \dfrac{h}{2}(b_1 + b_2)$. The perimeter $P = b_1 + b_2 + s_1 + s_2$.

    3. Radius of action, $R = 1,350$ miles.
      Area of coverage, $A = 5,728(10^3)$ square miles.

    5. Approximately 24.76 feet.

    7. 1 foot from the fulcrum on the side with the 6-pound weight.

    9. 173.

   11. Focal length, $f = 2.32$ feet (approx.).

   13. $1^2 + 2^2 + 3^2 + \cdots + n^2 = \dfrac{n(n + 1)(2n + 1)}{6}$.

15. Although the hands do not coincide precisely, they will "pass" within an arc of "one minute" on the clock face at 9:48:49 and 9:49:49. At 9:48:49 the angular displacement will be less than 2° of arc.

12.1: 1. (i) $\{(p_1,q_1), (p_2,q_1), (p_2,q_4)\}$, $D = \{p_1, p_2\}$, $R = \{q_1, q_4\}$.

     (ii) $\{(1,3), (1,4), (3,2), (3,3)\}$, $D = \{1, 3\}$, $R = \{2, 3, 4\}$.

     (iii) $\{(c,c), (b,b), (a,a)\}$, $D = R = \{c, b, a\}$.

     (iv) $\{(0,0), (0,6), (2,2), (4,4), (6,0), (6,6)\}$, $D = R = \{0, 2, 4, 6\}$.

     (v) $\{(d,b), (d,a), (k,b), (k,a)\}$, $D = \{d, k\}$, $R = \{b, a\}$.

     (vi) $\{(2,0), (2,2), (4,0)\}$, $D = \{2, 4\}$, $R = \{0, 2\}$.

     (c) (iii) and (iv) are symmetric, reflexive, and transitive.

12.2: 1. $P = \sqrt{58} + \sqrt{97} + \sqrt{53} \cong 24.745$

     $A = 27.5$ square units.

   3. A parallelogram. THEOREM: The line segments joining the midpoints of the sides of a quadrilateral form a parallelogram.

12.3: 1.

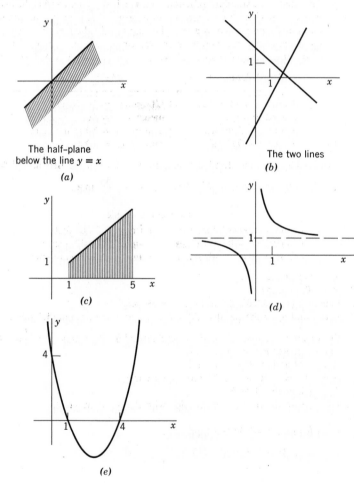

The half–plane
below the line $y = x$

(a)

The two lines

(b)

(c)

(d)

(e)

3. $16x^2 + 25y^2 = 400$.

5. $(x - 3)^2 + (y - 2)^2 = 9$.

12:　1. (a) There are 16 relations:

(1) ∅	(2) {(a,a)}	(3) {(a,b)}
(4) {(b,a)}	(5) {(b,b)}	(6) {(a,a), (a,b)}
(7) {(a,a), (b,a)}	(8) {(a,a), (b,b)}	(9) {(a,b), (b,a)}
(10) {(a,b), (b,b)}	(11) {(b,a), (b,b)}	(12) {(a,a), (a,b), (b,a)}
(13) {(a,a), (a,b), (b,b)}	(14) {(a,a), (b,a), (b,b)}	(15) {(a,b), (b,a), (b,b)}

(16) {(a,a), (a,b), (b,a), (b,b)}.

(b) The relations: (1), (2), (5), (8), (9), (12), (15), and (16) are symmetric relations.

(c) The relations: (8), (13), (14), and (16) are reflexive relations.

(d) The relations: (1), (2), (3), (4), (5), (6), (7), (8), (10), (11), (13), (14), and (16) are transitive relations.

7. $y = mx + b$.

9. $d = \dfrac{|y_0 - mx_0 - b|}{\sqrt{1 + m^2}}$

11. $xy = k$ where k is the constant (the sign may be either + or −).

13.1:　1.

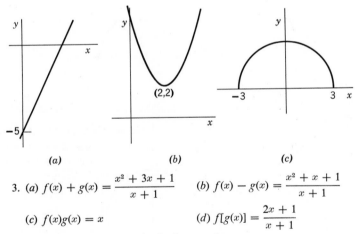

(a)　　　　　　　(b)　　　　　　　(c)

3. (a) $f(x) + g(x) = \dfrac{x^2 + 3x + 1}{x + 1}$　　(b) $f(x) - g(x) = \dfrac{x^2 + x + 1}{x + 1}$

(c) $f(x)g(x) = x$　　(d) $f[g(x)] = \dfrac{2x + 1}{x + 1}$

5. The arc of the circle R_1 in the first quadrant.

13.2:   1.

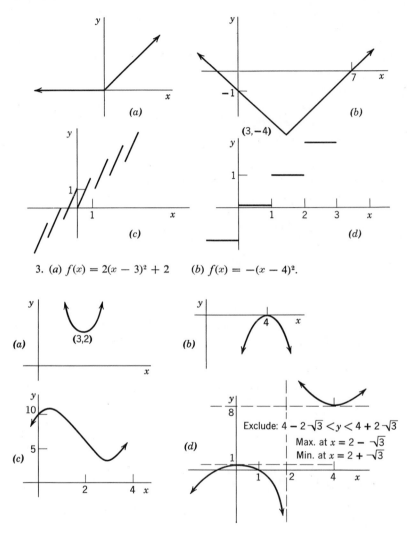

(a)

(b)

(3,−4)

(c)

(d)

3. (a) $f(x) = 2(x - 3)^2 + 2$ (b) $f(x) = -(x - 4)^2$.

(a)

(3,2)

(b)

4

(c)

10

5

2   4   x

(d)

8

Exclude: $4 - 2\sqrt{3} < y < 4 + 2\sqrt{3}$

Max. at $x = 2 - \sqrt{3}$

Min. at $x = 2 + \sqrt{3}$

5. (a) $f(x) = \log_{10} x$

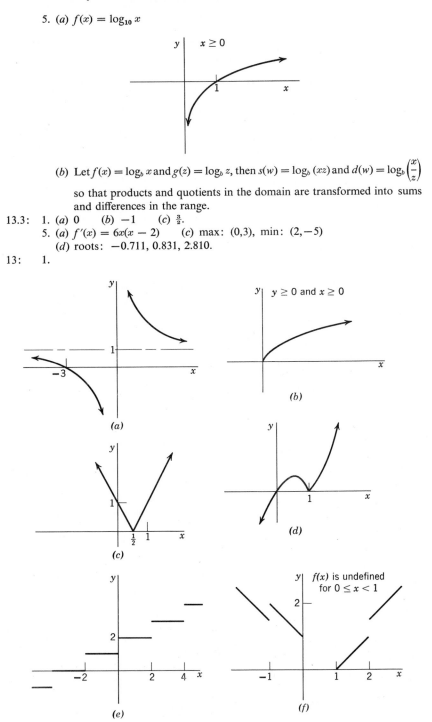

(b) Let $f(x) = \log_b x$ and $g(z) = \log_b z$, then $s(w) = \log_b (xz)$ and $d(w) = \log_b \left(\dfrac{x}{z}\right)$

so that products and quotients in the domain are transformed into sums and differences in the range.

13.3: 1. (a) 0   (b) −1   (c) $\frac{3}{2}$.

5. (a) $f'(x) = 6x(x − 2)$ (c) max: (0,3), min: (2,−5)

(d) roots: −0.711, 0.831, 2.810.

13: 1.

(a)

(b)

(c)

(d)

(e)

(f)

3. (a) $\dfrac{x(x^2 + x - 1)}{(x + 1)}$ (b) $x^2 - 2x + 1$

(c) $x^2 + 2x + 1$ (d) $\dfrac{-4x}{(x + 1)^2}$ (e) $\dfrac{x^2 - 2}{x^2}$

7. (a)

θ	0	$\dfrac{\pi}{6}$	$\dfrac{\pi}{4}$	$\dfrac{\pi}{3}$	$\dfrac{\pi}{2}$	π	$\dfrac{3\pi}{2}$	2π
$\sin \theta$	0	$\dfrac{1}{2}$	$\dfrac{1}{\sqrt{2}}$	$\dfrac{\sqrt{3}}{2}$	1	0	-1	0
$\cos \theta$	1	$\dfrac{\sqrt{3}}{2}$	$\dfrac{1}{\sqrt{2}}$	$\dfrac{1}{2}$	0	-1	0	1

9. (a) 0   (b) $\tfrac{7}{6}$.

11. 2 inches.

13. $P(4,3)$ and $Q(2,2)$.

15. (a) 11.1İ feet   (b) 66.6̇6 feet.

14.1: 1.

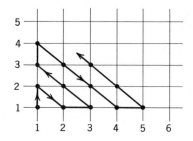

5. 17,576,000 including zeroes.

14.2: 1. (a) 120   (b) 7,560.
    3. (b) 96.

14.3: 5. (a) 1024.

14: 1. (a) For $n = 1$, $n(n + 1) = 1(2)$ even. If $n(n + 1)$ is even, we have
    $(n + 1)(n + 2) = n(n + 1) + 2(n + 1)$ and since $n(n + 1)$ and $2(n + 1)$
    are even, $(n + 1)(n + 2)$ is even.
    (b) $(2n + 1)(2m + 1) = 4nm + 2n + 2m + 1$ is odd.
    (c) $(2n)(2m) = 2(2mn)$ is even.
    3. (a) 89   (b) 4   (c) 50   (d) 1776.
    5. 12,144 without repetition. 13,824 with repetition.
    7. Including numbers starting with zero:
        120 without repetition; 216 with repetition.
    With nonzero number in the hundreds position:
        100 without repetition; 180 with repetition.
    11. $(4)(3)^9$ for no two questions the same.
        $(4)^{10}$ if questions can be answered the same.
    13. 288.

15. Multinomial theorem: For any natural number r and numbers $x_1, x_2, x_3, \cdots, x_s$ we have the expansion of $(x_1 + x_2 + x_3 + \cdots + x_s)^r$ is equal to the sum of the $\begin{pmatrix} s+r-1 \\ r \end{pmatrix}$ terms of the form $Cx_1{}^n x_2{}^m x_3{}^k \cdots x_s{}^p$ where $C = \dfrac{r!}{n!\, m!\, k! \cdots p!}$ and $n + m + k + \cdots + p = r$.

15.1: 1. $p(5) = \frac{1}{9}, p(8) = \frac{5}{36}$.
  3. p(four digits all alike) $= \frac{1}{1000}$.
  5. If 10% defective: p(one defective) $= (0.9)^9$
     If 20% defective: p(one defective) $= (0.8)^9(2)$.

15.2: 1. (a) Space with 2^5 outcomes: p(no more than two H) $= \frac{1}{2}$.
     (b) Space with 36 outcomes, experiment repeated: p(2 pr.) $= \frac{1}{36}$.
  3. (b) Since $2p(w) - p(r) = 0$, the game is "fair."

15.3: 1. Assume with replacement; use the binomial expansion.
     Mean is approx. $= 0.994$, Standard Deviation is approx. $= 0.933$.

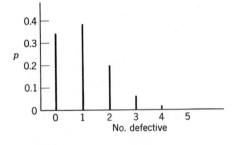

5. (a) Range   0   1   2   3
       Meas.   0.573   0.359   0.065   0.0035
   (b) Mean: $M = 0.50$, Standard Deviation: $S = 0.40$.

15: 1. (a) 0.002   (b) 0.0004   (c) 0.000015.
  3. $p = \frac{5}{16}$.
  5. (a) $\frac{47}{100}$ (b) $\frac{24}{100}$ (c) $\frac{17}{100}$.
  7. (a) $p = 0.43\dot{3}$ (b) $p = 0.958$.

  11. $p(A \mid C) = \dfrac{p(C \mid A)p(A)}{p(C)}, \quad p(B \mid C) = \dfrac{p(C \mid B)p(B)}{p(C)}$.

INDEX